Organic Photochemistry

McGraw-Hill Series in Advanced Chemistry

Organic Photochemistry

Robert O. Kan

Assistant Professor of Chemistry
Kent State University

McGraw-Hill Book Company

New York
St. Louis
San Francisco
Toronto
London
Sydney

Organic Photochemistry

33268

1234567890 MP 7321069876

Hoe warm het was en hoe ver. . . .

Nikolaas Beets

Preface

This short text has been written with the dual intention of providing an introduction to the subject of organic photochemistry for the practicing organic chemist and the student at the graduate level and of providing a review of the most significant recent developments in the field.

In presenting the subject I have made a rather arbitrary classification of photochemical processes, in the full realization that many reactions could have been discussed under any of the several headings chosen. For the sake of completeness, some processes are therefore mentioned more than once.

As a rule, instrumental details are not mentioned, mainly because lamp type and wattage and the filters used rarely identify the wavelength of the absorbed light and add little to an understanding of the processes involved. It is expected that the persons interested in these matters will consult the literature cited.

The subject matter is considered from the point of view of the organic chemist, and although the first chapter introduces some of the physical-chemical concepts and the terminology encountered in the literature, the discussion is kept very brief, principally because rather extensive treatments of these subjects are now becoming available.

The documentation provided is intended to be extensive rather than complete. No attempt has been made to provide an encyclopedia of organic photochemical reactions, even though a desire to expose the full scope of each reaction type may at times give that impression, for which I apologize.

The assistance of a number of friends and colleagues is acknowledged with great pleasure. I am particularly indebted to Drs. Albert Padwa, Christopher S. Foote, and Gary W. Griffin, who read the entire manuscript, and to Dr. Garnett R. McMillan and Dr. Howard Harris, who read part of it, for making extremely helpful comments and suggestions.

I would also like to thank Drs. John W. Reed and Vernon D. Neff for helpful discussions. Mr. George Newkome has been of great assistance in the checking of references, and Messrs. Robert Furey, Jim Engleman, James Sanders, and Kenneth Cerny have been of invaluable aid in proofreading.

Finally I am grateful to Dr. G. S. Hammond and the American Chemical Society for their permission to reproduce Figs. 2-1 and 2-2 and Table 2-1.

Robert O. Kan

Contents

1

Concepts

1-1 Introduction[1-4]

The subject of photochemistry deals with chemical reactions that are dependent on the action of visible or ultraviolet light. Despite the obvious importance of photochemical reactions for photosynthesis and allied phenomena, organic photochemistry received only limited attention until the 1940s. Many examples of organic photochemical reactions appeared in the literature before that time, but the only systematic studies that had been undertaken dealt with detailed analyses of a number of gas-phase reactions. Solution photochemistry was neglected, largely because techniques adequate to the task of resolving the complex mixtures which are often encountered had not yet been developed. Earlier investigators were also handicapped by the unavailability of artificial sources of visible and ultraviolet light of suitable intensity and spectral characteristics; with the sun as the chief source of radiation, progress in the field often depended on the weather!

The regions of the electromagnetic spectrum that are of interest to the photochemist are the far ultraviolet (100 to 2000 Å), the near ultra-violet (2000 to 4000 Å), and the visible region (4000 to 8000 Å). The wavelength, λ, is most often expressed in angstroms (1 Å = 10^{-8} cm) or in millimicrons (1 mμ = 10^{-7} cm = 10 Å).

A different method of classification is by frequency ν, related to the wavelength by $\nu = c/\lambda$, where c is the velocity of light. It may be seen from the relationships $E = h\nu$, $\nu = c/\lambda$, and $E = hc/\lambda$ that energy is inversely proportional to wavelength; the longer the wavelength, the lower the energy of the radiation.

The absorption of energy by molecules or atoms, which normally exist in a state of minimum electronic energy or *ground state*, raises them to a less stable state of higher electronic energy or *excited state*. The absorption process is usually referred to as "excitation." Excited species can lose their excess energy by a variety of means. The most common of these are the emission of radiation and the loss to the surroundings through collisions.

Each substance is selective in its absorption of radiation, depending on the presence of chromophores, which are atoms or functional groups which usually contain p electrons or π bonds. The various wavelength ranges at which absorption takes place are determined from the absorption spectra, which are plots of the wavelength against the amount of radiation absorbed on passing through a substance.

The total energy of the system consists of three components: rotational, vibrational, and electronic energies. The rotational energy levels of molecules lie very close together, while the energy difference between vibrational levels is 10 to 100 times larger than that between rotational levels. The vibrational energy can assume an important role, especially in polyatomic molecules, which have many vibrational modes. Although high vibrational and rotational energy levels are reached on excitation, the amount of energy involved in pure vibrational and rotational absorption is generally of only slight significance. Largest of the three energies is the electronic excitation energy; it is about 10 times the magnitude of the vibrational energy. It is associated with the transition of electrons from their normal low-energy orbitals to orbitals of higher energy, and the excitation energy thus acquired by the molecule is of such magnitude as to be comparable to the bond energies. It is therefore not surprising that many reactions involving the breakage of bonds can ensue.

The energy absorbed by the molecule at a specific wavelength may be readily calculated from the equation $E = h\nu$. After conversion to molar quantities the energy (in kilocalories per mole) is

$$E \text{ (kcal/mole)} = \frac{2.86 \times 10^4}{\lambda \text{ (m}\mu)}$$

Thus, absorption at 300 mμ is equivalent to an excitation energy of 95 kcal/mole.

In selecting a source of radiation, one must realize, however, that only radiation absorbed in a system may be effective in producing a chemical change. (This statement is often referred to as the first law of photochemistry or as the Grotthuss-Draper law.) The amount that is absorbed is related to the concentration of the substance in the path of the radiation by the Beer and Lambert laws, while the Stark-Einstein law of photochemical equivalence states that the amount of radiation absorbed is generally limited to one quantum per molecule taking part in a reaction. (Exceptions to the law have been observed in two-photon absorption processes.) It will be seen from these considerations that the efficiency of a process is variable. The efficiency is usually expressed in terms of the quantum yield Φ, which is defined as

$$\Phi = \frac{\text{number of molecules reacting or formed}}{\text{number of quanta absorbed}}$$

The number of quanta absorbed can be measured by an actinometer,[4a] which is a reaction system for which the quantum yield is known. The quantum yield of photochemical reactions, referring specifically to the primary process, is always $\leqslant 1$. The primary process is here defined as starting with the absorption of a photon and ending with the disappearance of the molecule or its deactivation to a nonreactive state.

1-2 *Electronic Orbitals*

It is useful to recall some features of atomic and molecular electronic orbitals. Atomic orbitals are one-electron wave functions expressing the probability of finding an electron at a certain distance from the nucleus. They may be physically represented by the space in which there is a relatively high probability of finding an electron. The Pauli exclusion principle, which states that no two electrons can have the same set of quantum numbers, limits the number of electrons per orbital to two, which must differ in spin quantum number (have opposite spins).

Bonds are considered to be spaces of high electron density between adjacent atoms; they are physical representations of molecular orbitals. The latter are again wave functions concerned with expressing the probability of finding electrons, and they can be expressed in terms of linear combinations of atomic orbitals.

In photochemistry we deal mostly with three types of molecular orbitals, characterized by their spatial properties: σ orbitals, in which the atomic orbitals overlap along the axis joining the atoms, π orbitals, which are antisymmetric with respect to a nodal plane through the atoms and which represent the sidewise overlap of atomic p orbitals (π orbitals may also result from atomic d orbitals, but such molecular orbitals are rarely of importance), and n orbitals, which contain the nonbonding electron pair on atoms such as oxygen and nitrogen and which are localized on those atoms. (The latter are properly defined as nonbonding orbitals, because the energy of the molecular orbital is identical with that of the atomic orbitals.)

In arranging the possible linear combinations of atomic orbitals in increasing order of energy, one obtains molecular orbitals which can be of lower, equal, or higher energy than the combining atomic orbitals. Those molecular orbitals which are of lower energy are usually populated in the ground state and are *bonding orbitals*. Those of higher energy are called *antibonding orbitals* (Fig. 1-1), and those of equal energy are the *nonbonding orbitals*, referred to above.

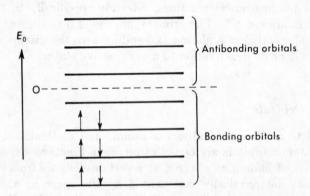

Fig. 1-1   Ground-state population of a molecule.

If the π orbitals of ethylene are considered to be standing waves, then it can be shown that bonding orbitals have waves with one node in the plane of the molecule, whereas antibonding orbitals have two nodes.

The most important difference between the two types of orbitals lies in the fact that interaction in the antibonding orbitals is repulsive.

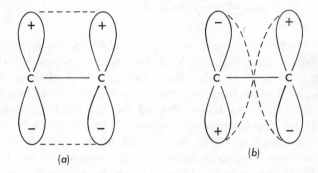

Fig. 1-2 *(a) Bonding and (b) antibonding π orbitals of ethylene.*

Each bonding (σ or π) orbital has an antibonding orbital, commonly denoted by σ^* and π^*, associated with it.

1-3 Electronic Transitions[3]

Excitations occur in photochemistry when the absorption of electronic energy results in the transition of an electron from either a bonding or a nonbonding orbital to an antibonding orbital. Such transitions are indicated by symbols such as σ-σ^*, π-π^*, and n-π^*.

According to the rules governing vibrational quantum numbers in the ground or excited state, several vibrational states may be populated in each. Electronic excitations can in theory *depart* from any of these and can *arrive* at any of these. Thus, the total energy associated with a specific electronic transition can vary within a range and absorption spectra in solutions never show single lines. The transition from a lowest vibrational level of ground state to a lowest vibrational level of excited state is referred to as the O-O transition.

Several types of notation[5] can be used to indicate electronic transitions. Spectroscopists often denote the absorption of radiation by ← and the emission by →, a practice we shall not follow. Frequently the capital letters N, V, Q, T, and R are encountered, each representing a different state. Thus, Q ← N corresponds to n-π^* (or $n \rightarrow \pi^*$) and V ← N to π-π^* (or $\pi \rightarrow \pi^*$). In this book we prefer to denote all excited states by the superscript *, the type of excitation in terms of the letters σ, π, and n, and the absorption of radiation by $\xrightarrow{h\nu}$. For example, the *n*-π* excitation of benzophenone is indicated as

$$\phi_2C{=}O \xrightarrow[n\text{-}\pi^*]{h\nu} \phi_2C{=}O^*$$

Normally in electronic excitations only one electron per molecule undergoes a transition to a higher orbital, leaving its original orbital half-vacant with only one electron. Since the promoted electron no longer has the same set of quantum numbers, its spin, relative to that in the half-vacant orbital, is no longer defined by the Pauli exclusion principle and may be either parallel or opposite. When referring to the relative spins of two such electrons, one speaks of the *multiplicity* of the molecule. The term originally referred to the number of spectral lines in the atomic absorption and emission spectra observed in magnetic fields of appropriate strength. It is defined by $2S + 1$, where S is the "total spin"—the absolute value of the sum of the spin quantum numbers involved ($+\frac{1}{2}$ or $-\frac{1}{2}$).

In most photochemical reactions (but excluding those involving ions or radical-ions) only two half-vacant orbitals are associated with a molecule in the excited state (the orbital from which the transition takes place and the antibonding orbital to which the electron is promoted), and consequently only two values for the multiplicity are obtained: 1 and 3. The former, in which the spin has been preserved, is called the "singlet state," and the latter, in which the spins are parallel, is the "triplet state." Most organic molecules in the ground state are singlets. (Notable examples of ground-state triplets are oxygen, nitric oxide, and diphenylmethylene. The latter is stable in glasses at 77°K, where it is formed by the photolysis of diphenyldiazomethane.)[6a]

The molar extinction coefficients at the height of the bands in an absorption spectrum (ϵ_{max}) are of great importance. The ϵ_{max} values can be obtained experimentally by applying Beer's law (if obeyed) and can sometimes be calculated[6] in terms of certain variables such as dipole-moment vectors and multidirectional transition moments. The significance of the ϵ_{max} values lies in the fact that they express the probability of the transitions taking place. When the value of the calculated intensity is zero, the corresponding transition is not allowed, or *forbidden;* when the calculated value is greater than zero, the transition is *allowed.* Such intensity calculations lead to a set of rules, called "selection rules," which state whether certain transitions are allowed or forbidden. Transitions that are forbidden according to the selection rules do take place, however, although the intensities of the bands associated with them are usually very low. More refined calculations of the intensities will then show that they are in fact not zero, but have a small finite value. There are two main types of forbidden transitions: spin-forbidden transitions and symmetry-forbidden transitions.

1. Spin-forbidden transitions. Selection rules predict that all singlet → triplet transitions are forbidden. The rules determining the multiplicity obtained on excitation are complex. Theory[7] predicts a singlet state for first-row elements upon excitation of their singlet ground states. The presence of heavy atoms, unpaired electrons, or a magnetic field results in a breakdown of the selection rules, and singlet → triplet conversions then take place, even though according to the rules of spin conservation they are not "allowed."

2. Symmetry-forbidden transitions. One type of transition belonging to this class is the parity-forbidden transition. When the wave function of a molecule changes sign on reflection through a center of symmetry, it is called ungerade (u), while those not changing sign on reflection are called gerade (g). Selection rules state that $g \rightarrow u$ and $u \rightarrow g$ transitions are allowed and that $g \rightarrow g$ and $u \rightarrow u$ transitions are forbidden. A discussion of other symmetry-forbidden transitions, dealing with specific bands, is beyond the scope of this text. For a more detailed description of them the reader is referred to the treatise by Jaffé and Orchin.[3]

It might be pointed out here that in calculations involving excited states one often considers the changes to be localized and neglects the interactions with other parts of the molecule.

Electronic transitions occur very rapidly (in about 10^{-15} sec), while the period of a vibration is about 10^{-13} sec. The Frank-Condon principle is an expression of this time difference. It states that since electronic transitions occur faster than a change in the nuclear positions, the geometry obtained upon excitation must be the same as that existing before excitation. Applied to the diagram of Fig. 1-3, where the potential energies of the states are plotted against the internuclear distances for a diatomic molecule, the principle implies that only vertical transitions take place.

It cannot be expected that the potential-energy curves have the same shape in the excited states as in the ground state, because the geometry of the states is not necessarily the same; a favorable internuclear distance in the ground state may be energetically unfavorable in the excited state. Thus although most ground-state molecules are usually in their lowest vibrational energy levels, Frank-Condon excitation will usually lead to higher vibrational levels of the excited state (Fig. 1-3). Since excited states possess less bonding character, a greater nuclear distance will be expected.

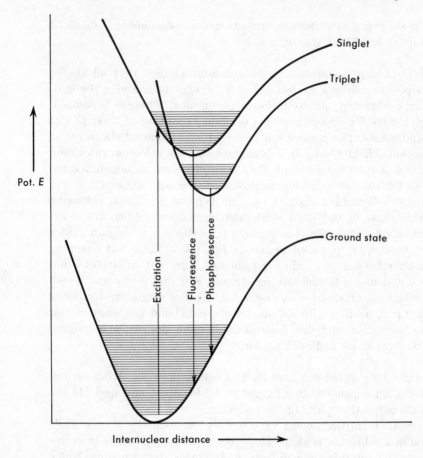

Fig. 1-3 Potential energy surface for a diatomic molecule.

The energies associated with electronic transitions in isolated chromophores often follow the order $\sigma\text{-}\sigma^* > n\text{-}\sigma^* > \pi\text{-}\pi^* > n\text{-}\pi^*$. The absorption maxima of $\sigma\text{-}\sigma^*$ bands are found in the far ultraviolet and are therefore not ordinarily observed by using conventional spectrophotometry. The $n\text{-}\sigma^*$ transition also lies at quite short wavelength. Its absorption maximum occurs at 190 mμ in acetone and at 213 mμ in methylamine.[8] $\pi\text{-}\pi^*$ excitations are much more commonly involved in organic photochemical reactions; they occur in aromatic, olefinic and other π systems. In benzene the transition is found at 203 mμ; in ethylene, at 180 mμ. The last of the series, $n\text{-}\pi^*$ excitation, is most prominent in organic photochemistry. Requiring the least energy, it occurs at about 277 mμ in acetone and at 665 mμ in nitrosobutane. It is pictorially represented by Fig. 1-4. Depending on selection rule restrictions, $\pi\text{-}\pi^*$

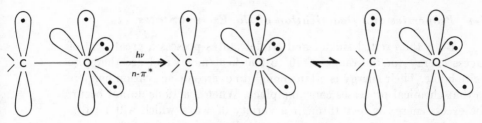

Fig. 1-4   An n-π* excitation of a carbonyl group.

transitions have extinction coefficients that vary from 1000 to 100,000. The n-π* transitions have extinction coefficients of 100 to 1000 (10 to 100 for unconjugated ketones), while those for spin-forbidden (doubly forbidden) transitions are as small as 10^{-3}. The values indicated for the wavelength associated with certain transitions are not meaningful unless the solvent is specified. An increase in the solvent polarity (hexane–alcohol–water–dilute hydrochloric acid) generally causes a hypsochromic or blue shift (a shift to shorter wavelength) in the n-π* bands and a bathochromic or red shift (a shift to longer wavelength) in π-π* bands.[9] The reason for the shifts of n-π* bands is that hydrogen bonding with the unshared electron pair lowers the ground-state energy in polar solvents, so that excitation requires additional energy to overcome the hydrogen bond. Hence, a shift to lower wavelength occurs. The magnitude of the shifts may be illustrated by the example of acetone. In aqueous solution its n-π* band is located at 265 mμ, while in hexane the band is shifted to 279mμ.[10] Other causes for shifts may be the formation of charge-transfer complexes or π complexes between solute and solvent. In all cases the net effect is an alteration in the effective dipole moment of the solute.[9]

Electronic transitions (intramolecular or intermolecular) resulting in the transfer of charge give rise to charge-transfer spectra. Charge-transfer spectra of the donor-acceptor type are often observed with aromatic compounds. For example, a 1:1 benzene/iodine complex is formed with intense absorption at 2900 Å. Other complexes include those of maleic anhydride with benzene, stilbene, styrene, or anthracene. They are identified by the appearance of absorption bands not found in the spectra of their components.

The shift of bands with solvent polarity provides a very useful method for identifying the types of transition, since n-π* and π-π* bands shift in opposite directions. In theory it is possible that the lowest-energy transition changes from n-π* to π-π* or to charge-transfer states in more polar solvents. Such cases have been observed, for example, with p-aminobenzophenone on going from hexane to isopropanol (Sec. 7-2).

1-4   Properties and Deactivation of the Excited States

Both the excited singlet and triplet states possess a great deal of excess energy (in the range of 40 to 200 kcal/mole) and are therefore quite labile. Their energy is often enough to overcome activation barriers so that chemical processes can take place. When reactions do not occur, the excess energy is lost through a variety of ways which will be discussed below.

Regardless of the nature of the deactivation of the excited states, the high energy of the states precludes stability and the lifetimes are often quite short. The average lifetime of the excited singlet state is 10^{-9} to 10^{-5} sec, while that of the excited triplet state is 10^{-5} to 10^{-3} sec. (In special cases the triplet states may even live for several seconds when observed in glasses or crystals.) Thus triplets are much longer lived than singlets. The greater lifetime of triplets may be understood when one considers that spin inversion must take place on return of the triplet to the singlet ground state; the transition is forbidden and therefore has only a low probability of occurring. Changes in geometry are more likely to occur in the triplet state to oppose the interaction of the unpaired electrons. Such change in geometry interposes an additional energy barrier to deactivation.

To a rough approximation the radiative lifetimes of excited states can be calculated by the equation

$$\tau = \frac{10^{-4}}{\epsilon_{max}}$$

For example, formaldehyde has a π-π^* band at 1700 Å with ϵ_{max} of 20,000 and an n-π^* band at 2500 Å with ϵ_{max} of 20. From these data the lifetimes of the two singlet states can be estimated at 5×10^{-9} and 5×10^{-6} sec, respectively. Such calculations suffer from the fact that the values of ϵ_{max} are solvent-dependent. More refined calculations employ the band area as a whole because it is much less solvent-dependent.

A second basic difference between the singlet and triplet states lies in their magnetic properties. Triplet states possess two electrons with parallel spins, thus making the molecule paramagnetic, whereas singlets are diamagnetic. Photochemical reactions involving the triplet state will be susceptible to quenching by paramagnetic salts and by free-radical scavengers such as oxygen and nitric oxide.† Certain paramagnetic quenchers are apparently also able to quench excited singlet states; the mechanism by which this quenching takes place is not known at

---

† Excited triplets can also transfer their excitation energy to a variety of organic acceptors by acting as sensitizers. This process is discussed in Sec. 1-5.

the present time.[10a] Occasionally the triplet state may be identified by electron spin resonance studies.

We have already indicated that the potential-energy curves of excited states are rarely identical with the curve of the ground state, because the most favorable geometry of the excited state is not necessarily identical with that of the ground state (Fig. 1-3); triplets tend to stabilize themselves by distortion, which relieves the interaction between the unpaired electrons. The extreme case of distortion would amount to 90°, where the electronic orbitals become orthogonal. Such a stabilization should occur only after the excitation step, in conformity with the Frank-Condon principle. In Chap. 2 we shall discuss some possible exceptions: cases in which nonvertical transitions are proposed.

The several modes of deactivation open to excited states may be divided into radiative and nonradiative processes. The conversions are best represented by the modified "Jablonski diagram" of Fig. 1-5. Two types of emission from radiative deactivations are recognized. The type associated with excited singlet → ground-state singlet emission is *fluorescence*, a short-lived (10^{-5} to 10^{-9} sec) emission of light; and the second type, the much longer lived (10^{-5} to 10^{-3} sec) emission associated with excited triplet → ground-state singlet deactivation, is *phosphorescence*. (More generally, fluorescence is defined as the emission between states of the same multiplicity and phosphorescence as the emission between states of different multiplicity.) It was seen earlier that excitation from the lowest ground-state vibrational level usually leads to an excited state of higher vibrational level. The loss of this excess vibrational energy through a "vibrational cascade" (a collisional transfer of vibrational energy) is extremely fast (10^{-9} to 10^{-12} sec), so that by the time emission occurs the lowest excited state vibrational level has been reached. Consequently, the energy of the light emitted is less than that of the light absorbed. This is an expression of Stokes' law. Almost all substances show Stokes behavior in that fluorescence wavelength is longer than that of the absorbed light.

Occasionally, thermal agitation can raise the excited state to a higher vibrational energy level prior to emission and the resulting fluorescence wavelength will be shorter than the wavelength of the absorbed light. Such cases are said to display "anti-Stokes behavior." Single atoms, being devoid of vibrational energy, can fluoresce at the same wavelength as the exciting radiation. Such fluorescence is termed "resonance fluorescence." Diatomic molecules at low pressures, where no loss of vibrational energy occurs before emission, similarly may exhibit resonance fluorescence.

Although only one electronic state is immediately populated in an electronic transition, processes as depicted in Fig. 1-5 allow other

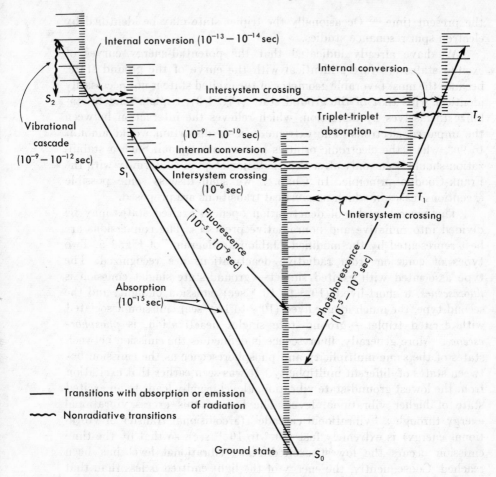

Fig. 1-5 Modified Jablonski diagram.

states to be populated as well. When those of higher energy are obtained, very rapid (10^{-13} to 10^{-14} sec) internal conversions to lower excited states occur. It may be seen from Fig. 1-5 that the latter processes are isoenergetic, leading to higher vibrational levels of the lower electronically excited states, which are further deactivated by vibrational cascades and by emission.

For every singlet excited state there exists a corresponding triplet state. The potential-energy curves associated with the states often overlap, and at the point where they cross (Fig. 1-3) the potential and kinetic energies of the states are identical. Here radiationless transition from one state to the other can take place through a process called *intersystem crossing:* the interconversion of states of different multi-plicities. Since ground state → triplet transitions are forbidden, inter-system crossing is the main source of excited triplets. The facility of intersystem crossing varies with each substance and its environment and depends to a large extent on the lifetimes of the excited singlet. Excited singlets of substances such as cyclohexenone are relatively long-lived ($\sim 10^{-5}$ sec); hence, the probability of intersystem crossing is greatly enhanced and the triplet state becomes heavily populated.

The fluorescence and phosphorescence spectra are often weak, because non-radiative deactivation processes of the singlet and triplet excited states often compete with emission. Internal conversion to one of the higher vibrational energy levels of the ground state may take place from the lowest excited singlet or, through intersystem crossing, from the lowest triplet. Excitation energy may be lost through collisions with the solvent or through interaction with other ground-state molecules, either with the formation of nonfluorescent dimers or through resonance interaction between ground-state and excited molecules. The latter process, called "concentration quenching," is observed as a decrease in fluorescence yield with an increase in the concentration.

Common techniques used to combat the radiationless deactivations are increasing the viscosity of the medium by the use of glassy solvents, diminishing the concentration, and lowering the temperature. Thus the fluorescence and phosphorescence spectra may often be observed and then can serve to identify the multiplicity of the excited state. Often, however, the observed emissions are caused by minute amounts of impurities, so that caution is warranted in the assignment of excited states from the emission spectra.

An alternative technique used to observe emission spectra is that of flash photolysis. During a short period of time (less than 10^{-4} sec), a flash of light of very high intensity is produced by discharging a high capacitance through a flash lamp. The intensity of the light ensures a relatively high concentration of excited species, the spectrum of which is studied immediately after the discharge. Except for a shift to longer wavelength, the fluorescence spectrum often has about the same shape as the absorption spectrum (Fig. 1-6) but is its mirror image.[3] The band adjacent to the point at which the absorption and emission spectra overlap is the O-O band. It is equidistant between the O-1 and 1-O bands.

While singlet-triplet intersystem crossings can take place fairly easily, the reverse reaction is quite unlikely; the triplet formed on inter-system crossing is not in its lowest vibrational level, and rapid vibrational cascade occurs. Conversion to even the first excited singlet then becomes an endothermic process and does not occur without further supply of

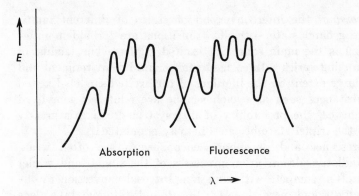

Fig. 1-6   Absorption and emission spectra of a typical electronic transition.

energy. Occasionally, the long-lived triplets do receive enough thermal excitation to undergo intersystem crossing and the fluorescence observed from the resulting singlets is longer-lived than usual. This is one type of delayed fluorescence. A second type of delayed fluorescence is obtained from the conversion of two excited triplets to an excited singlet and a ground-state singlet.[11]

Finally, the lowest excited state can, in theory, absorb more radiation and be converted to a higher energy state. Excited singlets are too short-lived for further excitation to take place, but absorption has been observed in the case of triplets. The bands associated with such conversions are triplet-triplet absorption bands.

1-5   Sensitization: The Transfer of Excitation Energy[12, 13]

We have seen that excited states may be deactivated by energy transfer in the form of vibrational energy to the surrounding solvent or to molecules of the same species by processes that must involve collisions. There is no reason why the energy cannot be utilized to excite another species electronically, provided some conditions are satisfied. The first condition is that the donor excited state be sufficiently long-lived to transfer its energy to an acceptor before various other non-radiative or radiative decays occur (Fig. 1-5). The second condition is that the excitation energy of the acceptor not exceed that of the donor; otherwise, the process would be endothermic and hence improbable. The third condition is that the total spin be conserved. Usually transfer occurs only with the production of an acceptor excited state of the same multiplicity as that of the excited donor species. Recently, however, some exceptions to the rule (i.e., triplet donor* + acceptor = donor + singlet acceptor*) have been observed.[17] When these conditions are satisfied, very efficient energy transfer can occur. The energy transfer, followed by emission or reaction of the acceptor, is called *sensitization.* From the lifetime requirements it is apparent that sensitizations involving triplets are more favorable than those involving singlets.

Sensitization provides the method of choice for exciting to their excited triplet states (such as π-π^* states) species that have poor efficiency of intersystem crossing or very high singlet excitation energies. (Singlet excitation can in such cases be effected only in certain mercury-sensitized processes.) The important feature in sensitized reactions is that the incident light need only be of the wavelength absorbed by the sensitizer; the acceptor can be entirely transparent. The occurrence of energy transfer in this manner can be easily demonstrated. On irradiation of a donor-acceptor mixture at the absorbing wavelength of the donor, the emission spectrum of the acceptor is obtained; further, the intensity of the emission spectrum of the donor decreases as the concentration of acceptor is increased. The process of triplet energy transfer is depicted in Fig. 1-7. It will be seen that exothermic transfer of triplet energy is most likely to occur. The energy difference between the two states is dissipated in the form of vibrational energy.

Little is known about the details of the energy-transfer step. For singlet energy transfer intermolecular distances may be as large as 50 Å; it is only necessary that the emission spectrum of the donor and the absorption spectrum of the acceptor overlap. Triplet energy transfer requires collisions or near-collisions; the process is diffusion-controlled, at least in the liquid phase. It is attractive to speculate that the spin properties of the donor are transferred by an actual exchange of electrons of opposite spin between the donor and acceptor. Triplet energy transfer can be represented by three consecutive steps (D = donor or sensitizer; A = acceptor):

$$D \xrightarrow{h\nu} D^* \text{ (singlet)}$$
$$D^* \text{ (singlet)} \rightarrow D^* \text{ (triplet)}$$
$$D^* \text{ (triplet)} + A \rightarrow D + A^* \text{ (triplet)}$$

The most effective sensitizers[14] are those that have very efficient intersystem crossing, that absorb preferably at longer wavelength than the acceptor but have a higher triplet energy than the acceptor, and that are photochemically unreactive. One of the most frequently used sensitizers is benzophenone with a triplet energy of 68.5 kcal/mole and 100% efficiency in intersystem crossing (when excited at 3665 Å).

An entire range of sensitizers whose triplet excitation energies have been determined[14] is known, and from their successful or unsuccessful

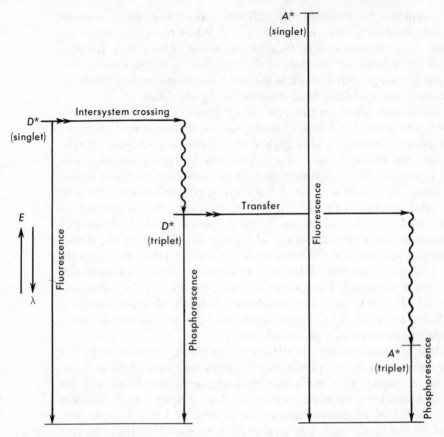

Fig. 1-7 *Triplet energy transfer in sensitization (D = sensitizer, A = acceptor).*

application to certain reactions the excitation energies of the reactants can be approximated. Similarly, the quenching efficiency of a number of unsaturated hydrocarbons on the emission from certain ketones has been determined and found to depend largely on ΔH of the reaction, especially when the energy-transfer process is endothermic.[14a] Intramolecular energy transfer has occasionally been observed. One example is 4-(1-naphthylmethyl) benzophenone. Radiation absorbed only by the benzophenone moiety of the molecule leads, on irradiation in the presence of an olefin, e.g., piperylene, to cis/trans ratios normally observed from naphthalene-sensitized isomerizations.[15] Triplet energy transfer from the benzophenone part to the naphthalene part apparently takes place. Transfer in the opposite direction seems to occur in the form of singlet energy.

4-(1-naphthylmethyl) benzophenone

A different example is found in the cis-trans isomerization of 4-hexenone-2.[18] Irradiation in pentane with light absorbed only by the carbonyl group of the trans olefin produces, along with other products, the

cis isomer. Other olefins present in the system are not isomerized through a bimolecular sensitization process. It is probable that intramolecular sensitization by energy transfer from the carbonyl group to the olefinic bond takes place, although other processes (thermal, dissociation-recombination, bond migration) have not been excluded.

A similar internal photosensitization has been reported for the cis-trans isomerization of the 1-phenyl-2-butenes.[16] It is likely that the fact that these systems are homoconjugated is of crucial importance. Since the triplet excitation energy of an isolated double bond is usually higher than that of a carbonyl group by about 6 kcal/mole, structural features might operate here to decrease or reverse such a difference. Alternatively, non-Frank-Condon transitions might be invoked to accommodate such unfavorable energy difference. The latter theory is more fully discussed in Chap. 2.

References

1. C. N. Rao, "Ultraviolet and Visible Spectroscopy," Butterworth, London, 1961.
2. C. Sandorfy, "Electronic Spectra and Quantum Chemistry," Prentice-Hall, Englewood Cliffs, N.J., 1964.
3. H. H. Jaffé and M. Orchin, "Theory and Applications of Ultraviolet Spectroscopy," Wiley, New York, 1962.

4. W. West in "Techniques in Organic Chemistry," vol. IX, chaps. 1 and 6, A. Weissberger (ed.), Interscience, New York, 1956.

4a. For a recent compilation of references concerned with actinometry, see E. E. Wegner and A. W. Adamson, *J. Am. Chem. Soc.*, **88**, 394 (1966).

5. J. N. Pitts, Jr., F. Wilkinson, and G. S. Hammond, in "Advances in Photochemistry," vol. I, W. A. Noyes, Jr., G. S. Hammond, J. N. Pitts, Jr. (ed.), Interscience, New York, 1963.

6. Ref. 3, chap. 6.

6a. W. A. Gibbons and A. M. Trozzolo, *J. Am. Chem. Soc.*, **88**, 172 (1966).

7. C. Reid, "The Triplet State," *Quart. Rev. (London)*, XII, 205 (1958).

8. Ref. 1, p. 11.

9. P. J. Orenski, S. F. Brady, and W. D. Closson, *Abstract of Papers, Am. Chem. Soc., Detroit*, April, 1965, 50P; J. E. Dubois, E. Goetz, and A. Bienvenue, *Spectrochim. Acta*, **20**, 1815 (1964).

10. Ref. 3, p. 187.

10a. G. S. Hammond and R. P. Foss, *J. Phys. Chem.*, **68**, 3739 (1964); R. P. Foss, D. O. Cowan, and G. S. Hammond, *J. Phys. Chem.*, **68**, 3747 (1964).

11. C. A. Parker, in "Advances in Photochemistry," vol. II, W. A. Noyes, Jr., G. S. Hammond, J. N. Pitts, Jr. (ed.), Interscience, New York, 1964.

12. V. L. Ermolaev and A. N. Terenin, *Akad. Nauk. SSSR, Pamyati S. I. Vavilova*, 137 (1952), *CA*, **47**, 7901h (1953).

13. G. Porter and M. R. Wright, *Discussions Faraday Soc.*, **27**, 18 (1959); T. H. Förster, *Discussions Faraday Soc.*, **27**, 1 (1959).

14. W. G. Herkstroeter, A. A. Lamola, and G. S. Hammond, *J. Am. Chem. Soc.*, **86**, 4537 (1964). See also Chap. 6, ref. 45.

14a. R. E. Rebbert and P. Ausloos, *J. Am. Chem. Soc.*, **87**, 5569 (1965).

15. P. A. Leermakers, G. W. Byers, A. A. Lamola, and G. S. Hammond, *J. Am. Chem. Soc.*, **85**, 2670 (1963).

16. H. Morrison, *J. Am. Chem. Soc.*, **87**, 932 (1965).

17. R. G. Bennett, R. P. Schwenker, and R. E. Kellog, *J. Chem. Phys.*, **41**, 3040 (1964).

18. H. Morrison, *Tetrahedron Letters*, **1964**, 3653.

2

Reactions Involving
the Olefinic Bond

2-1 Cis-Trans Isomerizations

The ability of olefins to undergo cis-trans isomerization upon irradiation with ultraviolet light is no recent discovery, even though the nature of the process continues to be the subject of extensive investigations.[1-3] The photochemical process can be effected by direct irradiation of the olefins or by irradiation in the presence of a sensitizer or a catalyst.

From the spectral properties of olefins information is obtained about their relative stabilities and the energy levels of their excited states. The cis isomers of conjugated olefins often absorb in the ultraviolet at slightly shorter wavelength and with lower extinction coefficients than the corresponding trans isomers. It has been suggested[4] that these shifts are caused primarily by a steric inhibition of resonance due to nonbonded interaction of the cis substituents. For example, *cis*-stilbene cannot be quite planar, because of interaction between the two ortho hydrogens, and is therefore less stable than the completely planar trans isomer. In the excited state these effects are felt more severely and there the difference between the energy levels is even greater, hence the lower wavelength of absorption of the cis isomer. Similar effects account for the greater stability of nonconjugated trans olefins relative to the cis isomers.

A common nonplanar transition state is obtained upon thermal agitation of either a cis or a trans olefin, and return to *that* ground state possessing the lowest energy is preferred. Since the trans isomers usually are of lower energy than the cis isomers, thermal cis-trans isomerization leads to a mixture in which the trans isomer generally predominates.

Electronic excitation of cis and trans olefins leads to two distinct excited states, the trans excited state usually being of lower energy than the cis excited state. Furthermore, the molar extinction coefficient of a cis olefin is generally lower than that of the trans isomer, so that at any given time more of the latter than of the former is being excited. Thus the trans excited state is more heavily populated, be it by direct excitation or through sensitization. The excited states may either interconvert through a rotational process (which is normally exothermic only for cis* → trans* conversions) or may, through radiative and nonradiative decay processes, return to the respective electronic ground states. The latter, however, are often in such a high vibrational level as to be indistinguishable from those involved in the thermal process, so that isomerization may still follow. It can thus be seen that the photochemical process leads to conversion into the cis isomer by virtue of the fact that a small but definite percentage of the trans excited species is continually being converted into the cis isomer, which is considerably less reactive photochemically. Were one to irradiate only at the absorption wavelength of one of the isomers, he could effect complete conversion to the other isomer because it, once formed, would not be able to undergo further excitation. Such a process, in which one can obtain a less stable, higher energy product merely because it is transparent to the incident light, is sometimes referred to as "optical pumping."

As a rule, continued irradiation with light absorbed by both isomers leads to a point where the ratio cis/trans in the mixture is no longer altered, because a constant ratio of the excited species is being generated, leading to a constant ratio of isomers on decay. Such a situation, referred to as a "photostationary state," is reached regardless of the isomer or mixture of isomers with which one starts.

The main two experimental facts of importance are the composition of the photostationary state and the quantum yield for cis-trans and trans-cis conversions (at low concentration). For high-energy sensitized reactions (where the sensitizer excitation energy is well above that of the cis and trans isomers) the ratios are equatable, since the products depend here only on

$$\frac{cis}{trans} = \frac{\Phi(trans - cis)}{\Phi(cis - trans)}$$

the decay process of the triplets. As long as the sensitizer has a high enough triplet excitation energy, one can also calculate what the ratio should be in the unsensitized reaction, since

$$\frac{cis}{trans} = \left(\frac{cis}{trans}\right)^{sens.} \left(\frac{\epsilon_{trans}}{\epsilon_{cis}}\right)$$

Thus the cis/trans ratio for stilbene is 1.45–1.49 when high-energy sensitizers are used,[2] and from the $\epsilon_{trans}/\epsilon_{cis}$ ratio of 7.2 at 3130 Å one obtains cis/trans = $7.2 \times 1.5 = 10.8$, or 91.5% cis. This is in excellent agreement with the experimental data (92 to 93% cis). Similarly, for 1,2-diphenylpropene the (high-energy) sensitized reaction leads to a cis/trans ratio of 1.23, whereas the ratio calculated for the unsensitized reaction is 2.74. The experimentally determined ratio was 2.64.

One type of photochemical cis-trans isomerization takes place in the presence of Br_2 or I_2 as catalyst. The most obvious mechanism for such a process would involve the photochemical production of halogen atoms, addition of the atoms to the olefin, followed by dissociation of the radical so formed to give a certain ratio of the cis and trans isomers:

$$X_2 \xrightarrow{h\nu} 2X\cdot$$

However, kinetic studies of the iodine-catalyzed isomerization of butene-2 indicate that the olefin may become tied up with the halogen atom in a π complex without undergoing isomerization.[120] The cis/trans ratios obtained are similar to those from thermal isomerizations, since the reaction is thermodynamically controlled in both cases.

Another photochemically generated inorganic species capable of catalyzing the interconversion of olefins is iron dodecacarbonyl, $Fe_3(CO)_{12}$.

On irradiation in the presence of 1-octene with light of wavelength above 4400 Å (where the olefin does not absorb but the catalyst does) isomerization to a mixture containing all linear cis and trans octenes takes place, possibly through the photochemical formation of $Fe(CO)_4$, which can form a complex with the olefin.[121]

Many detailed studies of sensitized isomerizations have been made by using sensitizers such as acetophenone, benzophenone, benzil, and α- or β-acetonaphthone, all of which have been found to be quite effective. Most significant contributions to the knowledge of the details of these processes have been made by Hammond and coworkers; the following discussion is largely based on ref. 3.

In the sensitized cis-trans isomerizations one is dealing largely with the triplet state. (It might be pointed out that although direct isomerization is most likely to involve decay by way of triplets, it is by no means a requirement for isomerization.) It will be recalled that energy from the sensitizer is transferred to the acceptor through either singlet or triplet excitations. The triplet state being much longer-lived, the triplet sensitizer is more prone to encounter an acceptor, since close contact is required for triplet transfer. Singlet transfer does not require such a close contact; however, severe restrictions are imposed on it in that it must be almost isoenergetic[3] and a large overlap between the fluorescence spectrum of the donor and the absorption spectrum of the acceptor is required.

In none of the cases examined by Hammond is this requirement fulfilled, but there does take place a very efficient singlet-triplet intersystem crossing in the sensitizers, and hence only the triplet state can be involved here.

One may generally represent the details of the isomerization by the following series of steps[3, 5] (S = sensitizer; Q = quencher; excited species are triplets):

1. Energy transfer:

$$S^* + \text{trans} \rightleftarrows S + \text{trans}^*$$
$$S^* + \text{cis} \rightleftarrows S + \text{cis}^*$$
$$\text{trans}^* + Q \rightarrow \text{trans} + Q^*$$
$$\text{cis}^* + Q \rightarrow \text{cis} + Q^*$$

2. Interconversion of excited states:

$$\text{trans}^* \rightleftarrows \text{cis}^*$$

3. Conversion to ground state:

$$\text{cis}^* \rightarrow \text{cis}$$
$$\text{trans}^* \rightarrow \text{trans}$$
$$\text{trans} + \text{trans}^* \rightarrow 2 \text{ trans}$$

(The last decay process may account for some self-quenching reactions suggested to explain some kinetic features observed in flash photolyses and for the fluorescence observed from excited dimers, or "excimers.")

The most interesting feature of the sensitized process is that the cis/trans ratio in the photostationary state changes with certain sensitizers, notably when the excitation energy of the sensitizer is lowered. Such variations have been studied in greatest detail with 1,2-diphenylpropenes. The results are given in Table 2-1, where the sensitizers

Table 2-1   *Sensitizers and* cis/trans *ratios for 1,2-diphenylpropenes*[3]

		cis/trans
1.	Acetophenone	1.18
2.	Benzophenone	1.24
3.	9,10-Anthraquinone	1.61
4.	Michler's ketone	1.51
5.	2-Acetonaphthone	2.59
6.	1-Naphthylphenyl ketone	2.81
7.	Benzil	4.56
8.	Fluorenone	8.30
9.	Duroquinone	9.00
10.	Benzoquinone	0.64
11.	Pyrene	4.62
12.	1,2-Benzanthracene	4.07
13.	Benzanthrone	4.21
14.	3-Acetylpyrene	2.77
15.	Acridine	
16.	Eosin	0.20
17.	9,10-Dibromoanthracene	0.50

are listed with the cis/trans ratios obtained from each, and in Fig. 2-1, where the ratios are plotted against the sensitizer triplet excitation energies.[3] The latter are obtained from emission spectroscopy.[6]

Figure 2-1 shows that a decrease in the sensitizer excitation energy E_t first causes an increase in the amount of cis isomer produced. The sensitizer becomes less efficient in the excitation of the isomer of highest energy, which in this case must be the cis isomer. Generally, all sensitizers having energies substantially greater than the minimum triplet excitation energy will give the same results. (Under these conditions transfer to both cis and trans acceptor is diffusion controlled.) As the energy decreases, the efficiency of the process decreases and reversibility of excitation transfer increases. In 1,2-diphenylpropene the rate of the

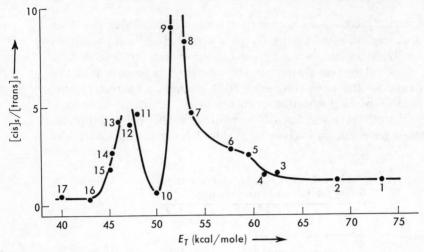

Fig. 2-1 *Sensitized isomerization of the 1,2-diphenylpropenes. (Reproduced from J. Am. Chem. Soc.,* **86,** 3197 (1964), *with permission from the authors and the American Chemical Society.*)

process $S^* + \text{trans} \rightarrow S + \text{trans}^*$ becomes much larger than that of $S^* + \text{cis} \rightarrow S + \text{cis}^*$; and cis remains. However, as Fig. 2-1 shows, there are places along the sensitizer energy scale where the decrease in cis excitation efficiency is much less than expected from the energy of the sensitizer.

Such discontinuous variations as observed in Fig. 2-1 have been accommodated by postulating excitation of the acceptor by a non-Frank-Condon process,[7] that is, by a nonvertical transition to a new triplet that differs from spectroscopic cis and trans triplets and from the ground-state configuration by having stabilized itself by distortion. Such triplets are referred to as "phantom triplets." These nonplanar, low-energy excited states are proposed to arise by a nonclassical energy transfer with a simultaneous change in geometry. Such processes are indicated in Fig. 2-2 for 1,2-diphenylpropene.[3]

To complete the isomerization mechanism, one should add the following steps to incorporate the possibility of nonvertical energy transfer (p = phantom triplet; excited states are triplets):

4. Additional modes of interconversion of excited states:

$$\text{trans}^* \rightleftarrows p^*$$
$$\text{cis}^* \rightleftarrows p^*$$

5. Additional modes of decay:

$$trans^* \rightarrow cis$$
$$cis^* \rightarrow trans$$
$$p^* \rightarrow trans$$
$$p^* \rightarrow cis$$

While triplet energy transfer is generally reversible if the energies are matched (as may be concluded from the phosphorescence or singlet-triplet absorption spectrum of donor and acceptor), the same cannot be

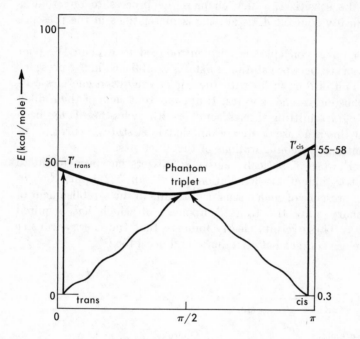

Angle of twist about central bond

Fig. 2-2 *Possible potential function for rotation in 1,2-diphenylpropene triplet state. (Reproduced from J. Am. Chem. Soc., 86, 3197 (1964), with permission of the authors and the American Chemical Society.)*

ascertained about the suggested nonvertical energy transfer in the flexible molecules; for after spectroscopic triplets have relaxed vibrationally to phantom triplets, the latter would be of too low an energy to reconvert the sensitizer to its excited state.

The effective functioning of low-energy sensitizers is thus visualized as being due both to the lowering of acceptor triplet excitation energy and to the irreversibility of the transfer process. One might ask why none of these processes takes place when high-energy sensitizers are employed. They probably do take place, but their efficiency must be very low compared with the production of spectroscopic triplets.

The theory presented here does not provide the only explanation of the variations observed in stationary-state composition with the sensitizer energy. Noting the fact that on a decrease in sensitizer energy the photostationary states tend to approach those of thermal isomerizations, the changes can be interpreted to mean that the role of these sensitizers is one of addition to the olefin and isomerization, followed by departure of the sensitizer, which changes the process to one that is thermodynamically controlled, as are the isomerizations in the presence of I_2 or Br_2.[122]

Finally, a novel concept has been introduced to explain the poor correlation observed between stationary states established in the presence of α-naphthil and of β-naphthil with the triplet excitation energies estimated from phosphorescence spectra. It appears that each of the α-diketones consists of *two* emitting species isomeric with each other. It has been suggested that this is a case of stereoisomeric triplet states[3,8] corresponding to the trans and cis configurations of the diketones.

Recently the use of optically active sensitizers has been found to effect assymetric induction; irradiation of *dl-trans*-1,2-diphenylcyclopropane in the presence of such a sensitizer results in the establishment of a photostationary state the trans component of which has acquired optical activity. These results clearly indicate that the energy-transfer step requires close contact between donor and acceptor.[132]

Of the many examples of cis-trans isomerizations known,[9] only a few will be listed here:

[10]

[11]

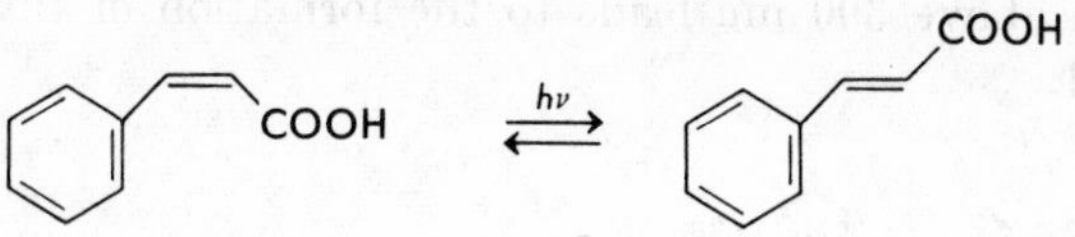

[12]

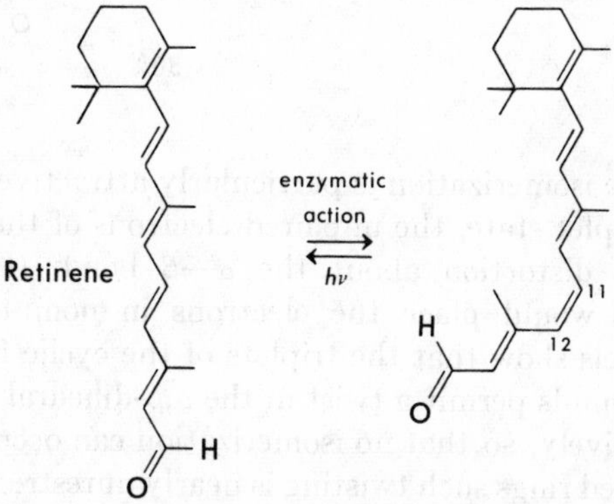

enzymatic
action

Retinene

[13]

The last reaction occurs in the retina of the eye; the all-trans retinene is isomerized to the 11,12-cis isomer by the action of an enzyme. The new isomer has the proper geometry to combine with proteins (opsins) to form a complex (rhodopsin). Light entering the eye reconverts the 11,12-cis isomer to retinene, which dissociates itself from the protein. The latter process, or those associated with it, probably gives rise to a nerve impulse.[13]

Subsequent reactions, such as cyclization and bond isomerization, often take place; most of these will be discussed in later sections. For example:

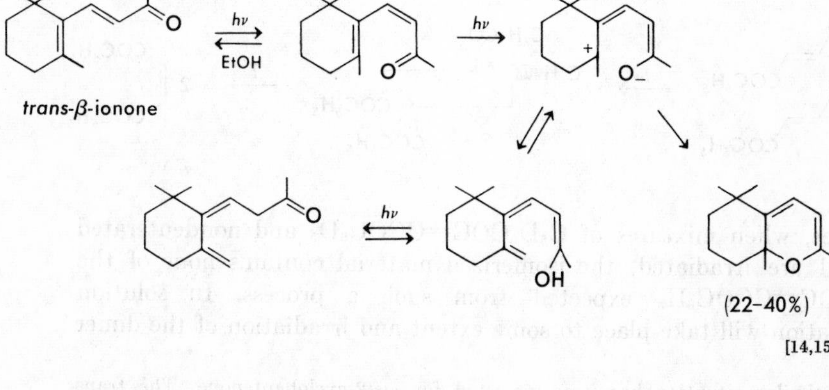

trans-β-ionone

(22–40%)

[14,15]

A particularly interesting case of cis-trans isomerization has been reported by Eaton for *cis*-2-cyclooctenone.[18] Irradiation of the cis isomer with light of wavelength above 300 mμ leads to the formation of the trans isomer in 80% yield:

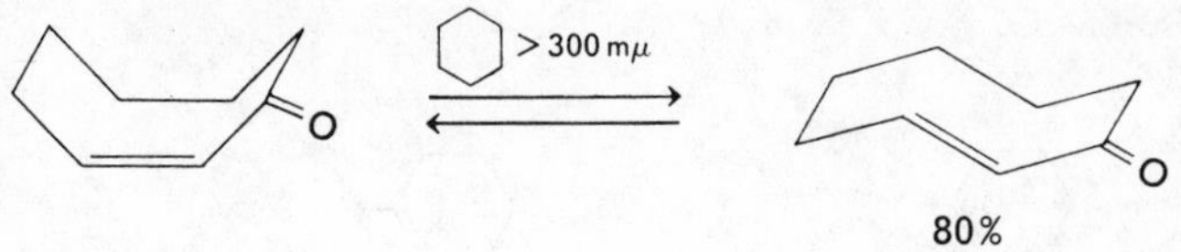

80%

The theory underlying the isomerization is particularly attractive;[18] since excitation leads to the triplet state, the unpaired electrons of the double bond induce a torsional distortion about the α—β bond. (Phantom triplet?) A twist of 90° would place the electrons in noninteracting orthogonal orbitals. Models show that the triplets of the cyclic five- and six-membered ring compounds permit a twist in the α,β-dihedral angle of only 20° and 60°, respectively, so that no isomerization can occur. However, in the eight-membered rings such twisting is nearly unrestricted, and isomerization occurs. The product dimerizes in the dark.†

Very unusual is the cis-trans isomerization that occurs on irradiation of dibenzoylethylene in the solid state:[19]

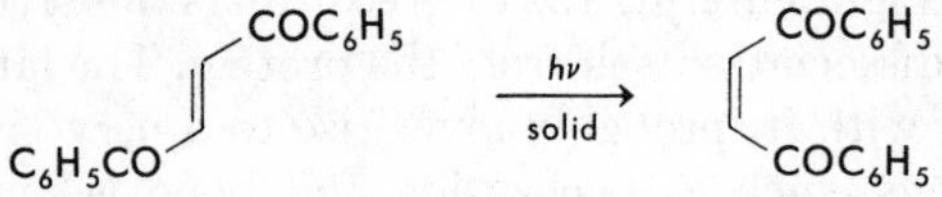

It might be thought that the process occurs through a dimerization:

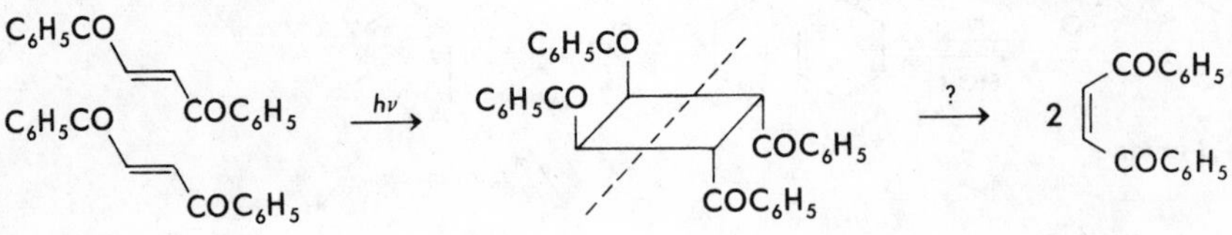

However, when mixtures of $C_6D_5COC{=}CCOC_6D_5$ and nondeuterated material are irradiated, the isomerized material contains none of the $C_6D_5COC{=}CCOC_6H_5$ expected from such a process. In solution dimerization will take place to some extent and irradiation of the dimer

† A similar situation has been reported for *cis*-2-cycloheptenone. The trans isomer has been observed spectroscopically upon irradiation of the cis isomer at low temperatures in an infrared cell (Chap. 6, refs. 11 and 12).

yields the cis isomer. Griffin[19] has suggested that the excited state for the dimerization (singlet) differs from that for the isomerization (triplet?).

Cis-trans isomerizations involving the N=N bond also will take place:

[20]

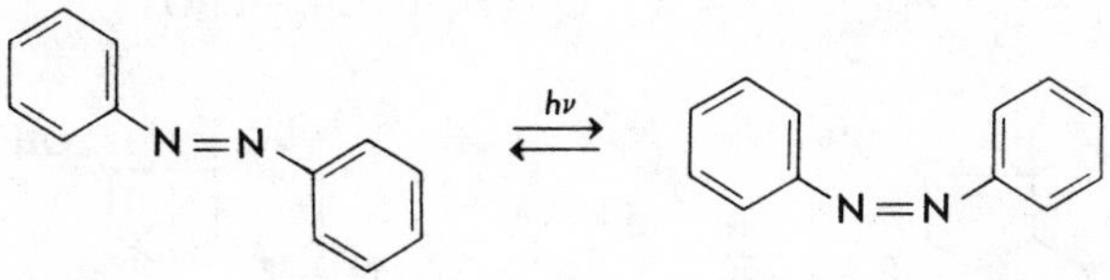

[21]

2-2 Migration of Olefinic Bonds

Double-bond migration frequently occurs through enolization. The migration, an example of the Norrish type II reactions which are discussed in detail in Chap. 3, takes place through a six-membered transition state involving γ-hydrogen abstraction, which has been demonstrated in the case of 5-methyl-3-hexenone-2 with the use of CH_3OD:[22]

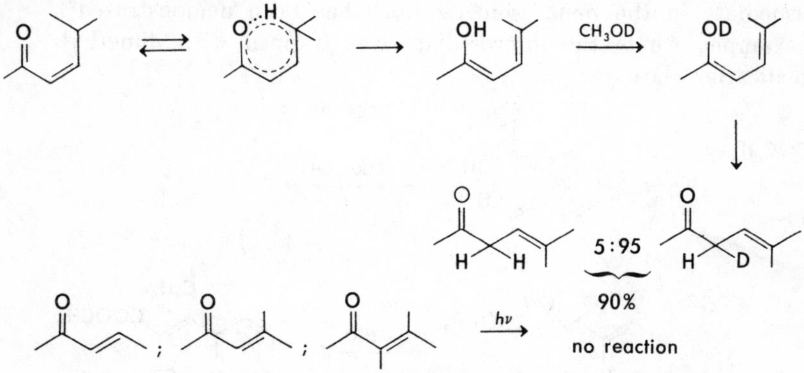

The loss of the 5-methyl group renders the ketone unreactive to bond migration, perhaps because the lowest triplet in this case has changed from n-π^* to π-π^*,[22] resulting in a reduced ability to abstract hydrogen. Similar observations have been made by Hammond in the reduction of certain naphthyl ketones, which may involve the π-π^* state as well (Sec. 7-2). Other examples of bond migration include the following:

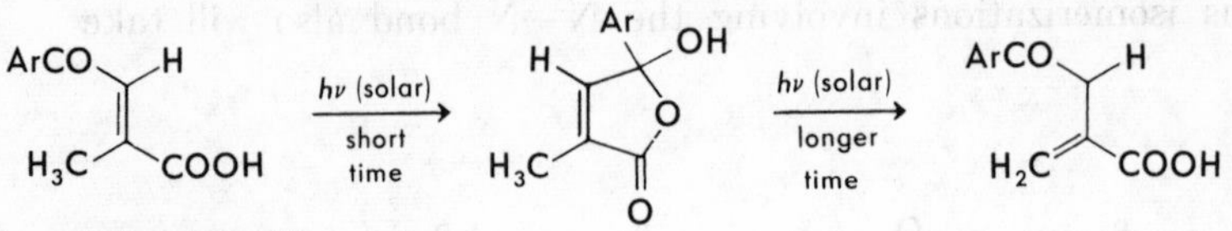

$$Ar = C_6H_5;\ 4\text{-}BrC_6H_4$$

[23]

$$CH_3-CH=CH-CHO \xrightarrow[\text{vapor}]{h\nu} CH_2=CH-CH_2-CHO$$

[25]

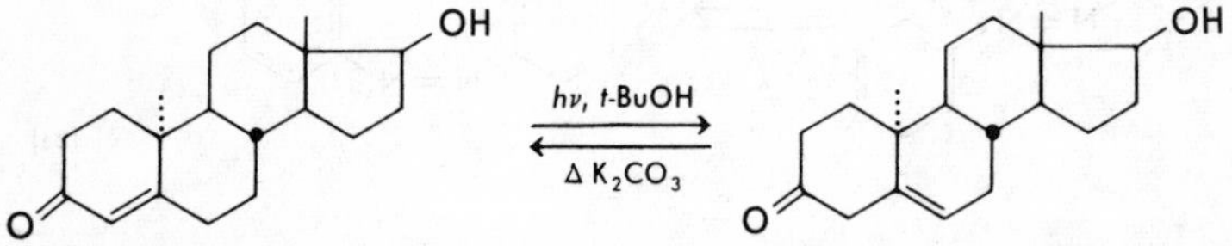

[26]

It will be seen that the reaction generally goes from a conjugated system to a nonconjugated one, presumably because of lack of absorption of the nonconjugated system. The isomerizations are thus examples of optical pumping.

The existence of the enol form during the vapor-phase photolysis of 2-pentanone has been demonstrated spectroscopically; the ketonization step occurs mostly at the walls of the vessel.[27] That the enolic form is also an intermediate in the bond isomerizations has been demonstrated[28] in one example, where the intermediate was trapped with dimethyl acetylenedicarboxylate:

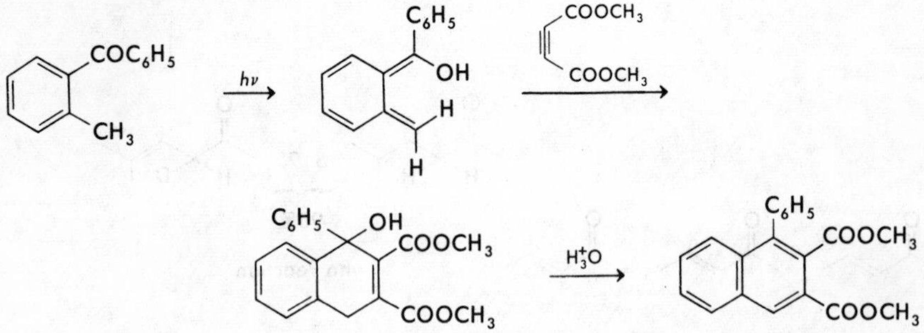

A second method used to demonstrate the intermediacy of enolic forms is that of deuterium exchange. Evidence of this nature has been obtained from the photolysis of 2,5-dimethylacetophenone in CH_3OD.[27a]

From a detailed study of the photochemistry of 2-benzyl- and

2-benzhydryl-3-benzoylchromone[27b] it has been shown that enolization, the principal reaction in the sensitized photolysis, proceeds exclusively via the triplet state. The enols undergo two photochemical processes. One is reketonization, occurring once again through the triplet state, and the other a photocyclization, taking place through singlet intermediates. The latter reaction, observed only in unsensitized irradiations, shows that intersystem crossing of the enol singlet is here an extremely inefficient process. The enolization reaction itself is inhibited at 77°K in saturated hydrocarbon glasses, but it can be promoted again by the addition of compounds possessing electron-donor properties. Other, poor electron-donor additives, while not catalyzing photoenolization, can activate phosphorescence of the substrate. The facilitating effect of donors might be sought in the formation of (triplet) charge-transfer complexes which might undergo enolization prior to dissociation. It seems then that the reaction proceeds through an n-π^* triplet of the ketone, which must pass through an activation-energy barrier on enolization. The phenomenon discussed here is useful in pointing out the dangers inherent in the interpretation of room-temperature processes with the aid of low-temperature spectroscopic data.[27b]

Similar isomerizations occurring in the ionone series show selectivity in the hydrogen-abstraction step.[16,17,24] The isomerization of β-ionone derivatives conducted in ethanol leads to no esterification of carboxyl groups; hydrogen is apparently abstracted from the methyl group:

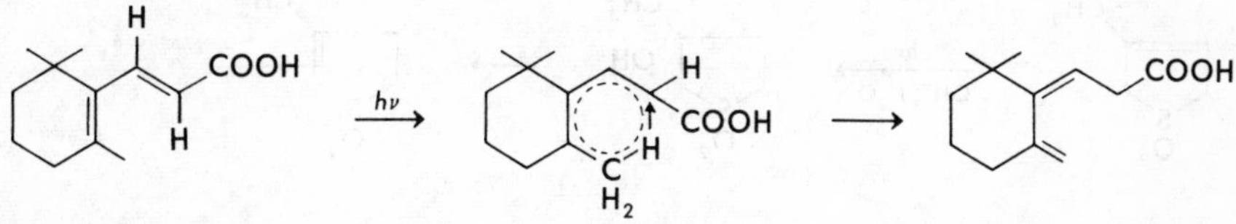

In the α-ionone derivatives the carboxyl group participates in the abstraction of hydrogen from the ring rather than from the methyl group; photolysis in ethanol leads to an ethyl ester:

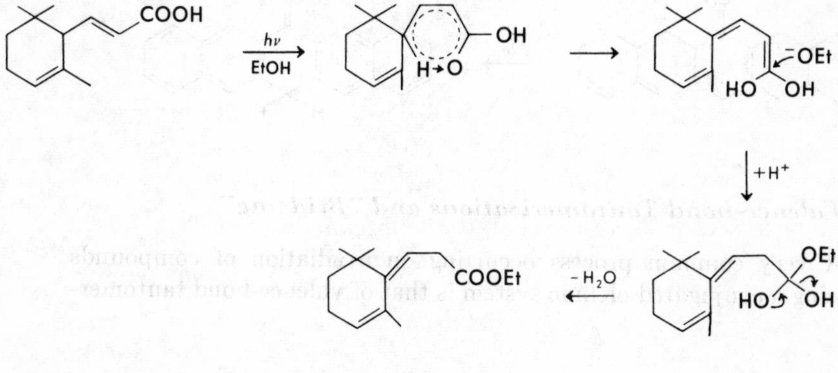

It has further been demonstrated that the introduction of additional double bonds into the cyclic system does not alter the reaction.[131] The formation of an allene from a conjugated diene system has also been observed:[29]

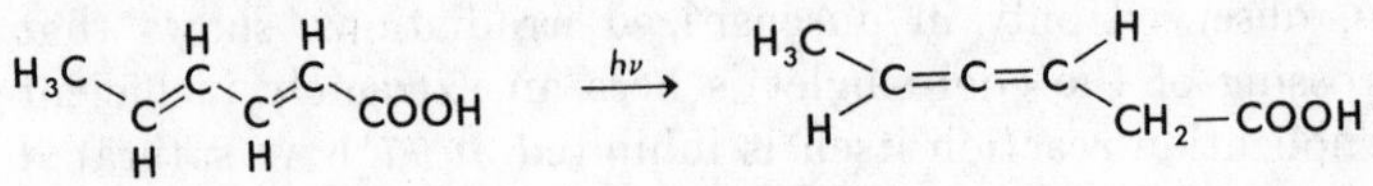

Since the aqueous salt solution of the acid does not undergo the isomerization, the non-ionized carboxyl group probably plays a role in the rearrangement:

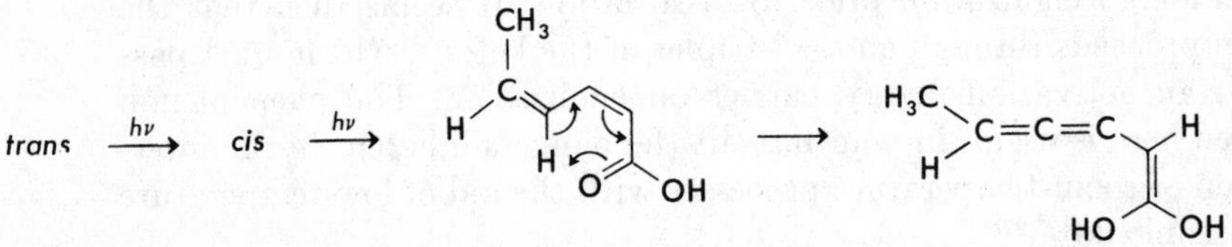

Bond migration involving a sulfone takes place upon irradiation in base:[30]

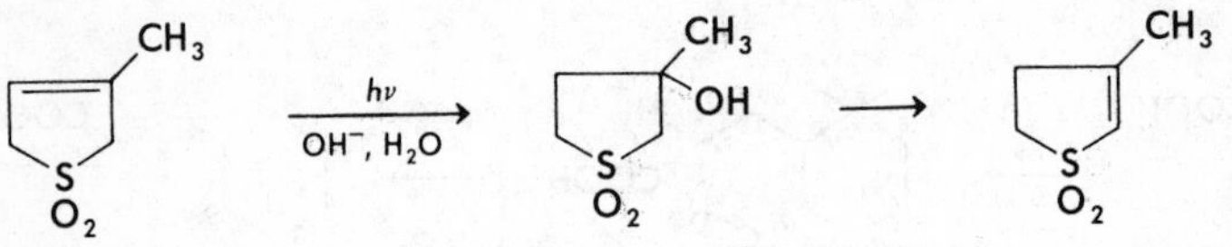

Another isomerization is that of methyl pentacene,[31] thought to react as follows:

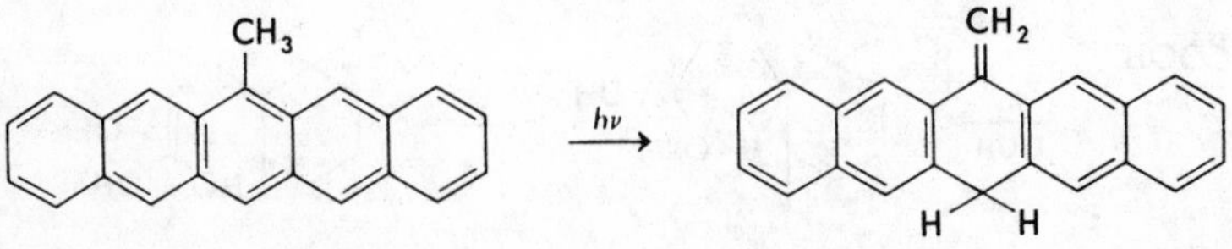

2-3 Valence-bond Tautomerizations and "Bridging"

A very common process occurring on irradiation of compounds possessing a conjugated olefinic system is that of valence-bond tautomerization leading either to the formation of a new ring (or "bridging") or to ring opening:

[32]

Simple 1,3-dienes as well as 1,3,5-trienes and polyenes have been observed to undergo both types of reaction, as illustrated by the following examples of unsensitized reactions:

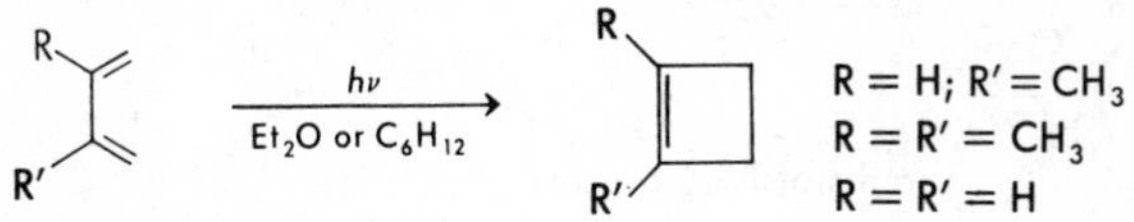

$R = H; R' = CH_3$
$R = R' = CH_3$
$R = R' = H$

[33]

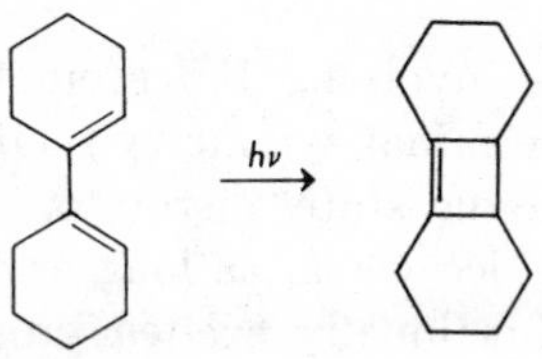

[34]

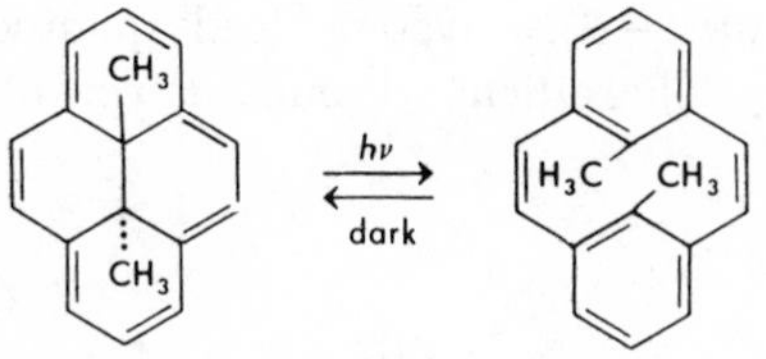

[123]

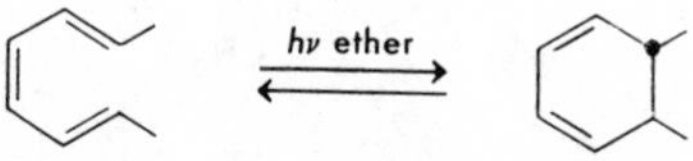

[36]

The stereochemistry shown in the last example can be correctly predicted on the basis of Hoffmann and Woodward's theory of "electrocyclic" reactions.[124] Such reactions are characterized by "the formation of a single bond between the termini of a linear system containing k π-electrons, and the converse process." The theory predicts that, in open-chain systems with $4n$ π-electrons, bond formation between the termini involves overlap (in the highest occupied ground-state orbital) of the orbital envelopes on opposite sides of the system, while in those systems with $(4n + 2)$ π-electrons an overlap on the same face of the system is involved.

The former reaction must take place by a *conrotatory* process, while the latter must involve a *disrotatory* displacement:

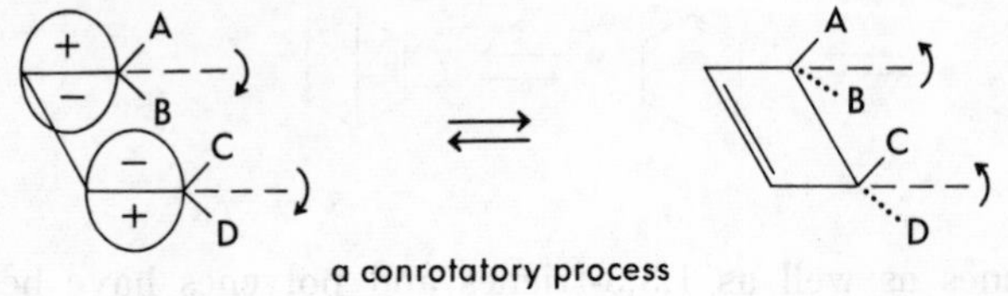

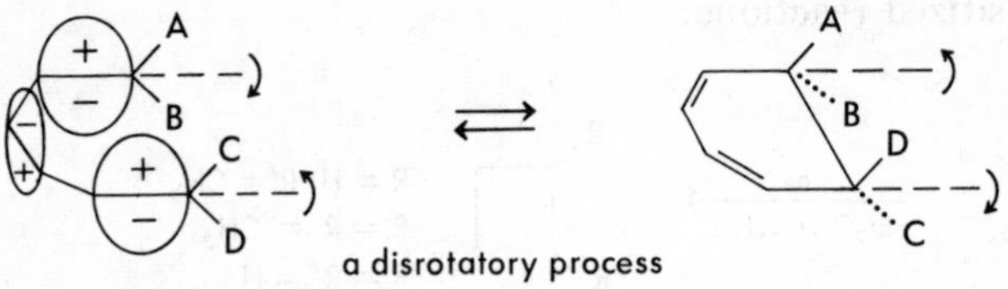

a conrotatory process

a disrotatory process

However, in photochemical processes involving the promotion of an electron to the first excited state the terminal symmetry relationship in the orbitals is reversed, so that ground-state disrotatory reactions are photochemically conrotatory, and vice versa, as long as the photochemical process does not involve vibrationally excited ground states in the bond-formation and -breakage step. Thus the cyclization of *trans,cis,trans*-2,4,6-octatriene, a $(4n + 2)$ π-system, leads photochemically to the *trans*-1,2-dimethylcyclohexadiene through a conrotatory process:

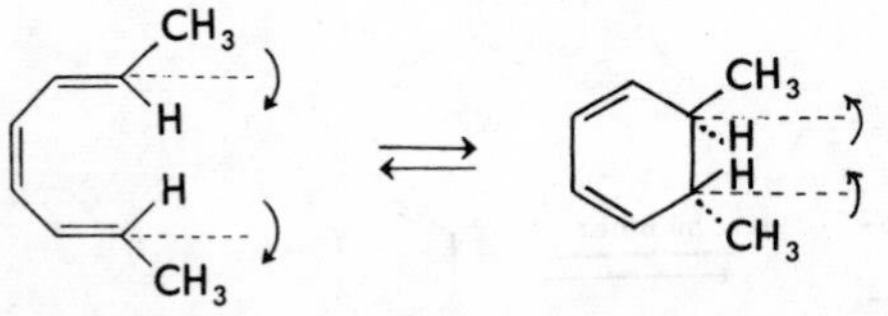

At present, only a few other photochemical reactions lend themselves to the application of the rules described above, but the situation will no doubt change in the near future.†

The course of the bridging reaction is quite dependent on the presence or absence of sensitizers. For example, myrcene leads primarily to the cyclobutane derivative and α-pinene on direct irradiation, while the sensi-

† Related selection rules have been proposed for bimolecular cycloaddition reactions and for reactions involving bond migrations.[124]

tized photolysis gives only the bicyclo[2.1.1]hexane:

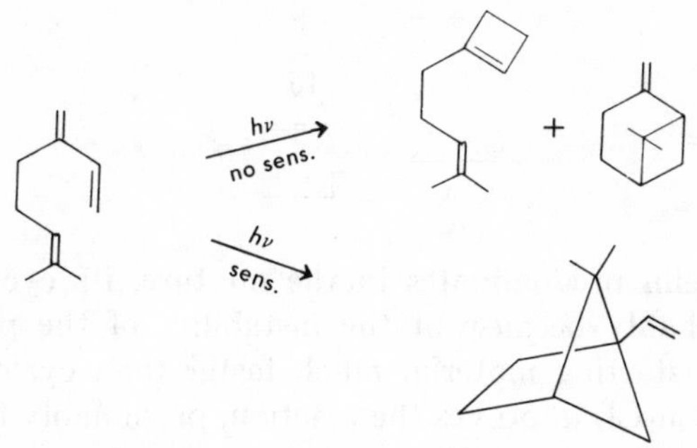

[36,108]

The course of bridging reactions cannot always be predicted, but generally the formation of four-membered rings seems to be a rather facile photochemical process. Thus the photolysis of *N,N*-dimethacrylyl-methacrylamide gives a 61% yield of the bridged cyclobutane; none of the anticipated adamantane derivative is formed:[125]

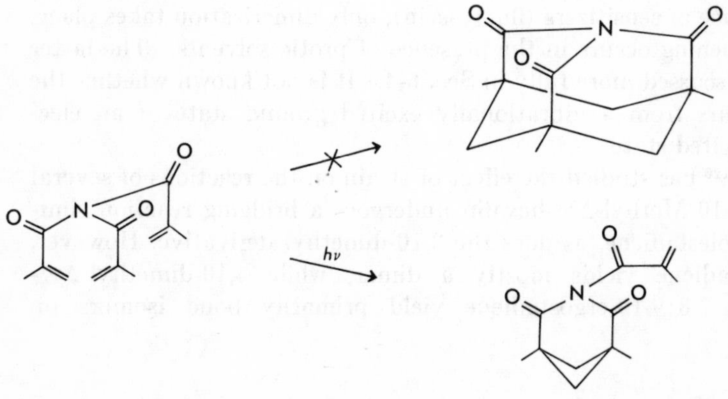

61%

It may be noted that in the reactions where destruction of the chromophore, the conjugated system, takes place the product is rendered unreactive. Such isomerizations are therefore no longer reversible.

Srinivasan[33,37] has studied the isomerizations of di- and triolefins in detail. Of special interest is the one-step synthesis of bicyclo[1.1.0]butane from butadiene:

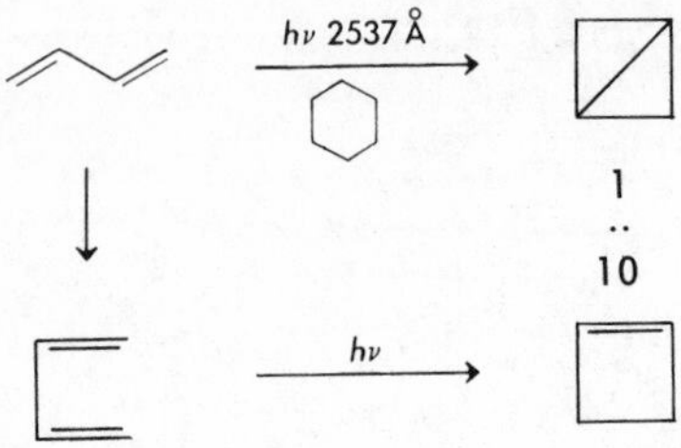

[38,39]

Although the trans olefin predominates in the mixture, its cyclization product does not, probably because of the instability of the product, which reverts back to starting material much faster than cyclobutene does. The presence of Cu_2Cl_2 improves the reaction, presumably through the formation of a π complex (page 52).

The formation of a (highly reactive) bicyclo[1.1.0]butane system on direct irradiation of 3,5-cholestadiene in pentane[126] bears analogy to the photolysis of butadiene:

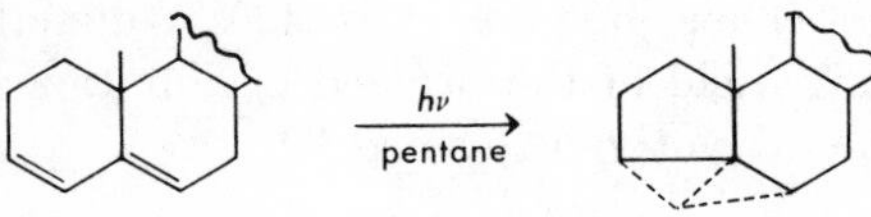

In the presence of sensitizers (fluorescein), only dimerization takes place, while ring opening occurs in the presence of protic solvents. (The latter reaction is discussed more fully in Sec. 6-4.) It is not known whether the reaction occurs from a vibrationally excited ground state or an electronically excited state.

Dauben[126] has studied the effect of strain on the reactions of several such dienes. 10-Methyl-$\Delta^{3,5}$-hexalin undergoes a bridging reaction similar to 3,5-cholestadiene, as does the 3,10-dimethyl derivative. However, B-norcholestadiene yields mostly a dimer, while 4,10-dimethyl-$\Delta^{3,5}$-hexalin and 7,8:9,10-ergostadiene yield primarily bond isomers on irradiation:

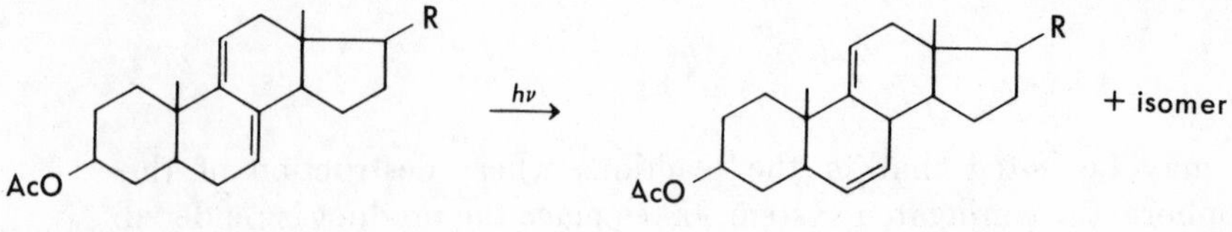

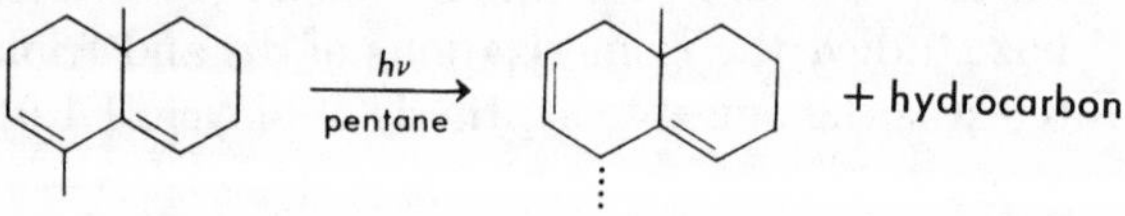

These bond migrations could conceivably involve the transient formation of the highly strained bicyclobutane intermediate with a subsequent 1,3-hydride shift:

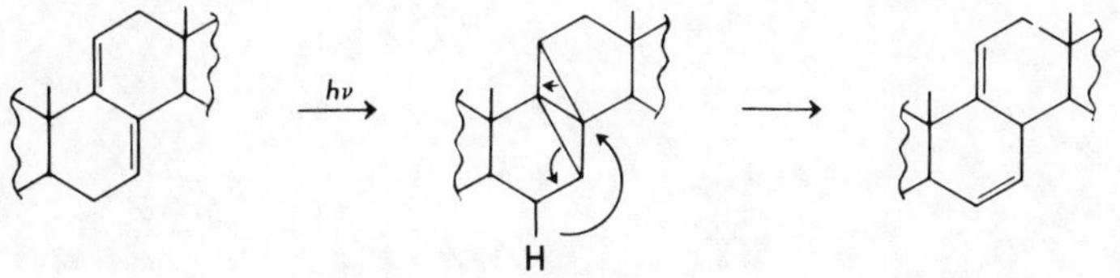

[126]

Bridging reactions have also been observed in a number of cyclic dienes. One example is found in levopimaric acid:

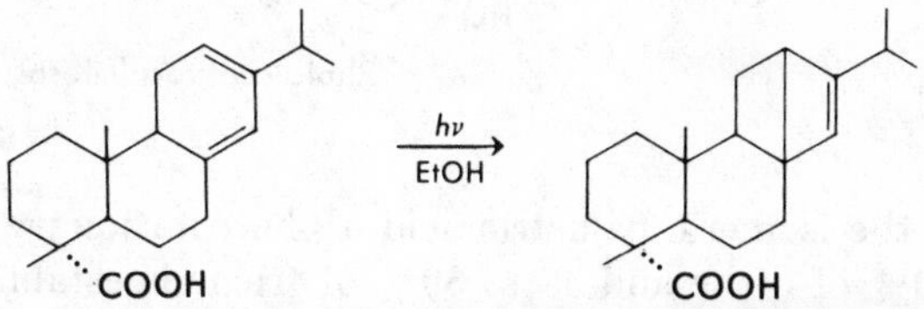

[40,41]

The excited state, thought to be a singlet, probably changes its geometry to a transition state of lower energy prior to deactivation:

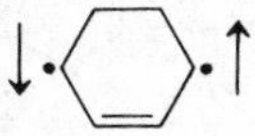

When the lowest-energy transition state approaches that of a half chair form (I), ring opening is likely to be the result of such collapse, whereas with the half boat form (II) as the lowest-energy transition state the formation of a new sigma bond would be consistent with the direction of the bonding *p* orbitals and the anticipated orbital overlap, so that bridging results.[40] This approach has been used successfully to accommo-

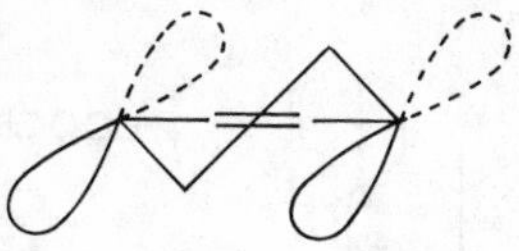

I

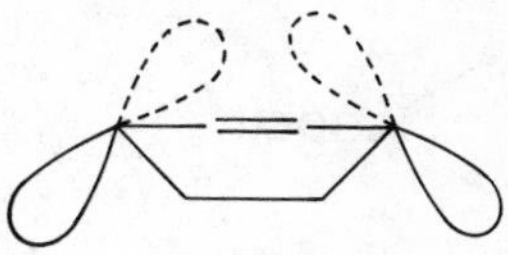

II

date the ring opening of cyclohexa-2,4-dien-1-ones and cyclohepta-3,5-dien-

1-ones and the bridging observed in the tropolones, cyclohepta-1,3-dienes, cyclohepta-1,3,5-trienes, and cyclohepta-2,4-dien-1-ones.

Another example of a bridging reaction is the formation of photo-isopyrocalciferol from isopyrocalciferol.

Isopyrocalciferol $\xrightarrow{h\nu}$ Photoisopyrocalciferol [44]

Interestingly, in the isomeric palustric acid a photostationary state consisting of 45 to 50% of diene and 55 to 50% of triene is established:

$$\underset{\text{pentane}}{\overset{h\nu}{\rightleftharpoons}}$$ [45]

Such equilibria must depend in part on the respective excitation energies and in part on steric factors. The latter are undoubtedly responsible for the ring opening of methyl dehydroursolate, and steric control also gov-

$\xrightarrow{h\nu}$ [46]

erns the epimerization at C_5 of 6,8-cholestadienol to 6,8-coprostadienol:

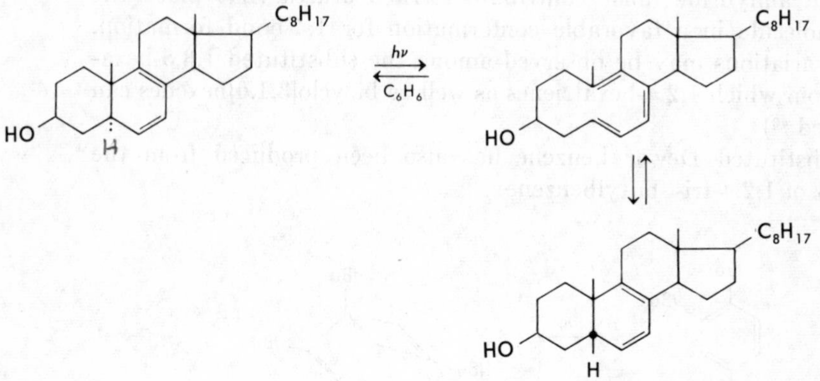

[47]

Finally, dehydroergosterol acetate reacts as follows on photolysis:

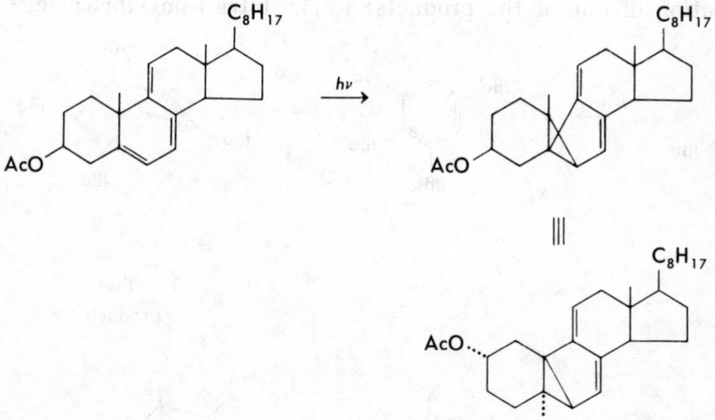

[48]

The bridging reaction has been applied successfully in the first reported synthesis of "Dewar benzene" (bicyclo[2.2.0]hexa-2,5-diene):

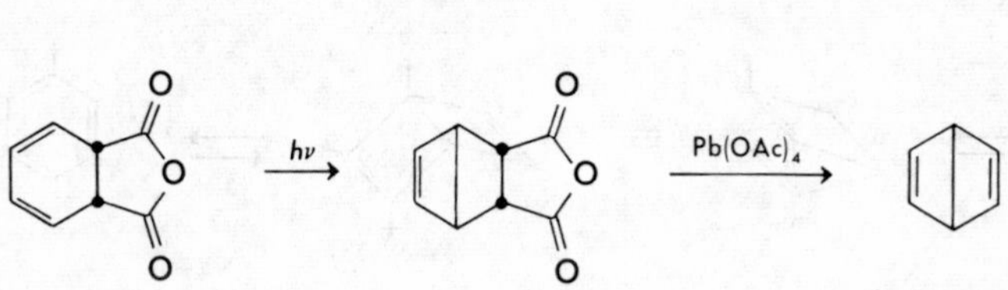

[49]

Irradiation of the related *trans*-1,3-cyclohexadiene-1,2-dicarboxylic acid leads exclusively to ring opening, yielding the all *trans*-α,ω-dicarboxylic acid;[42] the anhydride must contribute steric features that place the excited molecule in a favorable conformation for 1,4-bond formation. (Similar variations may be observed among the substituted 1,3,5-hexatrienes, from which 1,2,4-hexatrienes as well as bicyclo[3.1.0]hexenes can be obtained.[43])

A substituted Dewar benzene has also been produced from the photolysis of 1,2,4-tri-*t*-butylbenzene:

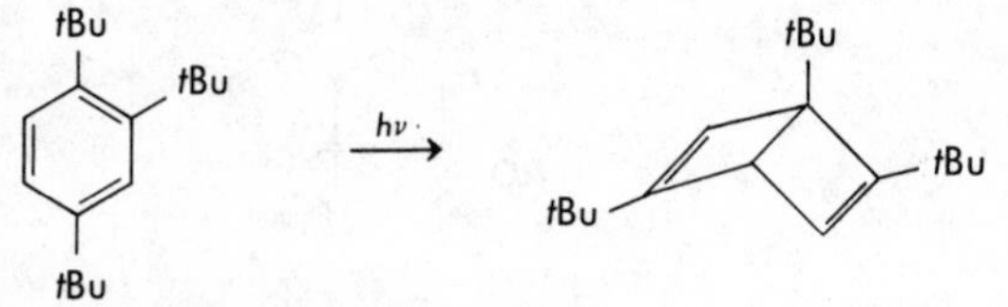

[50]

The photolysis of 1,2,4,5-tetra-*t*-butylbenzene is even more unusual in that it suggests the intermediacy of both Dewar and Ladenburg structures in the formation of one of the products: 1,2,3,5-tetra-*t*-butylbenzene:[51]

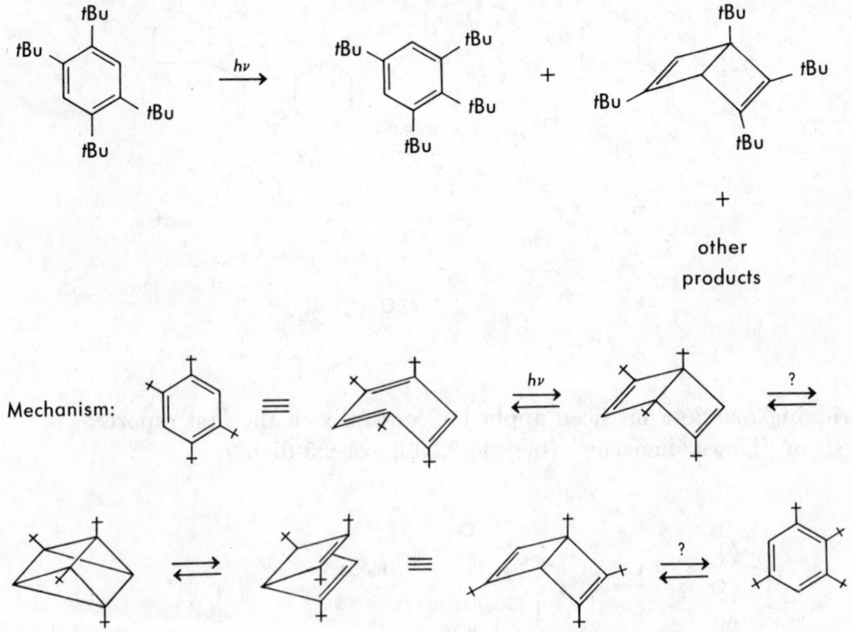

+

other products

Mechanism:

Here the driving force for valence-bond tautomerization is likely to be the relief of interaction between the two adjacent bulky substituents in the planar molecule. A similar isomerization occurs with di-*t*-butyl-benzenes. *Ortho-*, *meta-*, or *para*-di-*t*-butylbenzene produces the same 1:4 mixture of *meta-* and *para*-di-*t*-butylbenzene on photolysis.[52]

The reaction is intramolecular, since neither the monosubstituted nor the trisubstituted benzene produces any of the disubstituted material; it probably also takes place through the prismane, or Ladenburg structure:[53]

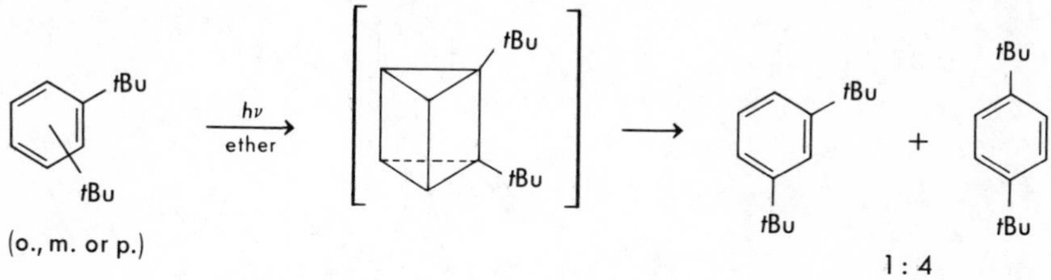

The fact that alkyl groups themselves do not migrate has been demonstrated in the photolysis of mesitylene-1,3,5-$C_3{}^{14}$ in isohexane. The product, 1,2,4-trimethylbenzene, was labeled exclusively in the 1, 2, and 4 positions:[127]

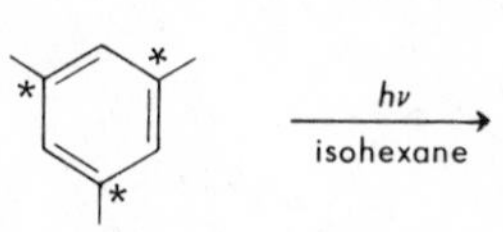

Arguing that steric factors cannot be responsible for the statistical preference for the 1,2 shift of ring carbons observed here, as compared with the 1,3 shifts encountered in the photolysis of dimethyl- and dimethylethylbenzenes, Kaplan and coworkers have suggested that a combination of mechanisms may be in operation.[127] One would involve the Ladenburg structure (or a set of three folded Dewar structures), while a second possibility involves the intermediacy of a tricyclohexene:

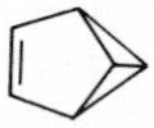

Wilzbach and Kaplan,[127] on careful reexamination of the photolysis of 1,2,4-tri-*t*-butylbenzene, have isolated all three possible intermediates from the reaction mixture. The Dewar and Ladenburg structures, as well as the substituted tricyclo[2.1.1.0^{5,6}]-2-hexene (named benzvalene) possess moderate stability. The following series of interconversions has been observed:

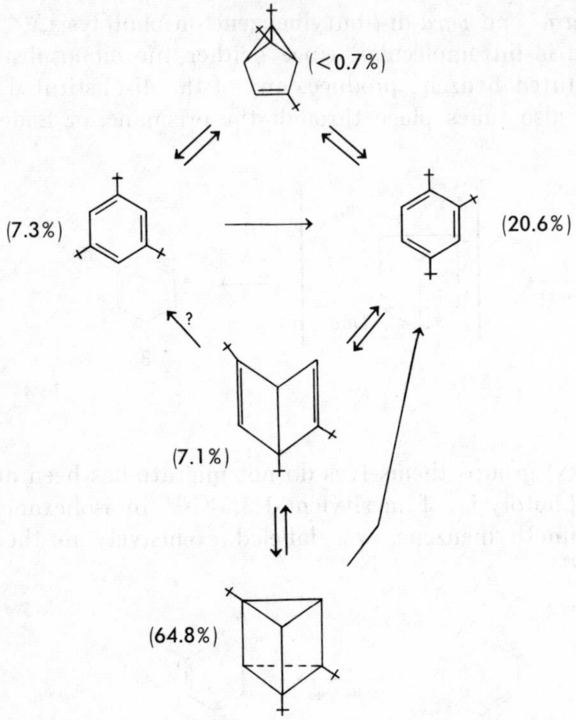

Heterocyclic analogs of the six-membered ring dienes can also undergo bridging, which may be seen from the following two examples:

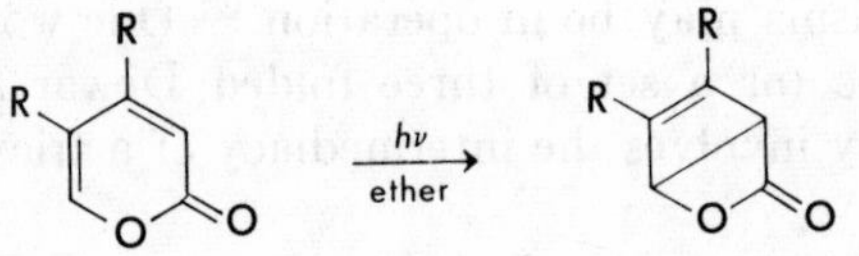

R = H, C$_6$H$_5$

[54,55]

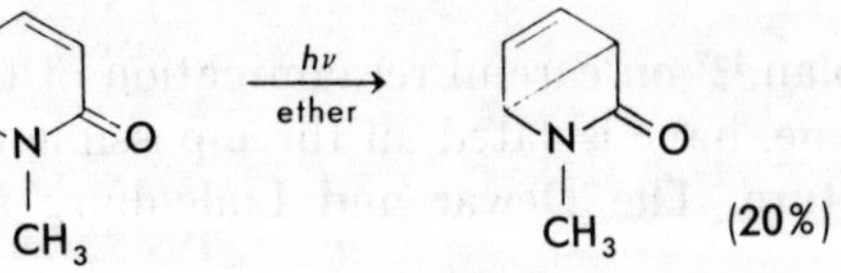

[54]

When these reactions are run in more concentrated solutions, however, dimerization will take place (Sec. 5-7). 2-Pyrone may alternatively lead to fission (Sec. 3-4). Another case probably involving the bridged Dewar-type intermediate is that of 2,6-dimethyl-4-aminopyrimidine:

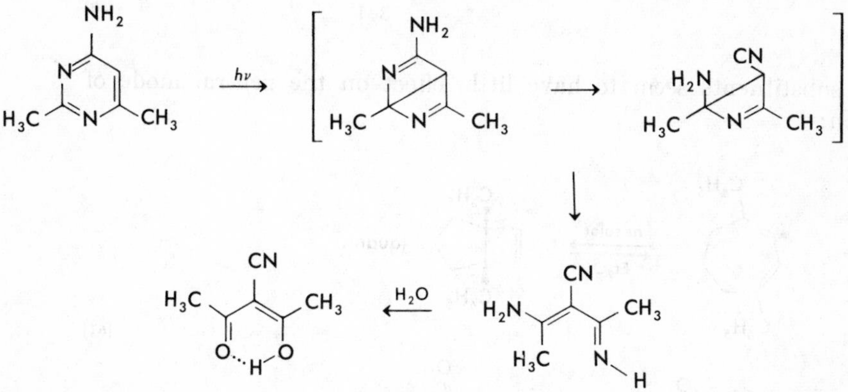

[56]

By far the greatest number of bridging reactions is found among seven-membered ring systems. For example, 1,3-cycloheptadiene forms bicyclo[3.2.0]heptene-6 on photolysis:

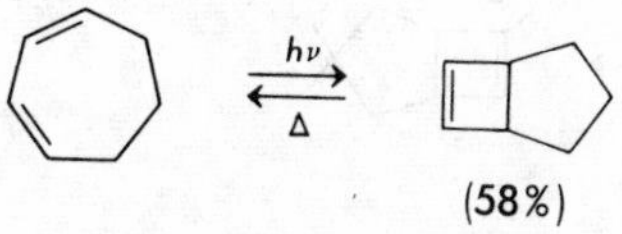

(58%)

[57–59]

The behavior of the triene depends largely on the medium employed. In ether the bicycloheptadiene is the main product, while the neat sample undergoes a rapid series of intramolecular 1,2-hydride shifts, demonstrated by using 7-deuterocycloheptatriene and 7-phenylcycloheptatriene.[128] The vapor-phase photolysis also yields some toluene, probably formed from a vibrationally excited ground state.[60]

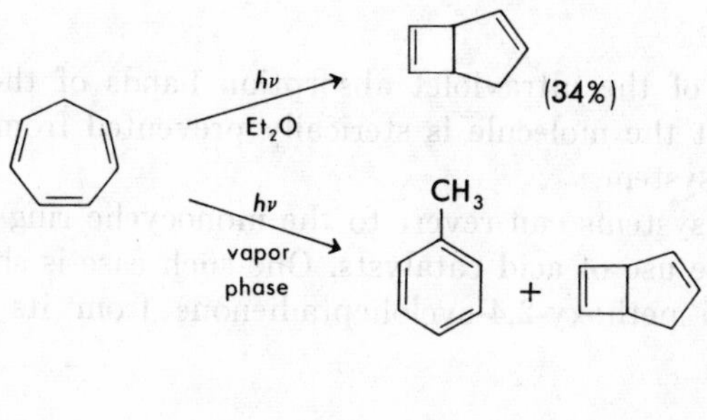

(34%)

[57]

[60]

From 3,5-cycloheptadienol or its γ-enol ether two epimers are formed:

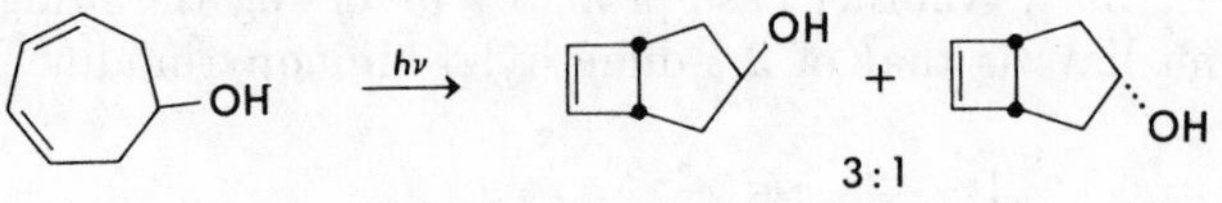

3:1

[58]

Other substituents seem to have little effect on the general mode of reaction:

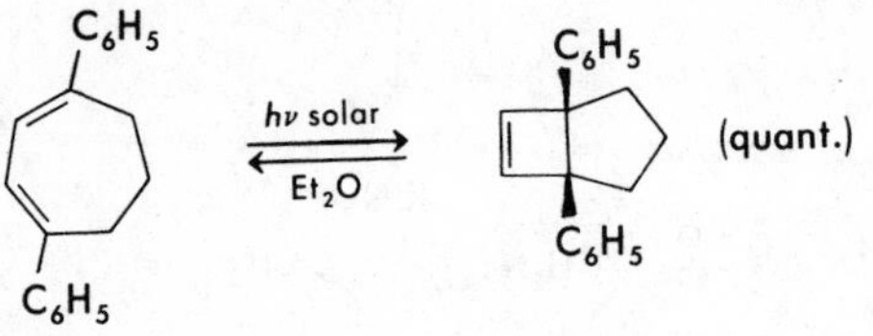

(quant.)

[61]

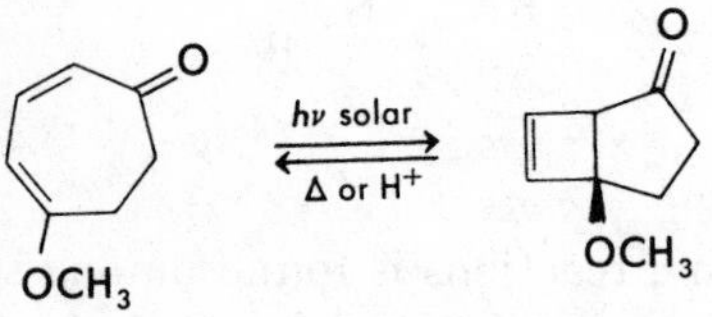

[58]

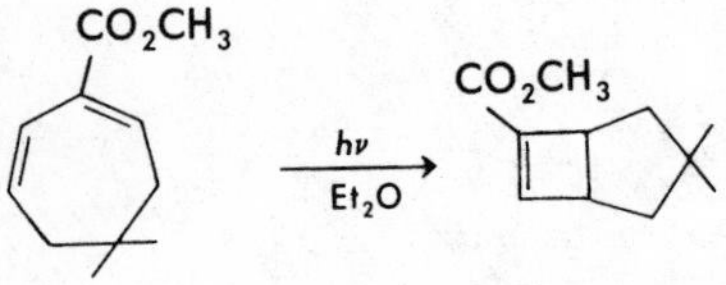

[62]

However, 3,5-cycloheptadienones lead to ring fission:

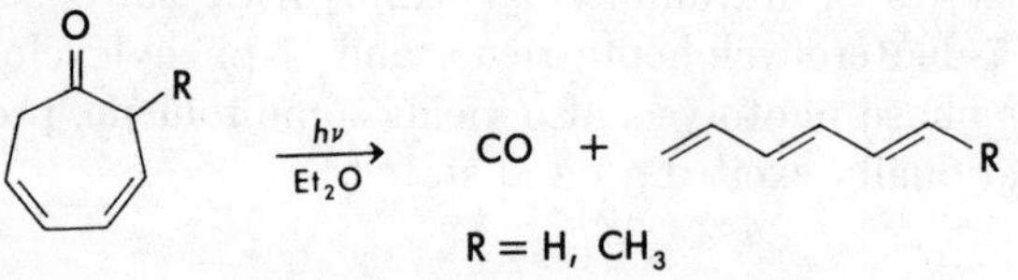

$$CO + \text{...} R$$

R = H, CH₃

[57,63]

The low wavelength of the ultraviolet absorption bands of the cyclic dienone indicates that the molecule is sterically prevented from acting as a true conjugated system.

Bridged bicyclic systems can revert to the monocyclic ring system on heating or with the use of acid catalysts. One such case is shown in the reformation of 5-methoxy-2,4-cycloheptadienone from its photoisomer shown above,[58] while a photolytic ring opening is seen in the case of *cis*-bicyclo[4.3.0]nona-2,4-diene.[129]

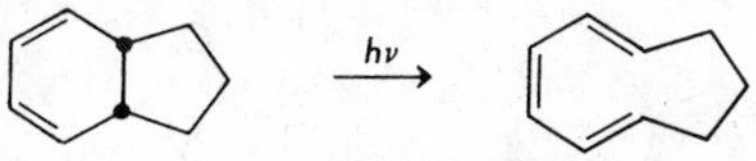

It frequently happens that the primary photoproduct reacts further photochemically. At times none of the primary product is observed, a fact which poses formidable problems in rationalizing the routes by which the final products might have been obtained. An example of such consecutive reactions among seven-membered dienes may be found in eucarvone:

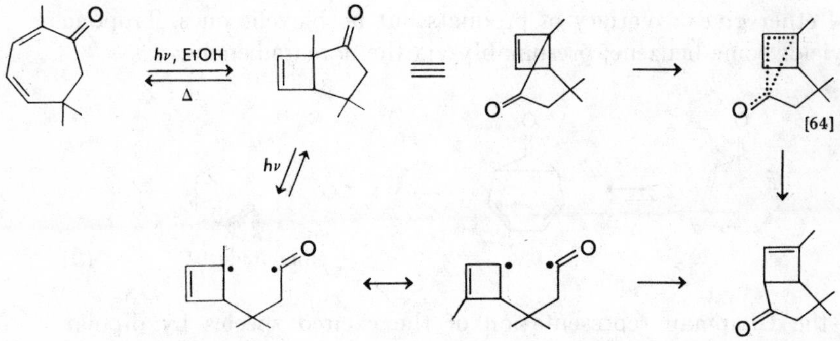

Two additional bicyclic products were isolated by different workers. Their structure and possible mode of formation are indicated below:

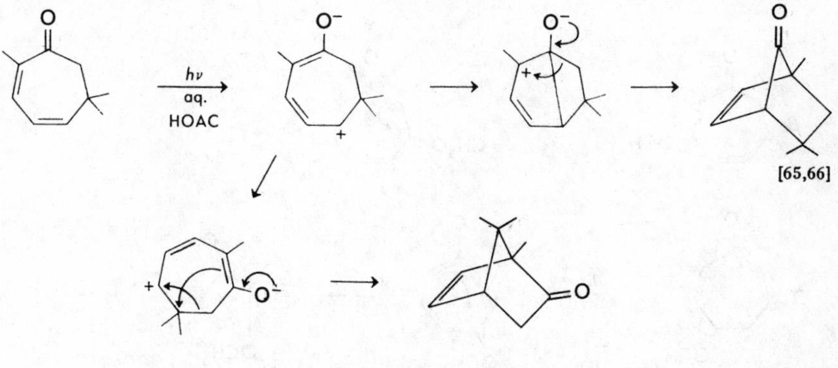

The tropolones have been studied in great detail. γ-Tropolone methyl ethers and α-tropolone methyl ethers behave similarly, while β-tropolone

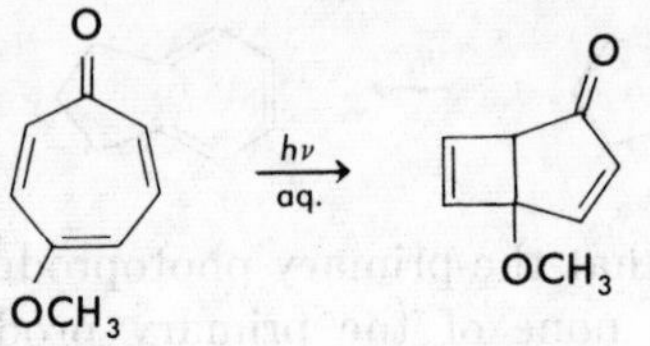

$$\xrightarrow[\text{aq.}]{h\nu}$$

[68]

$$\xrightarrow{h\nu}$$

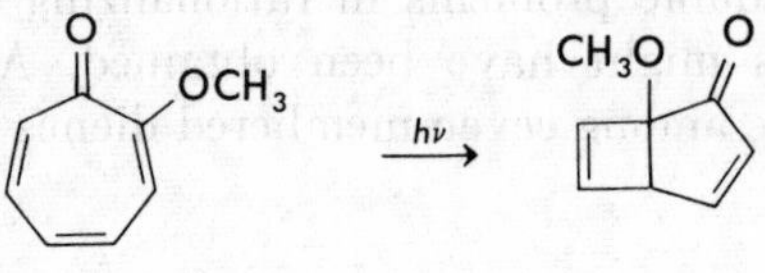

[69,70]

methyl ether gives a variety of products but no bicyclic ones. Tropone itself yields some benzene, presumably via the norcaradienone:

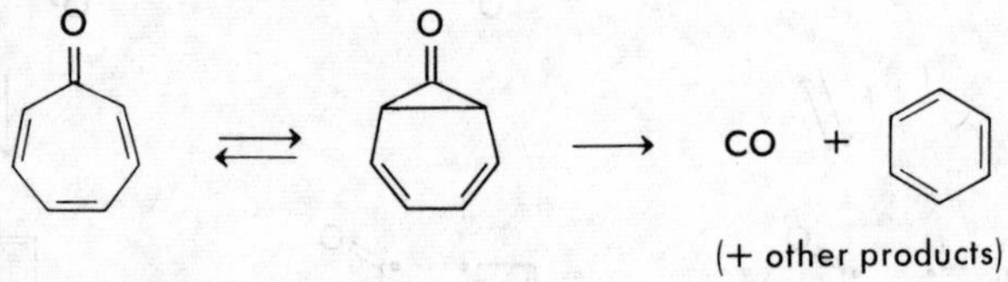

$$\rightleftharpoons \qquad \longrightarrow \quad CO \; + \quad$$

(+ other products)   [71]

Using the Chapman representation of the excited species by dipolar structures (Chap. 4), the cause for these differences may be seen in the effect exerted by the methoxyl group:

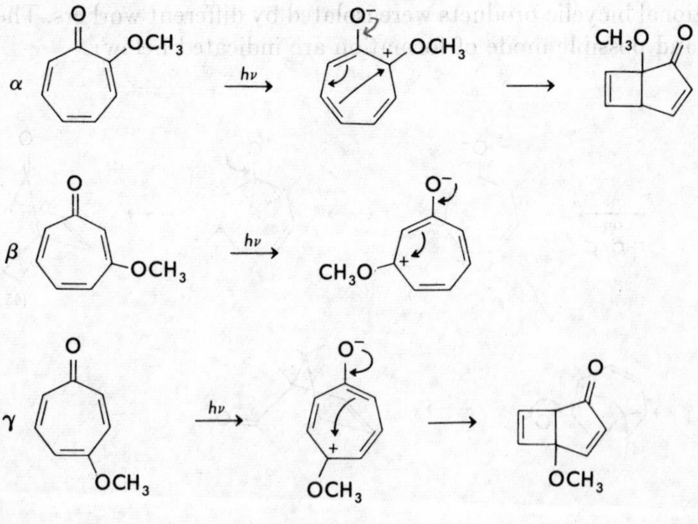

α $\xrightarrow{h\nu}$ $\longrightarrow$

β $\xrightarrow{h\nu}$

γ $\xrightarrow{h\nu}$ $\longrightarrow$

In the case of the β isomer no collapse to the bicyclic product can take place by analogous electron distributions, and slower processes become competitive.[71]

In quartz vessels the irradiation of the α-methyl ether leads to fission, apparently through hydration of a double bond in the primary product. The free alcohol behaves analogously.

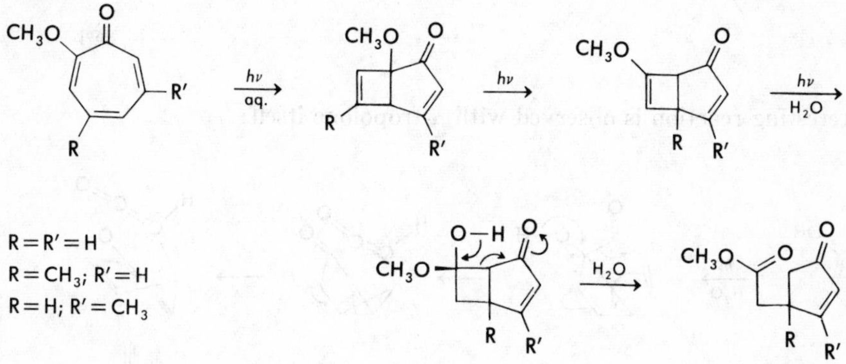

$$R = R' = H$$
$$R = CH_3; \ R' = H$$
$$R = H; \ R' = CH_3$$

[69,72]

The rearrangement as observed in the bicyclic product is analogous to the secondary process seen in the eucarvone photolysis. A third representation of the possible mechanistic details is shown here:

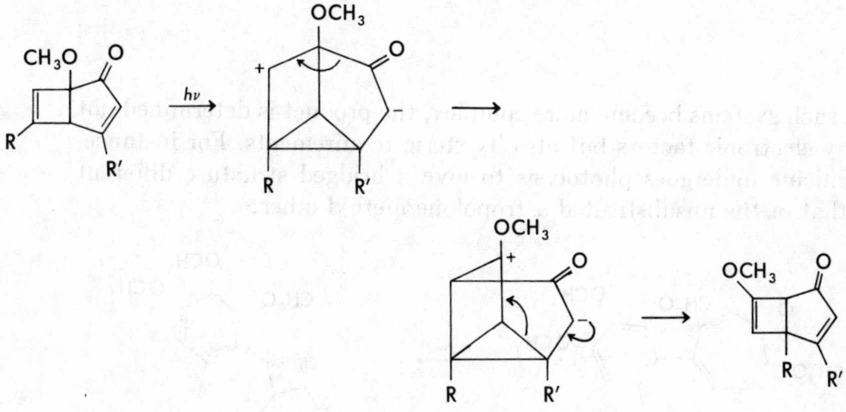

[69,70]

The initial photoproduct from γ-thujaplicin is found to rearrange in a similar fashion:

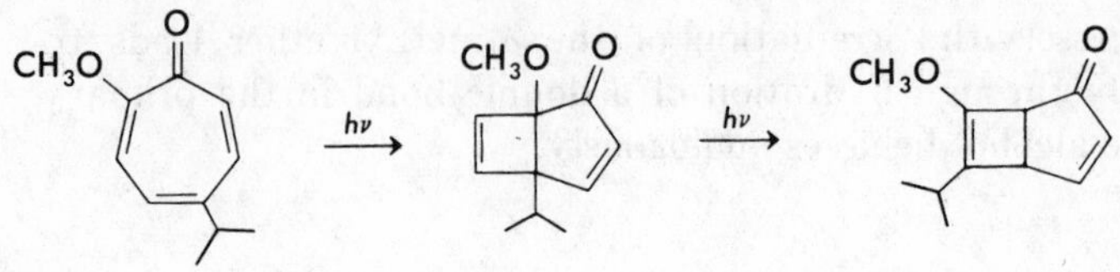

[69]

An interesting reaction is observed with α-tropolone itself:

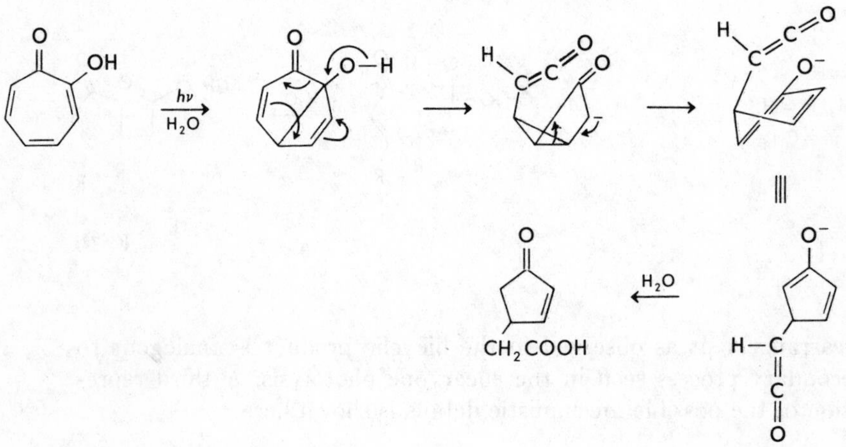

[70]

When such systems become more complex, the product is determined not only by electronic factors but also by steric requirements. For instance, isocolchicine undergoes photolysis to give a bridged structure different from that of the unsubstituted α-tropolone methyl ether:

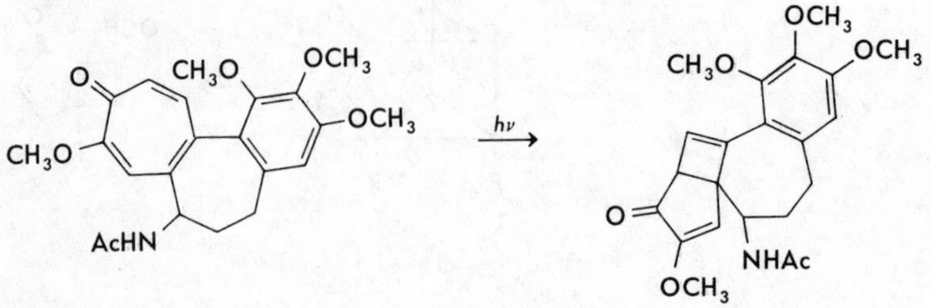

[71]

When fused to an aromatic ring, ring contraction is observed, but the solvent does not become incorporated in the product:

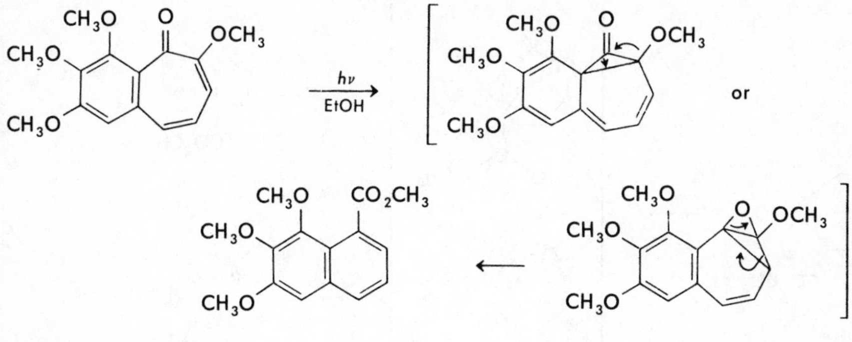

[72]

Colchicine itself yields two bridged products differing only in stereochemistry, similar to isocolchicine, as well as a third one, found to be a head-to-head dimer (Sec. 5-6):

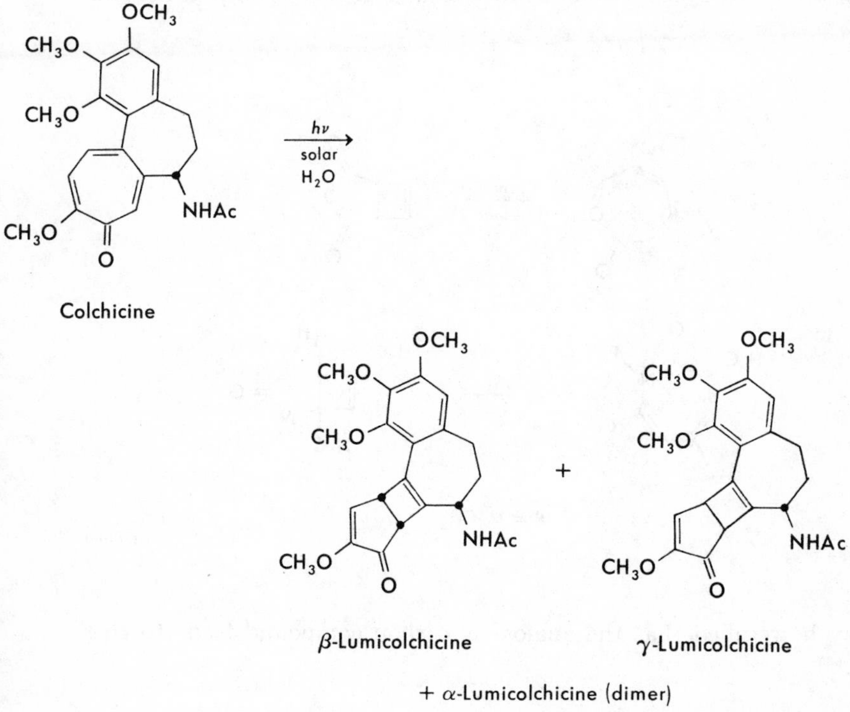

Colchicine

β-Lumicolchicine   γ-Lumicolchicine

+ α-Lumicolchicine (dimer)

[73–76]

An example of a Wagner-Meerwein rearrangement has been observed in the case of methyl thujate:

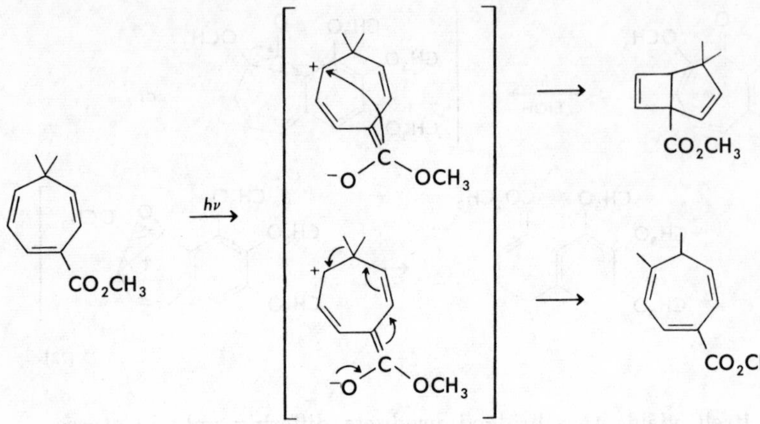

[77]

Among the heterocyclic seven-membered analogs two examples may be noted:

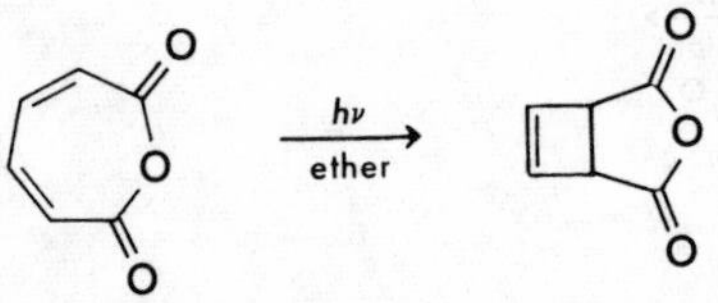

[78]

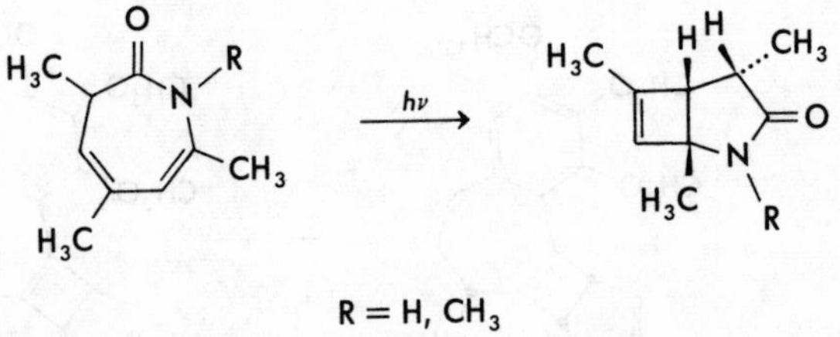

R = H, CH₃

[79,80]

(It may be recalled that the analogous carbon compound leads to ring fission.[63])

Eight-membered ring systems behave as expected, which may be seen from the example of 1,3-cyclooctadiene (and similarly 1,3,5-cyclooctatriene):

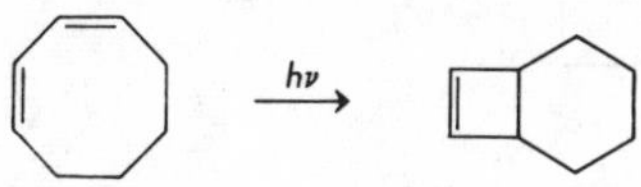

[80–83]

However, the mercury-sensitized photoisomerization of 1,5-cyclooctadiene does not lead to the simple bridged product but instead yields that resulting from "crossover":

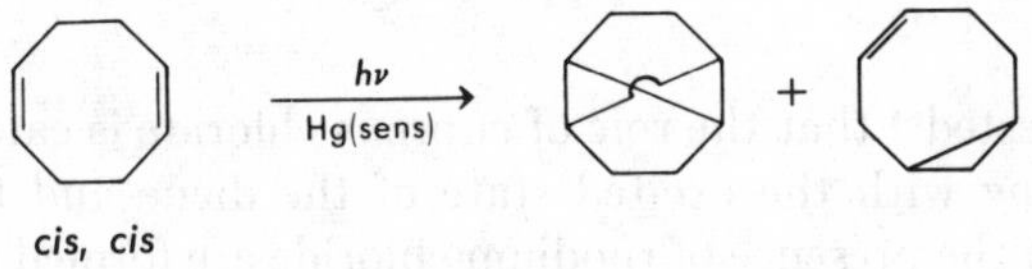

cis, cis

[84,85,39]

For the formation of bicyclo[5.1.0]octene-3, observed as the second product, a hydrogen migration must be postulated. Baldwin and Greeley[85] have shown that the formation of the tricyclic hydrocarbon does not occur by a purely intramolecular process, as in dibenzocyclooctatetraene (p. 53); 3-deuterio-*cis,cis*-1,5-cyclooctadiene yields a mixture of deuteriotricyclo[3.3.0.0²,⁶]octane and unlabeled tricyclooctane. It is therefore likely that this reaction proceeds by way of free-radical intermediates. A similar crossover product, as shown above, is obtained on photolysis of the six-carbon open-chain olefin:†

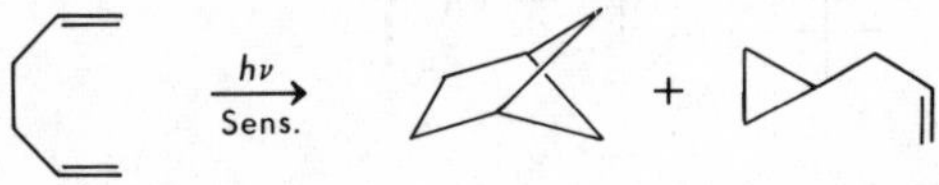

[86]

The use of π complexes of an olefin as a photochemical reactant or catalyst has recently been investigated.[39,84] While the complex of cuprous chloride with 1,5-cyclooctadiene leads to the same bridged product as that obtained from the uncomplexed material, the rhodium complex, presumably similar in structure, leads to different products:

† The decomposition of 1,6-heptadiene takes a similar course.[84]

Srinivasan has suggested[84] that the role of cuprous chloride is catalytic in nature by complexing with the excited state of the diene and that the products obtained in the presence of rhodium chloride are formed through excitation of the π complex itself:

vs:

Bicyclo[4.2.0]octene-7 probably forms from a secondary process involving 1,3-cyclooctadiene:

[84]

The crossover reaction of 1,5-cyclooctadiene finds its analogy in the rearrangement of the substituted dibenzo(a,e)cyclooctatetraene reported by Stiles and Burckhardt:[86]

$R_1 = R_2 = C_6H_5$; p-CH$_3$-C$_6$H$_4$; p-Br-C$_6$H$_4$; COOCH$_3$; $R_1 = C_6H_5$, $R_2 = $ p-Br-C$_6$H$_4$

It was shown that the thermal counterpart proceeds intramolecularly, without going through an intermediate dimerization step or a dissociation-recombination reaction. (For example, intermediates such as benzocyclobutadiene would give rise to scrambling of nonidentical substituents R and R'.) Cyclooctatrienes undergo several bridging reactions. While the photolysis of 1,3,5-cyclooctatriene is relatively straightforward, the isomeric 1,3,6-triene gives a variety of products, perhaps formed through one or more 1,2-hydride shifts. The sequence can be schematically represented as follows:

[87]

The related ketone may undergo both bridging and ring opening, depending on the medium employed, in a process similar to that observed with cyclohexanone (Sec. 3-2):

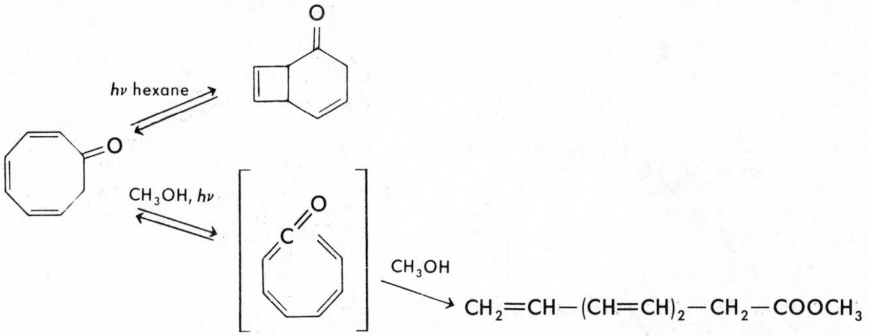

[89]

Derivatives of cyclooctatetraene also undergo valence-bond tautomerization on photolysis, as shown below:

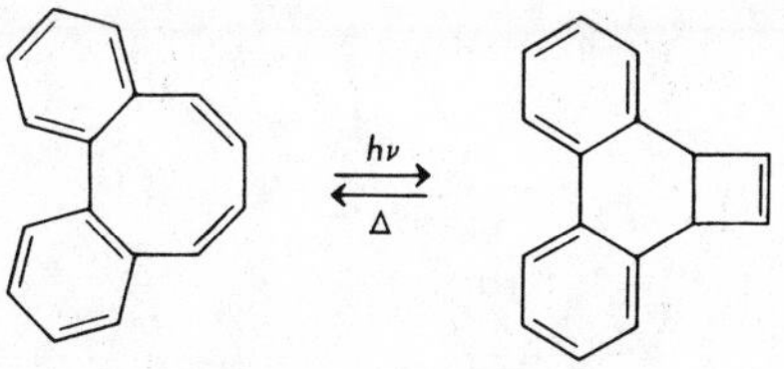

[88]

It may be appropriate to conclude this section with an example that will give the reader a taste of the variety, complexity, and perfidity of organic photochemistry: the vitamin D_2 series:[90-96]

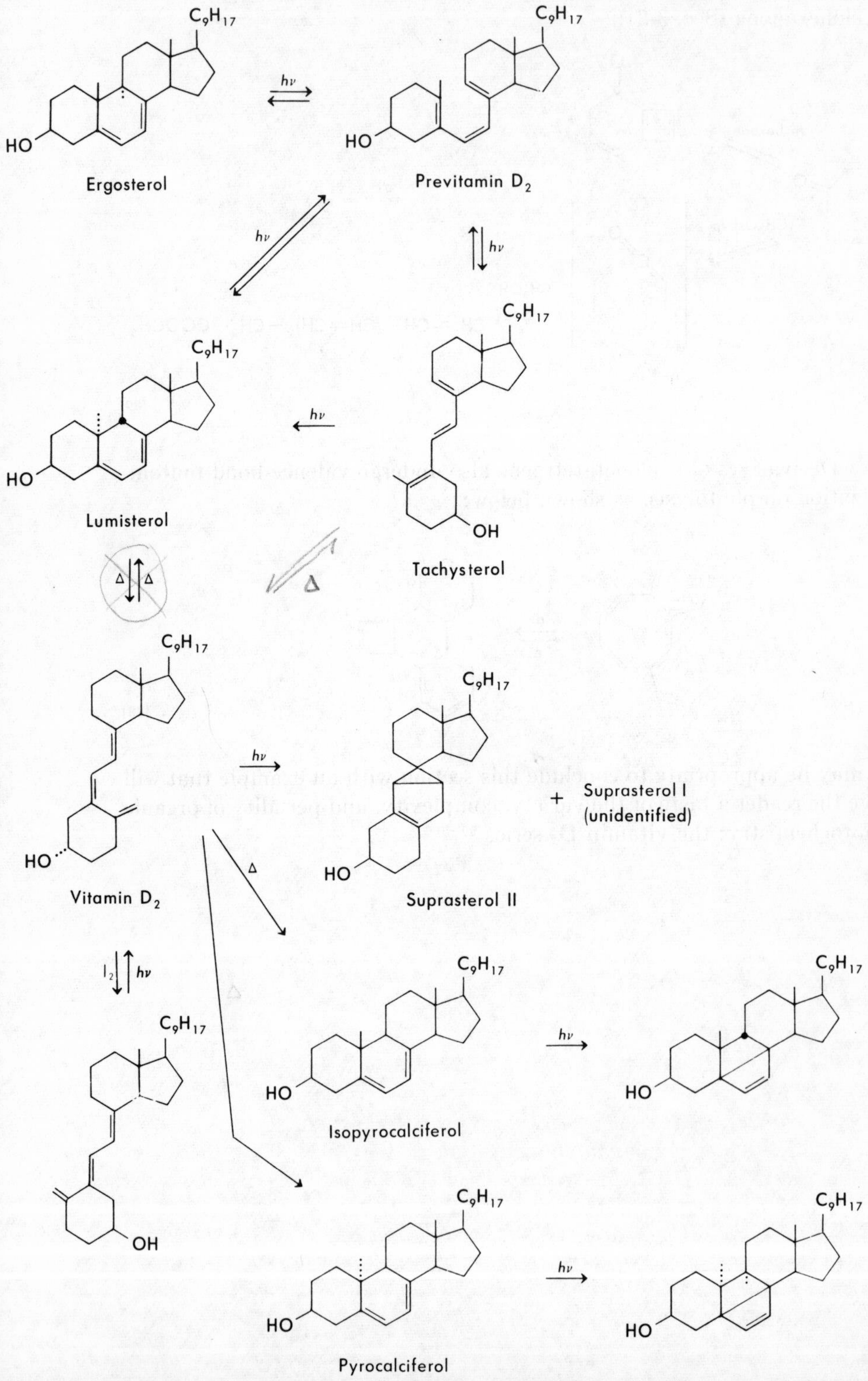

C_9H_{17}
HO
Ergosterol
hν
Previtamin D_2
hν
hν
hν
Lumisterol
Tachysterol
OH
Δ
Δ Δ
Vitamin D_2
hν
Suprasterol II
+ Suprasterol I (unidentified)
Δ
I_2 hν
Isopyrocalciferol
hν
Pyrocalciferol
hν

Relevant to the vitamin D_2 example, it should be noted that a mixture of pyrocalciferol and isopyrocalciferol is obtained by heating vitamin D_2,[94,95,97,98] while previtamin D_2 and vitamin D_2 establish a thermal equilibrium. The equations above give a good example of bridging, cis-trans isomerizations, and bond isomerizations.

2-4 Internal Cycloadditions Resulting from Valence-bond Tautomerizations

When situated in the appropriate location with respect to each other, two olefinic bonds may undergo "internal addition" with the formation of a cyclic or polycyclic compound. For example:

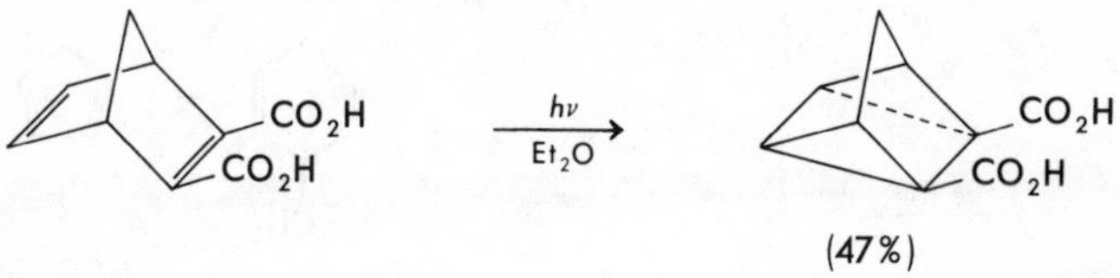

The second of these cyclizations may be effected either without sensitizers[98] or in the presence of benzophenone or acetophenone.[99] It is remarkable, however, that the *reverse* process is also a facile photochemical reaction taking place in the presence of sensitizers. Since the starting material in the reverse reaction possesses more energy than the product, less excitation energy is required and higher reactivity of low-energy sensitizers is expected and has indeed been observed.[99] The sensitization step, unusual in that it involves energy transfer which is followed by the breakage of single bonds in the acceptor, might lead directly to a triplet of quadricyclene similar in configuration to that formed from the diene (but not identical with it). Alternatively, a stepwise process in which a diradical is produced initially on breakage of one of the quadricyclene bonds may be envisaged:[99]

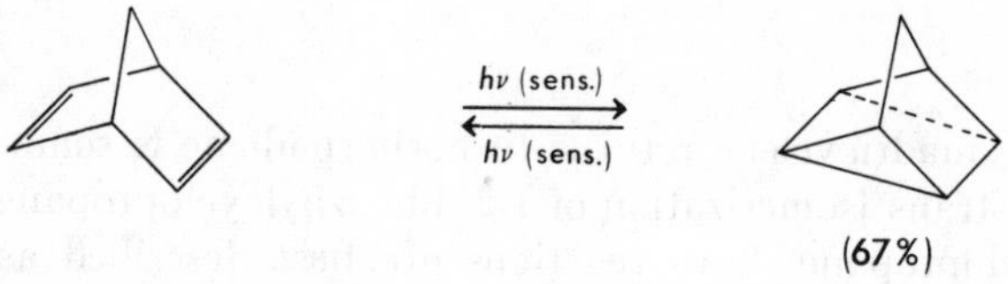

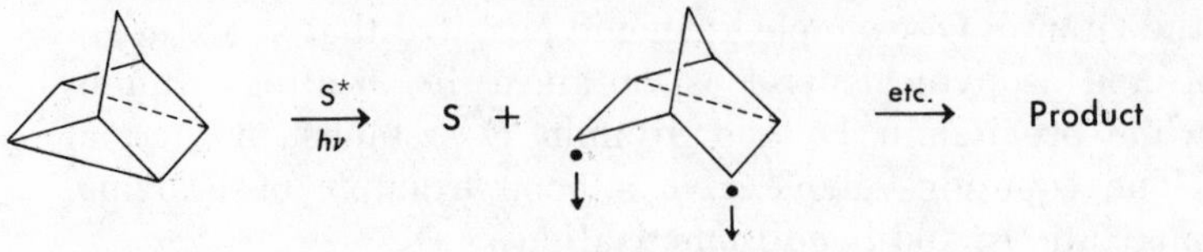

While the formation of quadricyclene takes place in solution, the photolysis of norbornadiene in the gas phase yields cyclopentadiene, toluene, and acetylene.[102] Toluene probably forms in a diradical process, while the remaining products can be generated by a "reverse Diels-Alder" reaction.†

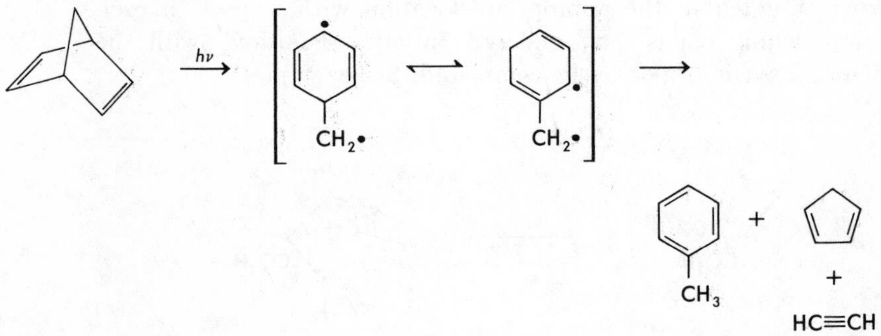

[102]

The reaction by which quadricyclene returns to norbornadiene is somewhat similar to the cis-trans isomerization of 1,2-dibenzoylcyclopropane and of 1,2-diphenylcyclopropane; both reactions are best described as involving breakage of the weakest bond in the three-membered rings:

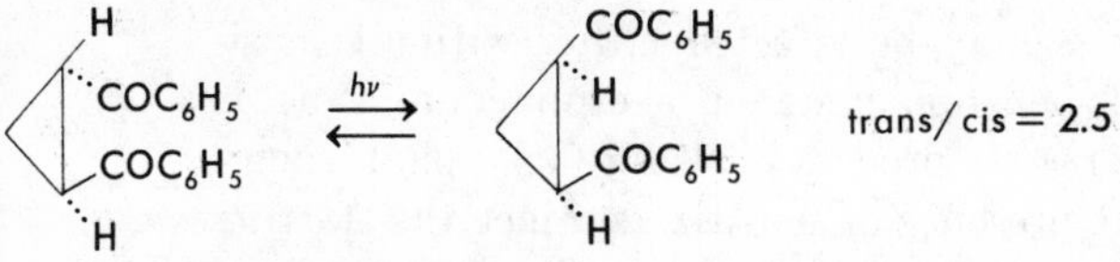

trans/cis = 2.5

[100]

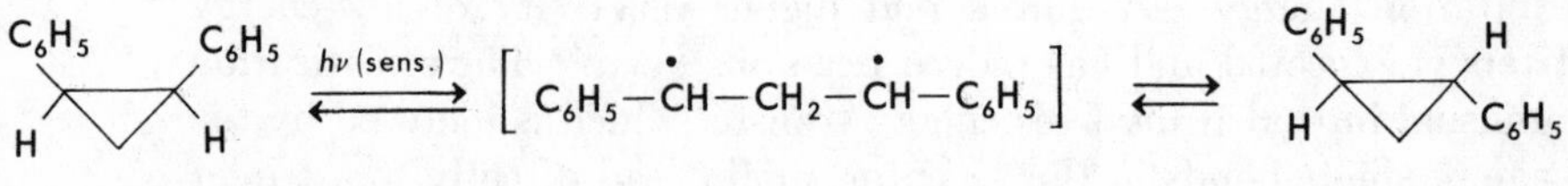

[99,101]

† The photolysis of barrelene (bicyclo[2.2.2]octatriene) leads to analogs of bullvalene.[102a]

Griffin and coworkers[101] found that, on prolonged irradiation of *trans*-1,2,-diphenylcyclopropane, the following products are obtained:

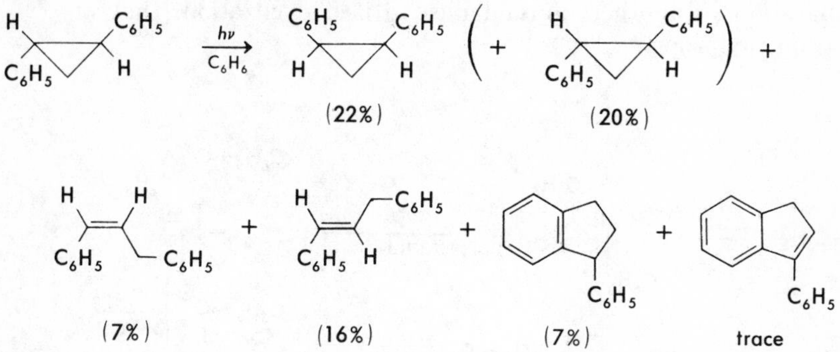
H
C6H5
hν
C6H6
(22%)
(20%)
(7%)
(16%)
(7%)
trace

[101]

While the cyclic cis isomer, the indene, and indane may form from the diradical shown above, by recombination and attack on one of the aromatic rings, respectively, the diphenylpropenes must arise either by a 1,2 hydrogen migration or by a phenyl migration. (Had the latter taken place, one might have expected other, branched products.) Most remarkable is the fact that the reverse reaction may be observed on prolonged unsensitized irradiation of *trans*-1,3-diphenylpropene:

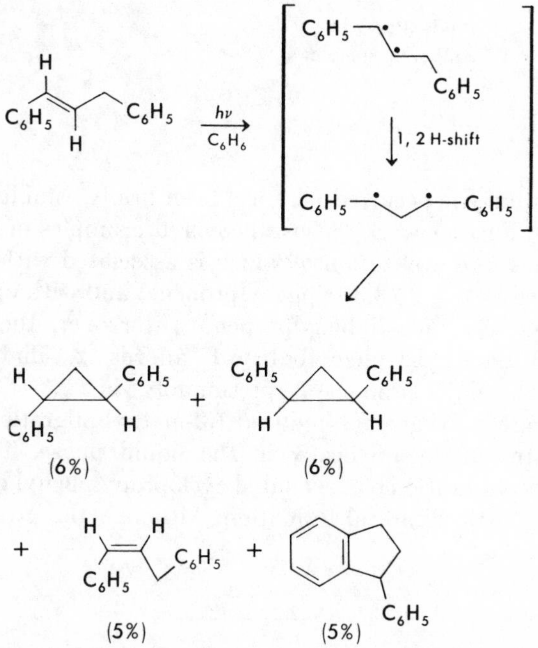
H
C6H5
hν
C6H6
1, 2 H-shift
(6%)
(6%)
(5%)
(5%)

[101]

It is clear that 1,2 migration of hydrogen or phenyl occurs in this cyclization, a rather unusual phenomenon in solution reactions. It is not certain whether hydrogen or phenyl is migrating, but there is precedent for the phenyl migration in another unusual unsensitized cyclization, that of 1,1,3,3-tetraphenylpropene:

(identical with
authentic sample)

[101]

That phenyl migration has occurred here has been firmly established by chemical means.[101a] Further work[101b] has uncovered examples of phenyl-substituted propenes, the cyclization of which is associated with phenyl migration in some cases (e.g., 3,3,3-triphenylpropene) and with hydrogen migration in others (e.g., 1,1-diphenylpropene). Moreover, the photocyclization of 3,3-dimethyl-1-phenylbutene-1 affords 2,3-dimethyl-4-phenylbutene-1 as the major product[101c] (presumably via 2,2,3-trimethyl-1-phenylcyclopropane) so that photoinduced 1,2-methyl migrations have now been demonstrated unequivocally in the liquid phase. The gas-phase photolytic decomposition of the related cyclopropylphenyl methane apparently involves little diradical formation. Although the presence of oxygen causes a decrease in the relative amounts of some of the gases formed (methane, ethane, propane, propene, cyclopropane, etc.), the amount of ethylene increases relative to methane.[130] It might be concluded that ethylene is formed either in a one-step process, depicted below, or that the biradical does in fact form, but that cleavage occurs much faster than combination with oxygen:

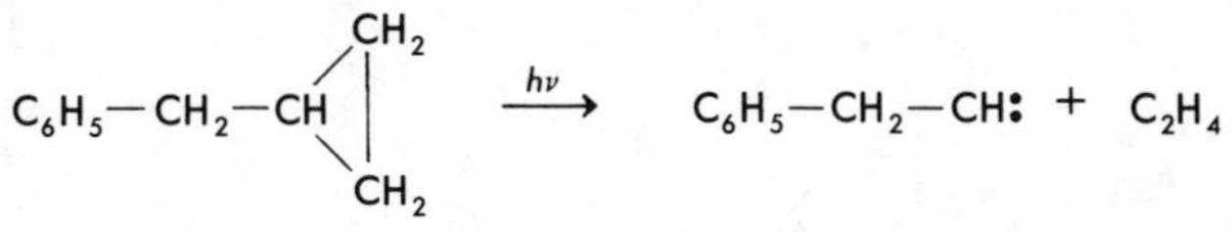

Although the yields of internal cycloadditions may at times be far from spectacular, the products are often not available by any other means, and they may possess features of great value in many synthetic routes. For

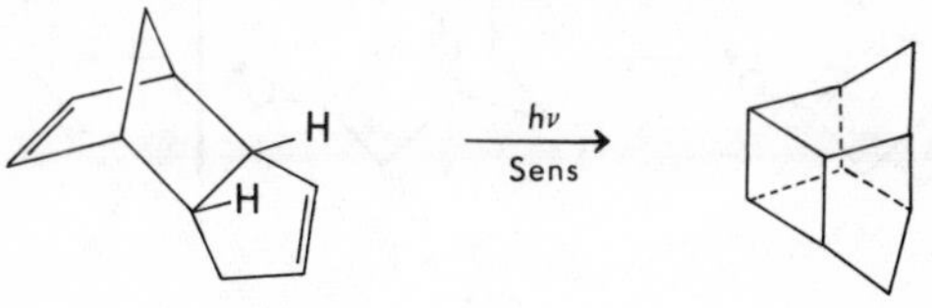

[103]

instance, a most elegant application of the cycloaddition of the Diels-Alder adduct of cyclopentadiene may be encountered in the synthesis of cubane:

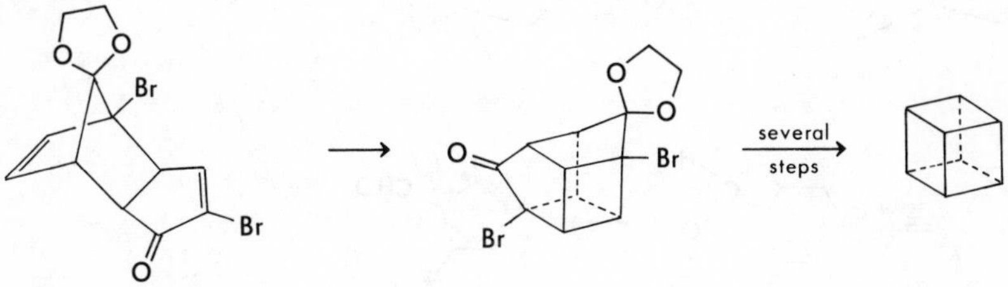

[104]

Other cycloadditions of interest are shown in the following examples:

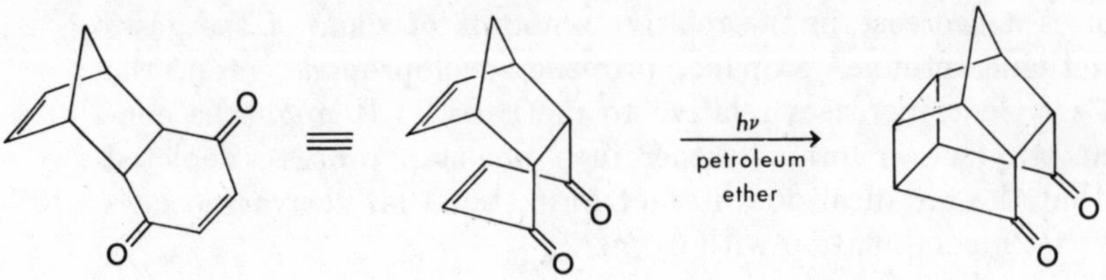

[105]

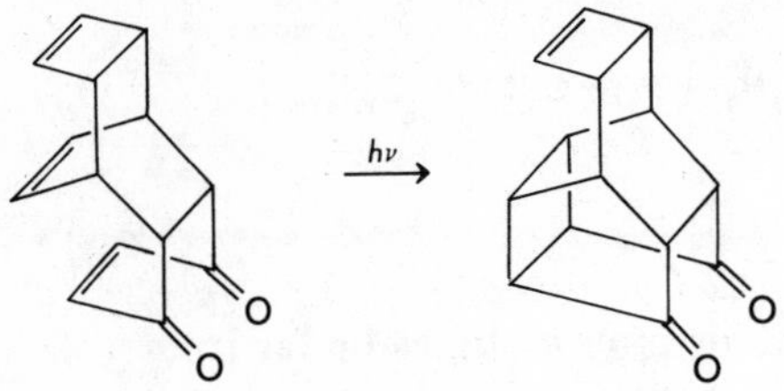

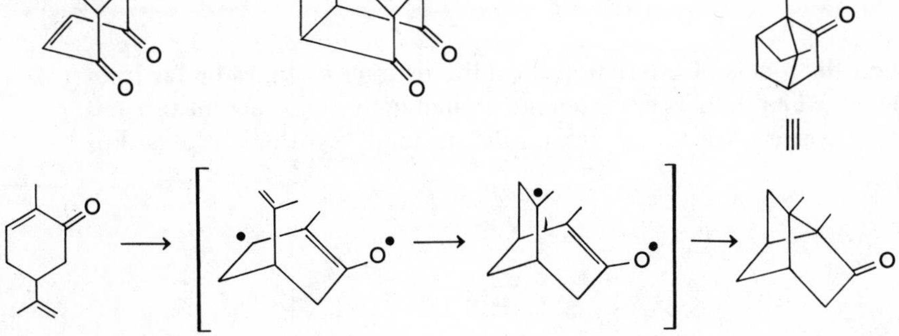

[105]
[106]

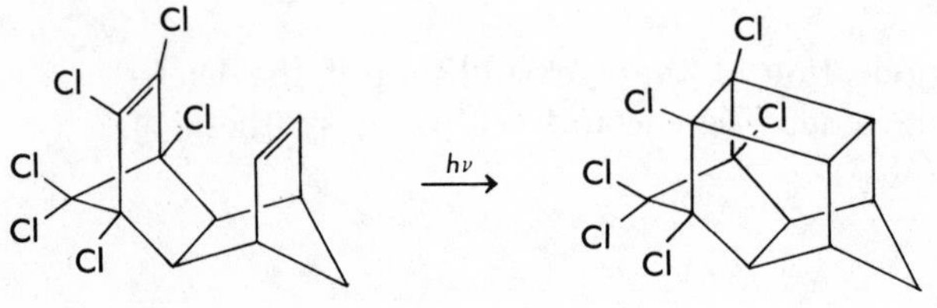

[107]

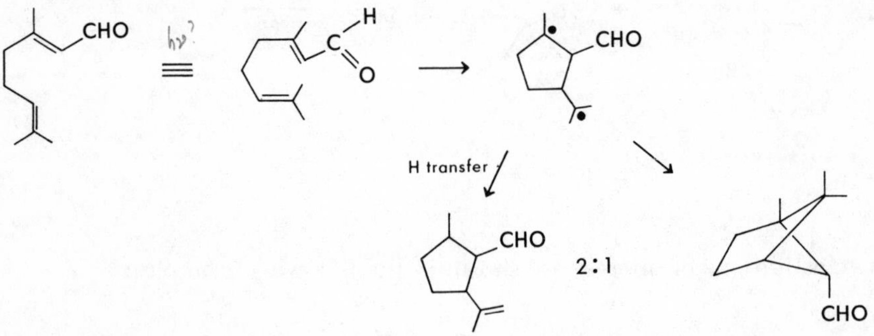

2:1

[109]

An attempt to prepare the Ladenburg isomer of benzene through a cycloaddition instead resulted in the formation of hexaphenylbenzene:

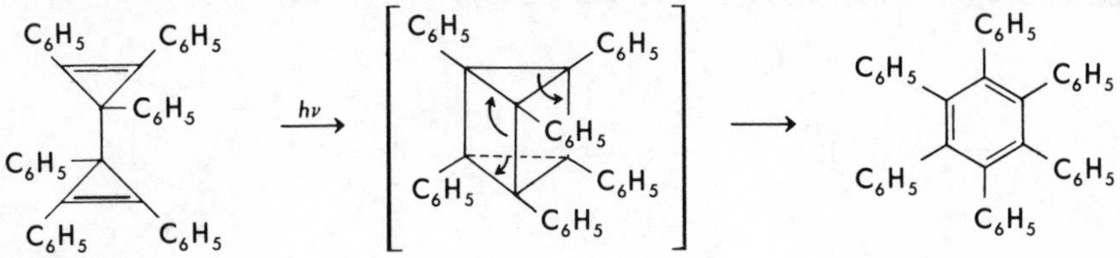

[110]

Cycloaddition through γ-hydrogen abstraction followed by ring closure has been observed in a number of ketones.[111,112] The reactions are further examples of the Norrish type II process (Sec. 3-1).

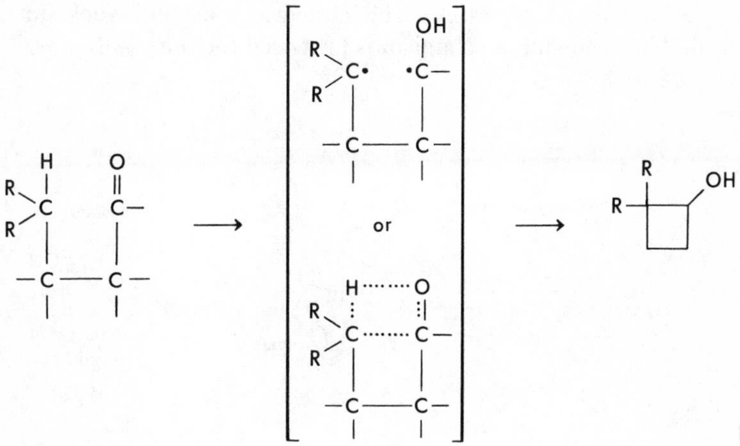

[113]

Either the intermediate is cyclic or ring closure occurs much faster than rotation about the single bond, which may be seen from the fact that the products derived from optically active ketones display partial retention:

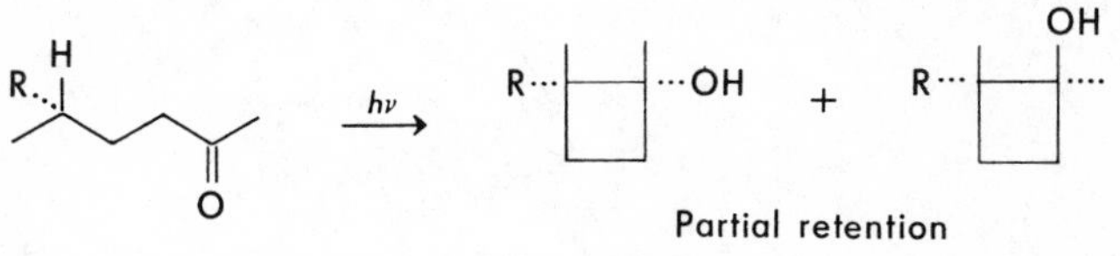

Partial retention

[113]

Evidence for a free-radical mechanism was first deduced from the fact that 6-hepten-2-one, which could form a diradical capable of undergoing allylic rearrangement, formed small amounts of the cyclized product resulting from such a rearrangement.[112] Additional evidence for a two-step mechanism is described in Sec. 4-2 (Chap. 4, ref. 85). However,

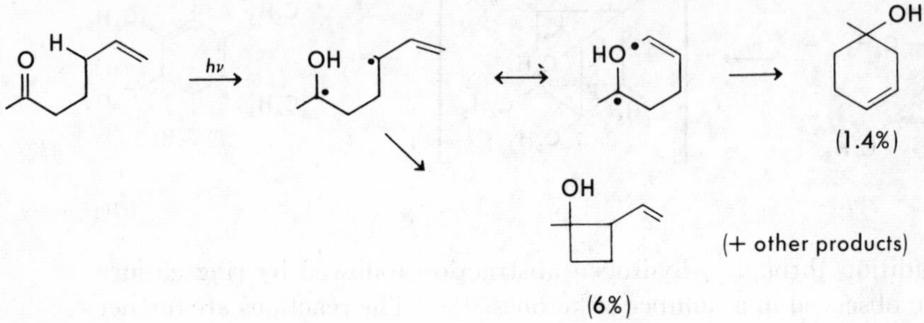

(1.4%)

(6%)

(+ other products)

6S-2,6-dimethyloct-7-en-3-one forms the analogous cyclohexane derivative with a high degree of retention, which seems to exclude such an allylic diradical. The following mechanism is proposed for the reaction:[114]

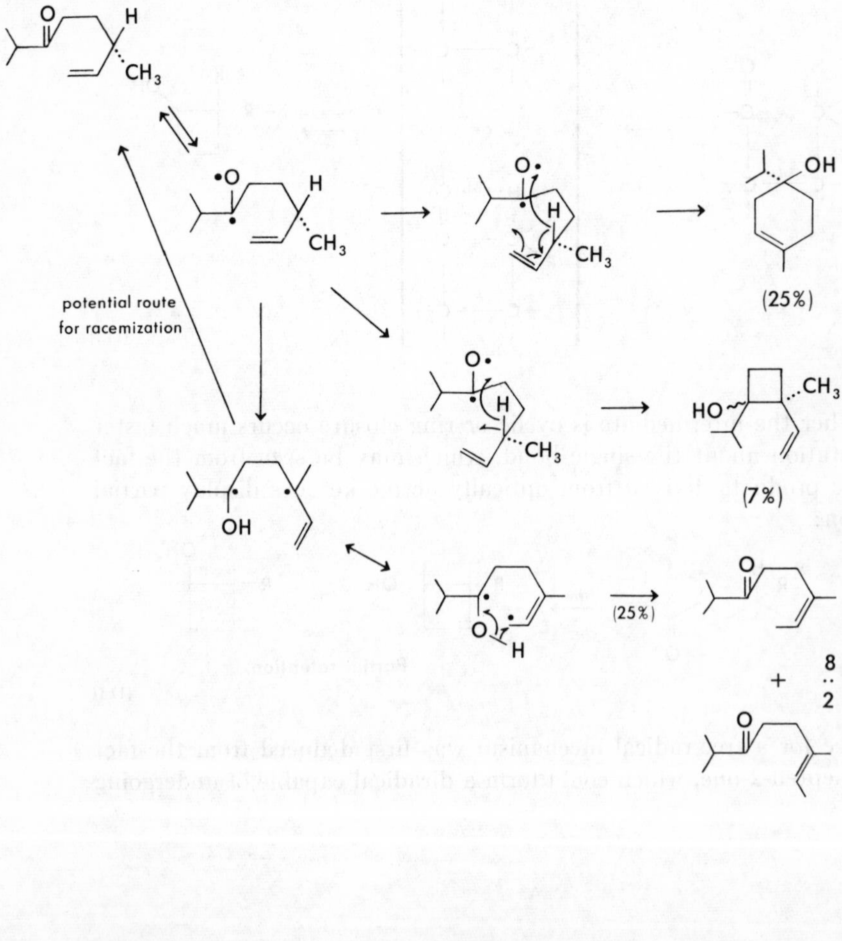

potential route
for racemization

(25%)

(7%)

(25%)

8
::
2

Several other examples have been observed among steroidal ketones:

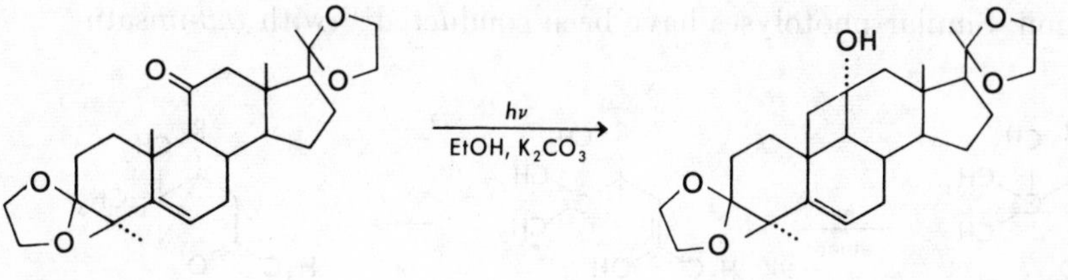

[115,116]

A similar kind of cycloaddition may be found in the formation of 2-hydroxycyclobutanones from 1,2-diketones upon their photolysis:

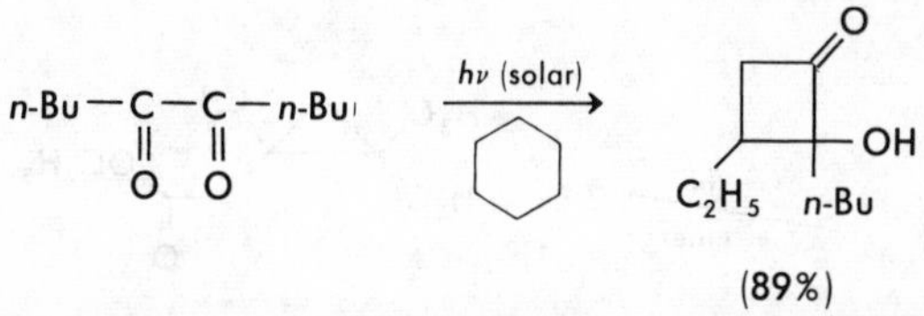

(89%)

[117]

It has been suggested that a triplet state is involved in these reactions, as seen by the pronounced effect of quenchers (O_2, naphthalene, anthracene).[117] Even ordinary 2,3-pentanedione undergoes the reaction, although the product dimerizes upon standing.

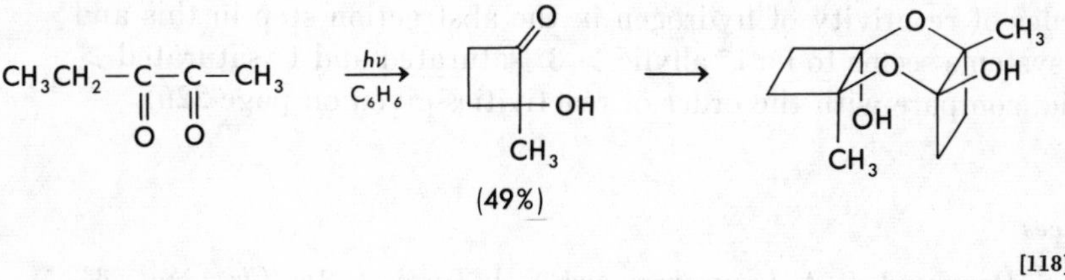

(49%)

[118]

One other example of an α-diketone photolysis is shown below:

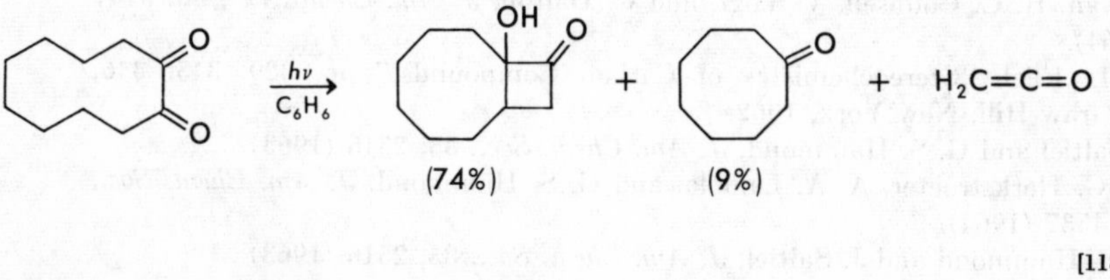

(74%)   (9%) $H_2C=C=O$

[118]

The formation of an acetonyl cyclopropane from the α,β-unsaturated ketone shown below apparently proceeds through the rare δ-hydrogen abstraction. Similar photolyses have been conducted[119] with α,β-unsatu-

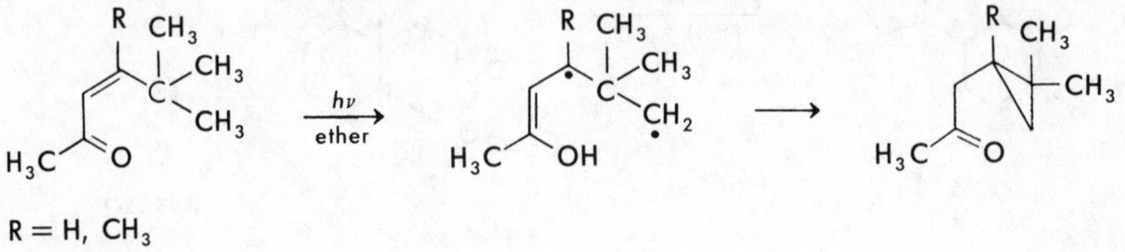

R = H, CH₃

[119]

rated esters; the reaction is dependent on the solvent employed, as shown below:

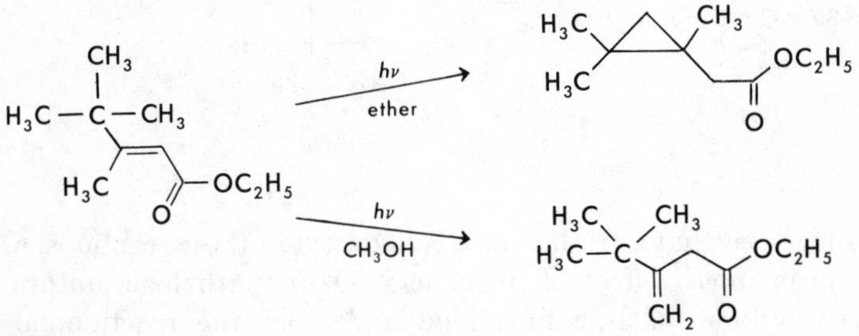

(The order of reactivity of hydrogen in the abstraction step in this and related systems seems to be 1° allylic > 3° saturated and 1° saturated > 1° allylic; compare with the order of reactivities given on page 226).

References

1. G. S. Hammond, P. A. Leermakers, and N. J. Turro, *J. Am. Chem. Soc.*, **83**, 2396 (1961).
2. G. S. Hammond and J. Saltiel, *J. Am. Chem. Soc.*, **84**, 4983 (1962).
3. G. S. Hammond, J. Saltiel, A. A. Lamola, N. J. Turro, J. S. Bradshaw, D. O. Cowan, R. C. Counsell, V. Vogt, and C. Dalton, *J. Am. Chem. Soc.*, **86**, 3197 (1964).
4. E. L. Eliel, "Stereochemistry of Carbon Compounds," pp. 329, 345, 346, McGraw-Hill, New York, 1962.
5. J. Saltiel and G. S. Hammond, *J. Am. Chem. Soc.*, **85**, 2515 (1963).
6. W. G. Herkstroeter, A. A. Lamola, and G. S. Hammond, *J. Am. Chem. Soc.*, **86**, 4537 (1964).
7. G. S. Hammond and J. Saltiel, *J. Am. Chem. Soc.*, **85**, 2516 (1963).

8. W. G. Herkstroeter, G. S. Hammond, and J. Saltiel, *J. Am. Chem. Soc.*, **85**, 482 (1963).
9. G. M. Wyman, *Chem. Rev.*, **55**, 625 (1955); L. Zechmeister, "Cis-Trans Isomeric Carotenoids, Vitamin A and Arylpolyenes," Academic, New York, 1962.
10. G. Büchi and N. C. Yang, *J. Am. Chem. Soc.*, **79**, 2318 (1957).
11. A. R. Olson and F. L. Hudson, *J. Am. Chem. Soc.*, **55**, 1410 (1933).
12. R. Stoermer, *Ber.*, **42**, 4865 (1909); **44**, 637 (1911).
13. G. Wald, *Sci. Am.*, **201**, 92 (1959).
14. G. Büchi and N. C. Yang, *Chem. Ind. (London)*, **1955**, 357.
15. P. de Mayo, J. B. Stothers, and R. W. Yip, *Can. J. Chem.*, **39**, 2135 (1961).
16. G. Büchi and N. C. Yang, *Helv. Chim. Acta*, **38**, 1338 (1955).
17. M. Mousseron-Canet, M. Mousseron, and P. Legendre, *Bull. Soc. Chim. France*, **1961**, 1509.
18. P. E. Eaton and K. Lin, *J. Am. Chem. Soc.*, **86**, 2087 (1964).
19. G. W. Griffin, E. J. O'Connell, and J. M. Kelliher, *Proc. Chem. Soc.*, **1964**, 337.
20. B. G. Gowenlock and J. Trotman, *J. Chem. Soc.*, **1955**, 4190.
21. D. Webb and H. H. Jaffé, *Tetrahedron Letters*, **1964**, 1875.
22. N. C. Yang and M. J. Jorgenson, *Tetrahedron Letters*, **1964**, 1203.
23. R. E. Lutz, P. S. Bailey, C. K. Dien, and J. W. Rinker, *J. Am. Chem. Soc.*, **75**, 5039 (1953).
24. R. Y. Levina, V. N. Kostin, and P. A. Gembitskii, *J. Gen. Chem. USSR (Eng. Transl.)*, **29**, 2421 (1959); *Zhur. Obshchei Khim.* **29**, 2456 (1959).
25. C. A. McDowell and S. Sifniades, *J. Am. Chem. Soc.*, **84**, 4606 (1962).
26. H. Wehrli, R. Wenger, K. Schaffner, and O. Jeger, *Helv. Chim. Acta*, **46**, 678 (1963).
27. G. R. McMillan, J. G. Calvert, and J. N. Pitts, Jr., *J. Am. Chem. Soc.*, **86**, 3602 (1964).
27a. G. Wettermark, *Photochem. & Photobiol.*, **4**, 621 (1965).
27b. W. A. Henderson, Jr. and E. F. Ullman, *J. Am. Chem. Soc.*, **87**, 5424 (1965); K. R. Huffman and E. F. Ullman, *ibid*, **87**, 5417 (1965).
28. N. C. Yang and C. Rivas, *J. Am. Chem. Soc.*, **83**, 2213 (1961).
29. K. J. Crowley, *J. Am. Chem. Soc.*, **85**, 1210 (1963).
30. H. J. Backer and J. Strating, *Rec. Trav. Chim.*, **54**, 618 (1935); E. Eigenberger, *J. Prakt. Chem.*, [2], **129**, 312 (1931).
31. E. Clar, *Ber.*, **82**, 495 (1949).
32. D. H. R. Barton, *Helv. Chim. Acta*, **42**, 2604 (1959); R. J. de Kock, N. G. Minnaard, and E. Havinga, *Rec. Trav. Chim.*, **79**, 922 (1960). For a complete discussion see E. E. van Tamelen, *Angew. Chem.*, **77**, 759 (1965).
33. R. Srinivasan, *J. Am. Chem. Soc.*, **84**, 4141 (1962).
34. K. J. Crowley, *Proc. Chem. Soc.*, **1962**, 334; *Tetrahedron*, **21**, 1001 (1965).
35. K. J. Crowley, *Proc. Chem. Soc.*, **1962**, 245.
36. G. J. Fonken, *Tetrahedron Letters*, **1962**, 549. For additional examples see K. J. Crowley, *Tetrahedron Letters*, **1965**, 2863, and J. Meinwald, A. Eckell, and K. L. Erickson, *J. Am. Chem. Soc.*, **87**, 3534 (1965).
37. R. Srinivasan, *J. Am. Chem. Soc.*, **84**, 3982 (1962).
38. R. Srinivasan, *J. Am. Chem. Soc.*, **85**, 4045 (1963).
39. R. Srinivasan, *J. Am. Chem. Soc.*, **85**, 3048 (1963).
40. W. H. Schuller, R. N. Moore, J. E. Hawkins, and R. V. Lawrence, *J. Org. Chem.*, **27**, 1178 (1962).
41. W. G. Dauben and R. M. Coates, *J. Am. Chem. Soc.*, **86**, 2490 (1964).
42. P. Courtot and J. M. Robert, *Bull. Soc. Chim. France*, **1965**, 3362.
43. H. Prinzbach and E. Druckrey, *Tetrahedron Letters*, **1965**, 2959.

44. W. G. Dauben and G. J. Fonken, *J. Am. Chem. Soc.*, **79**, 2971 (1957).
45. W. G. Dauben and R. M. Coates, *J. Org. Chem.*, **29**, 2761 (1964).
46. R. L. Autrey, D. H. R. Barton, and W. H. Reusch, *Proc. Chem. Soc.*, **1959**, 55.
47. A. Windaus and G. Zühlsdorff, *Ann.*, **536**, 204 (1938).
48. D. H. R. Barton and A. S. Kende, *J. Chem. Soc.*, **1958**, 688; D. H. R. Barton, R. Bernasconi, and J. Klein, *J. Chem. Soc.*, **1960**, 511.
49. E. E. van Tamelen and S. P. Pappas, *J. Am. Chem. Soc.*, **85**, 3297 (1963).
50. E. E. van Tamelen and S. P. Pappas, *J. Am. Chem. Soc.*, **84**, 3789 (1962). For a review, see H. G. Viehe, *Angew. Chem.*, **77**, 768 (1965).
51. E. M. Arnett and J. M. Bollinger, *Tetrahedron Letters*, **1964**, 3803.
52. A. W. Burgstahler and P. L. Chien, *Abstract of Papers, Am. Chem. Soc., Chicago*, September, 1964, 27S.
53. A. W. Burgstahler and P. L. Chien, *J. Am. Chem. Soc.*, **86**, 2940 (1964).
54. E. J. Corey and J. Streith, *J. Am. Chem. Soc.*, **86**, 950 (1964). See also L. A. Paquette, J. H. Barrett, R. P. Spitz, and R. Pitcher, *J. Am. Chem. Soc.*, **87**, 3417 (1965).
55. A. Padwa and R. Hartman, *J. Am. Chem. Soc.*, **86**, 4212 (1964).
56. K. L. Wierzchowski, D. Shugar, and A. R. Katritsky, *J. Am. Chem. Soc.*, **85**, 827 (1963).
57. W. G. Dauben and R. L. Cargill, *Tetrahedron*, **12**, 186 (1961).
58. O. L. Chapman, D. J. Pasto, G. W. Borden, and A. A. Griswold, *J. Am. Chem. Soc.*, **84**, 1220 (1962).
59. O. L. Chapman and D. J. Pasto, *Chem. Ind.* (*London*), **1961**, 53.
60. R. Srinivasan, *J. Am. Chem. Soc.*, **84**, 3432 (1962).
61. J. Rigaudy and P. Courtot, *Tetrahedron Letters*, **3**, 95 (1961).
62. D. J. Pasto, *J. Org. Chem.*, **27**, 2786 (1962).
63. O. L. Chapman and G. W. Borden, *J. Org. Chem.*, **26**, 4185 (1961).
64. G. Büchi and E. M. Burgess, *J. Am. Chem. Soc.*, **82**, 4333 (1960).
65. O. L. Chapman, in "Advances in Photochemistry," vol. I, p. 355, W. A. Noyes, Jr., G. S. Hammond, J. N. Pitts, Jr. (ed.), Interscience, New York, 1963.
66. J. J. Hurst and G. H. Whitham, *J. Chem. Soc.*, **1963**, 710.
67. D. I. Shuster, M. J. Nash, and M. L. Kantor, *Tetrahedron Letters*, **1964**, 1375.
68. O. L. Chapman and D. J. Pasto, *J. Am. Chem. Soc.*, **80**, 6685 (1958).
69. W. G. Dauben, K. Koch, O. L. Chapman, and S. L. Smith, *J. Am. Chem. Soc.*, **83**, 1768 (1961).
70. W. G. Dauben, K. Koch, S. L. Smith, and O. L. Chapman, *J. Am. Chem. Soc.*, **85**, 2616 (1963).
71. Ref. 65, pp. 326–327.
72. E. J. Forbes and R. A. Ripley, *J. Chem. Soc.*, **1959**, 2770.
73. E. J. Forbes, *J. Chem. Soc.*, **1955**, 3864.
74. F. Santavy, *Biol. Listy*, **31**, 246 (1951).
75. P. D. Gardner, R. L. Brandon, and G. R. Haynes, *J. Am. Chem. Soc.*, **79**, 6334 (1957).
76. O. L. Chapman, H. G. Smith, and R. W. King, *J. Am. Chem. Soc.*, **85**, 803, 806 (1963).
77. O. L. Chapman and S. L. Smith, *J. Org. Chem.*, **27**, 2291 (1962).
78. G. J. Fonken, *Chem. Ind.* (*London*), **1961**, 1575.
79. O. L. Chapman and E. D. Hoganson, *J. Am. Chem. Soc.*, **86**, 498 (1964).
80. L. A. Paquette, *J. Am. Chem. Soc.*, **86**, 500 (1964).
81. W. G. Dauben and R. L. Cargill, *J. Org. Chem.*, **27**, 1910 (1962).
82. O. L. Chapman, G. W. Borden, R. W. King, and B. Winkler, *J. Am. Chem. Soc.*, **86**, 2660 (1964).

83. W. R. Roth and B. Peltzer, *Angew. Chem.*, **76**, 378 (1964).
84. R. Srinivasan, *J. Am. Chem. Soc.*, **85**, 819 (1963); **86**, 3318 (1964); R. Srinivasan, *J. Phys. Chem.* **67**, 1367 (1963); R. Srinivasan and K. A. Hill, *J. Am. Chem. Soc.*, **87**, 4988 (1965).
85. J. E. Baldwin and R. H. Greeley, *J. Am. Chem. Soc.*, **87**, 4514 (1965).
86. M. Stiles and U. Burckhardt, *J. Am. Chem. Soc.*, **86**, 3396 (1964).
87. J. Zirner and S. Winstein, *Proc. Chem. Soc.*, **1964**, 235.
88. E. Vogel, W. Frass, and J. Wolpers, *Angew. Chem.*, **75**, 979 (1963).
89. G. Büchi and E. M. Burgess, *J. Am. Chem. Soc.*, **84**, 3104 (1962).
90. Ref. 65, pp. 381–383.
91. E. Havinga, R. J. de Kock, and M. P. Rappoldt, *Tetrahedron*, **11**, 276 (1960).
92. G. M. Sanders and E. Havinga, *Rec. Trav. Chim.*, **83**, 665 (1964).
93. R. J. de Kock, G. van der Kuip, A. Verloop, and E. Havinga, *Rec. Trav. Chim.*, **80**, 20 (1961).
94. L. F. Fieser and M. Fieser, "Steroids," chap. 4, Reinhold, New York, 1959.
95. H. H. Inhoffen, *Angew. Chem.*, **72**, 875 (1960); H. H. Inhoffen and K. Irmscher, *Fortschr. Chem. Org. Naturstoffe*, **17**, 70 (1959); B. Lythgoe, *Proc. Chem. Soc.*, **1959**, 141.
96. W. G. Dauben and G. J. Fonken, *J. Am. Chem. Soc.*, **81**, 4060 (1959).
97. S. J. Cristol and R. L. Snell, *J. Am. Chem. Soc.*, **80**, 1950 (1958); **76**, 5000 (1954).
98. W. G. Dauben and R. L. Cargill, *Tetrahedron*, **15**, 197 (1961).
99. G. S. Hammond, P. Wyatt, D. C. DeBoer, and N. J. Turro, *J. Am. Chem. Soc.*, **86**, 2532 (1964).
100. G. W. Griffin, E. J. O'Connell, and H. A. Hammond, *J. Am. Chem. Soc.*, **85**, 1001 (1963).
101. G. W. Griffin, J. Covell, R. C. Petterson, R. M. Dodson, and G. Klose, *J. Am. Chem. Soc.*, **87**, 1410 (1965).
101a. G. W. Griffin, private communication.
101b. G. W. Griffin, A. F. Marcantonio, H. Kristinsson, R. C. Petterson, and C. S. Irving, *Tetrahedron Letters*, **1965**, 2951.
101c. H. Kristinsson and G. W. Griffin, *J. Am. Chem. Soc.*, **88**, 378 1966).
102. B. C. Roquitte, *J. Am. Chem. Soc.*, **85**, 3700 (1963).
102a. H. E. Zimmerman and G. L. Grunewald, *J. Am. Chem. Soc.*, **88**, 183 (1966).
103. G. O. Schenck and R. Steinmetz, *Ber.*, **96**, 520 (1963).
104. P. E. Eaton and T. W. Cole, Jr., *J. Am. Chem. Soc.*, **86**, 962, 3157 (1964).
105. R. C. Cookson, E. Crundwell, and J. Hudec, *Chem. Ind. (London)* **1958**, 1003; R. C. Cookson, E. Crundwell, R. R. Hill, and J. Hudec, *J. Chem. Soc.*, **1964**, 3062.
106. G. Büchi and I. M. Goldman, *J. Am. Chem. Soc.*, **79**, 4741 (1957).
107. R. C. Cookson and E. Crundwell, *Chem. Ind. (London)*, **1958**, 1004.
108. R. S. H. Liu and G. S. Hammond, *J. Am. Chem. Soc.*, **86**, 1892 (1964).
109. R. C. Cookson, J. Hudec, S. A. Knight, and B. R. D. Whitear, *Tetrahedron Letters*, **1962**, 79; *Tetrahedron*, **19**, 1995 (1963).
110. R. Breslow and P. Gal, *J. Am. Chem. Soc.*, **81**, 4747 (1959).
111. N. C. Yang and D. H. Yang, *J. Am. Chem. Soc.*, **80**, 2913 (1958).
112. N. C. Yang, A. Morduchowitz, and D. H. Yang, *J. Am. Chem. Soc.*, **85**, 1017 (1963); P. Yates and A. G. Szabo, *Tetrahedron Letters*, **1965**, 485.
113. I. Orban, K. Schaffner, and O. Jeger, *J. Am. Chem. Soc.*, **85**, 3033 (1963).
114. K. H. Schulte-Elte and G. Ohloff, *Tetrahedron Letters*, **1964**, 1143.
115. J. I. Rieute, K. Schaffner, and O. Jeger, *Helv. Chim. Acta*, **46**, 1599 (1963).
116. M. S. Heller, H. Wehrli, K. Schaffner, and O. Jeger, *Helv. Chim. Acta*, **45**, 1261 (1962).

117. W. H. Urry and D. J. Trecker, *J. Am. Chem. Soc.*, **84**, 118 (1962).

118. W. H. Urry, D. J. Trecker, and D. A. Winey, *Tetrahedron Letters*, **1962**, 609.

119. M. J. Jorgenson and N. C. Yang, *J. Am. Chem. Soc.*, **85**, 1698 (1963); M. J. Jorgenson, *Chem. Commun.* **1965**, 137.

120. M. H. Back and R. J. Cvetanović, *Can. J. Chem.*, **41**, 1396 (1963).

121. M. D. Carr, V. V. Kane, and M. C. Whiting, *Proc. Chem. Soc.*, **1964**, 408.

122. G. O. Schenck and R. Steinmetz, *Bull. Soc. Chim. Belges*, **71**, 781 (1962).

123. H. R. Blattmann, D. Meuche, E. Heilbronner, R. J. Molyneux, and V. Boekelheide, *J. Am. Chem. Soc.*, **87**, 130 (1965). See also T. Sato, E. Yamada, Y. Okamura, T. Amada, and K. Hata, *Bull. Chem. Soc. (Japan)*, **38**, 1049 (1965).

124. R. B. Woodward and R. Hoffmann, *J. Am. Chem. Soc.*, **87**, 395, 2511 (1965); R. Hoffmann and R. B. Woodward, *J. Am. Chem. Soc.*, **87**, 2046 (1965).

125. R. T. LaLonde and R. I. Aksentijevich, *Tetrahedron Letters*, **1965**, 23.

126. W. G. Dauben and W. T. Wipke, *Pure Appl. Chem.*, **9**, 539 (1964).

127. L. Kaplan, K. E. Wilzbach, W. G. Brown, and S. S. Yang, *J. Am. Chem. Soc.*, **87**, 675 (1965); K. E. Wilzbach and L. Kaplan, *J. Am. Chem. Soc.*, **86**, 2307 (1964); K. E. Wilzbach and L. Kaplan, *J. Am. Chem. Soc.*, **87**, 4004 (1965).

128. A. P. Ter Borg and H. Kloosterziel, *Rec. Trav. Chim.*, **84**, 241 (1965).

129. E. Vogel, W. Grimme, and E. Dinné, *Tetrahedron Letters*, **1965**, 391.

130. P. A. Leermakers and G. F. Vesley, *J. Org. Chem.*, **30**, 539 (1965).

131. M. Mousseron, *Pure Appl. Chem.*, **9**, 481 (1964).

132. G. S. Hammond and R. S. Cole, *J. Am. Chem. Soc.*, **87**, 3257 (1965).

Reactions Proceeding through Bond Dissociation

3-1 Norrish Type I and Type II Reactions

We mentioned in Chap. 1 that, the magnitude of excitation energies being comparable to that of bond energies, bond dissociations can occur without much difficulty. Where homolytic fissions are concerned, the stability of the radicals to be formed and the relative bond-dissociation energies will play a role in determining which bonds undergo breakage. When one considers the magnitude of bond-dissociation energies which fall in the order

$$\geq\!C\!-\!H \;>\; \geq\!C\!-\!C\!\leq \;>\; \geq\!C\!-\!CO\!-\!C\!\leq \;>\; \searrow\!C\!=\!CH\!-\!CH_2\!-\!C\!\leq$$

it can be seen that C—C bonds adjacent to carbonyl groups and allylic to olefinic bonds are prone to dissociate in photochemical reactions. The fragmentation patterns are rather similar to those observed in mass spectrometry.

The course that the photochemical reactions of carbonyl compounds take greatly depends on the reaction phase employed; when the photolyses are conducted in the liquid phase, the choice of solvent is often critical. The presence in vapor-phase reactions of vibrationally excited ground states generated from electronically excited species assumes major proportions, and the products derived from the reactions are analogous to those obtained from thermal, nonphotochemical reactions. The effect of added inert gases or of an increase in the pressure of the substrate is to increase the number of collisions and to cause rapid dissipation of vibrational energy over the entire system. Such experimental variations cause changes in the quantum yield and in the product distribution.

Two main routes are generally followed in the photolysis of aldehydes and ketones. The first, referred to as a Norrish type I process, can be formally represented by the cleavage of a $-\overset{}{\underset{\overset{\|}{O}}{C}}-C\!\!\!\overset{}{\underset{}{\leqslant}}$ bond followed by decarbonylation of the resulting acyl radical formed. The radicals present after the decarbonylation step may recombine, abstract hydrogen, or undergo secondary fission reactions to yield hydrocarbons and olefins:

Norrish type I process

The second route is the Norrish type II reaction. It is characterized by a hydrogen transfer to the carbonyl group; in many cases studied such transfer apparently occurs through a six-membered transition state. In saturated ketones the bond α,β to the carbonyl group is often broken, so that olefins and methyl carbonyl derivatives may result. For reactions

Norrish type II process

of this type to take place it is necessary that more than two carbons be present in one of the adjacent alkyl groups. Variations of the type II process have already been encountered in the bond migration of α,β-unsaturated ketones (page 29), the formation of cyclobutanols from γ-hydrogen-containing carbonyl derivatives (pages 63 and 65), and in the formation of acetonyl cyclopropanes discussed on page 66. The reactivity of substances that are inherently capable of undergoing type II reactions depends in part on the character of their lowest triplet state. For example, the lowest triplets of *para*-substituted butyrophenones that do not undergo the reaction have been shown to be π-π*, rather than n-π* in character.[1a]

Both types of processes may occur simultaneously, as is the case, for example, in the photolysis of isovaleraldehyde:

[1]

The type I process is especially prominent in gas-phase photolyses, while in the liquid phase the loss of carbon monoxide is observed only with small- or intermediate-sized ring compounds. Reactions of type II can be observed in both gas- and liquid-phase photolyses, but the formation of a ketene is observed only in the presence of a nucleophilic solvent capable of adding to it. Further, there apparently exists a relationship between the ring size, the number of conjugated double bonds, and the type of process taking place on photolysis of conjugated unsaturated ketones (page 96).

3-2 *Saturated Ketones*

a. Vapor-phase Reactions. Vapor-phase reactions[2] have been carried out with a number of cyclic ketones. The products obtained from some of them are indicated below, and the possible routes of formation are indicated schematically. It is not certain whether the loss

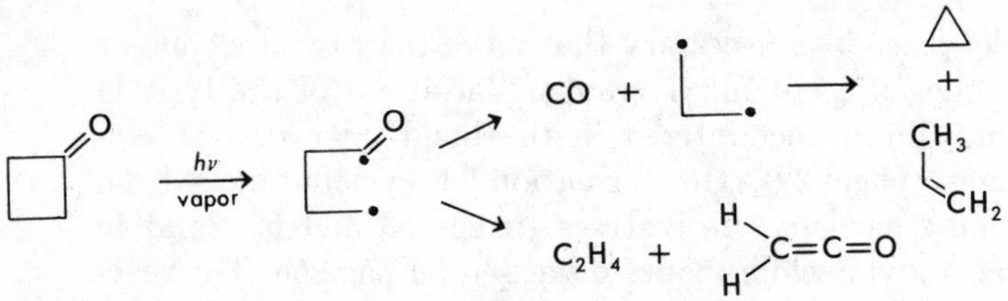

hν
vapor
CO +
CH3
CH2
C2H4 +
H
C=C=O
H

[4,5]

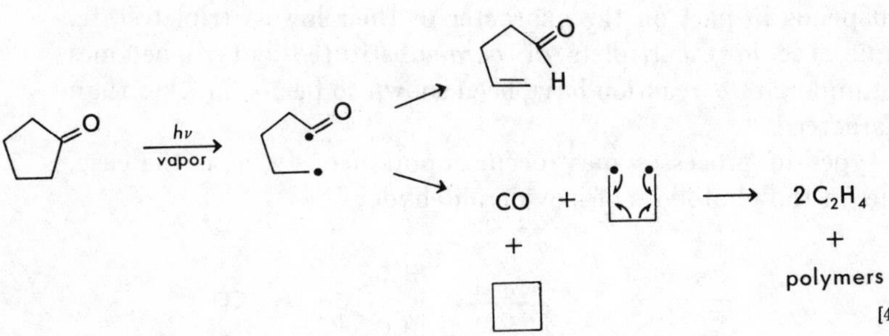

hν
vapor
H
CO +
+
2 C2H4
+
polymers

[4–6]

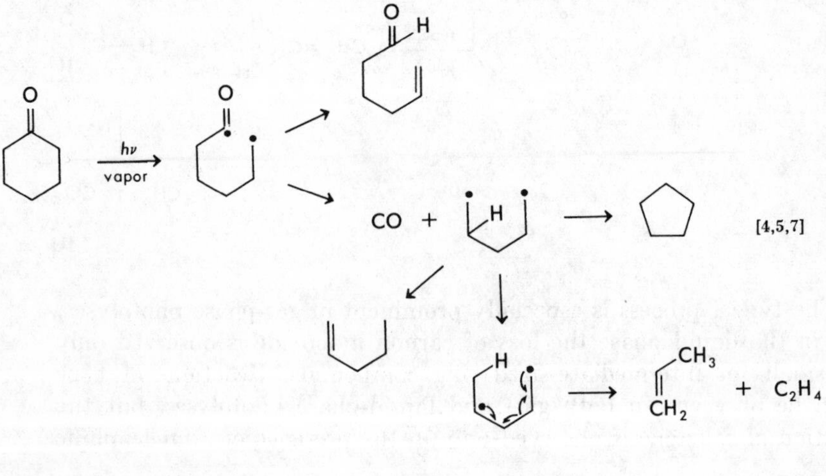

O
H
hν
vapor
CO +
H
H
CH3
CH2
+ C2H4

[4,5,7]

of CO and subsequent steps are in fact consecutive or concerted, but the slight influence that added O_2 exerts on the reaction seems to discount the existence of an intermediate diradical and points to a concerted process.[9] The alternative path would be one involving very fast diradical processes (faster than 10^{-10} sec) or processes resulting from vibrationally excited ground states. The absence of quenching effects from the addition of oxygen is only an indication that no long-lived diradical species are present. Contrary conclusions are drawn from the results obtained from the vapor-phase photolysis of *cis-* and *trans*-2,6-dimethylcyclohexanone. Either of the two compounds leads to the same ratio of products and at a faster rate than cis-trans isomerization occurs. The nonstereospecificity observed points to the formation of a common diradical in the primary step:[10]

It is probable that the mode of decomposition of cyclic ketones depends on the vibrational energy of the excited state.[11] That an electronically excited singlet (or a vibrationally excited ground state) is involved is inferred from the fruitless attempts to observe phosphorescence.[9]

The formation of radicals of the types $\cdot CH_2-CH_2-CH_2-CO-CH_2-CH_2\cdot$ and $\cdot CH_2-CH_2-CO-CH_2-CH_2\cdot$ has been postulated[6,7] to account for the facile formation of simple olefins, but evidence is still lacking, especially since other olefinic products that can possibly be derived from them have thus far not been isolated, for example,

$$\bullet CH_2CH_2CH_2\underset{\underset{O}{\|}}{C}CH_2CH_2\bullet \longrightarrow CH_3-CH=CH_2 + CH_2=CH_2 + CO$$

The photolyses of deuterated ketones have shown[6] that hydrogen abstraction in type II reactions that yield aldehydes takes place from the γ position (or the β position when one considers the molecule prior to fission).

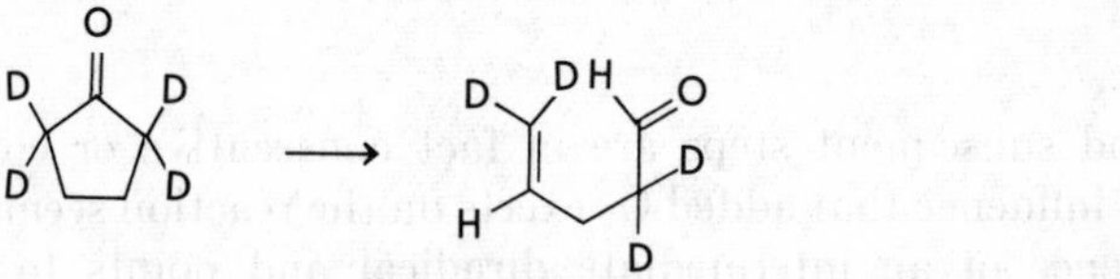

[6]

Such a process, if concerted, would make the formation of 3-butenal from cyclobutanone unlikely because of the greater distance separating the β position from the carbonyl group in the parent molecule. Indeed, one observes little, if any, of the aldehyde.

The presence of substituents in the ring of cyclic ketones does not basically alter the photochemical process. Bicyclic ketones lead to interesting strained systems by the loss of carbon monoxide followed by recombination of the radicals or by hydrogen abstraction:

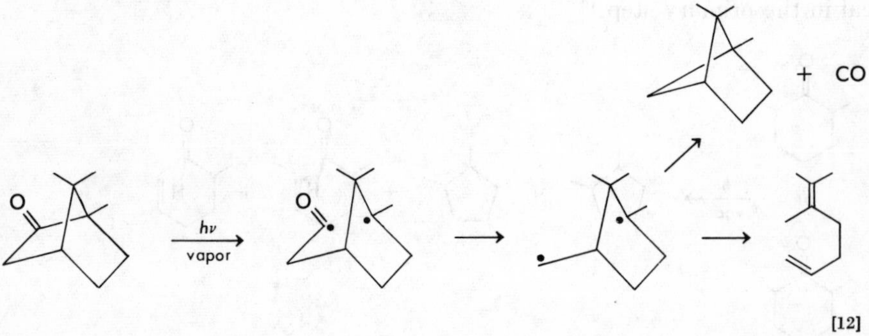

[12]

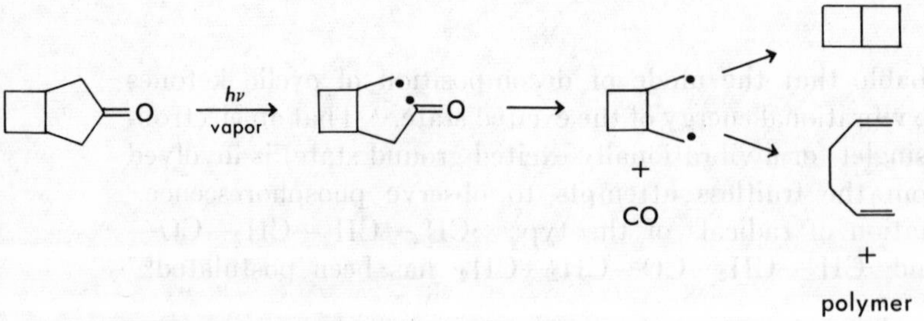

[13]

The use of sensitizers can alter the product ratios as well as product identity. For example, the unsensitized photolysis of norcamphor is relatively uncomplicated:

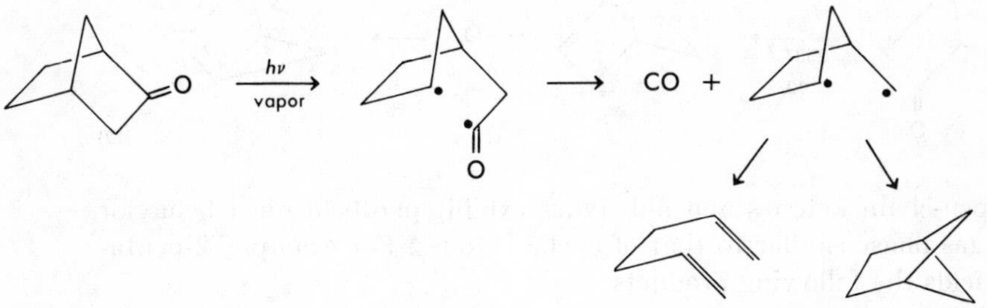

[14]

In the presence of mercury vapor, which through excitation acts as a triplet sensitizer, additional products form:

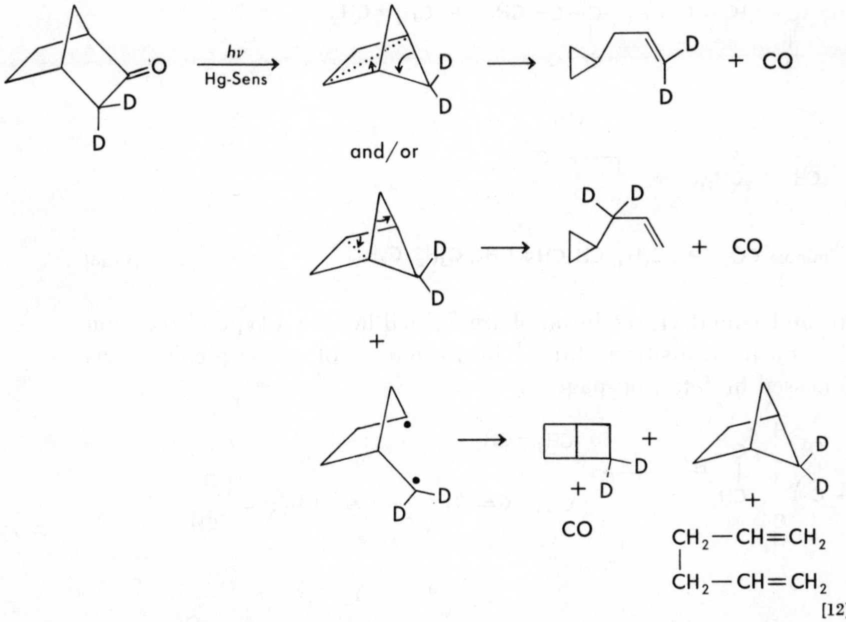

[12]

The formation of nortricyclene as a by-product is very unusual because it involves the loss of atomic oxygen. Since the C=O bond-dissociation energy is of the order of 165 kcal/mole, it would be attractive to speculate that a two-photon transition is involved; in it the second absorption step would take place from an electronically excited state to yield a new excited state of very high energy. Alternatively, it is possible that energy transfer occurs from mercury atoms possessing such high excitation energy.

$$\text{(structure)} \xrightarrow[\substack{2537\ \text{Å} \\ (\text{Hg})}]{h\nu} \text{(structure)} + \cdot O \longrightarrow \text{(structure)}$$

[12]

Open-chain ketones and aldehydes exhibit photochemical behavior in the gas phase similar to that of cyclic ketones. For example, 2-pentanone yields the following products:

$$CH_3-\overset{\overset{\textstyle O}{\|}}{C}-CH_2CH_2CH_3 \xrightarrow[vapor]{h\nu} \begin{bmatrix} CH_3-\underset{\cdot}{C}=O & CH_3CH_2CH_2\cdot \\[2mm] CH_3\cdot & \cdot\overset{\overset{\textstyle }{}}{C}-CH_2CH_2CH_3 \\ & \underset{O}{\overset{\|}{}} \end{bmatrix} \longrightarrow$$

$$CH_3-\overset{\overset{\textstyle }{}}{\underset{\underset{O}{\|}}{C}}-CH_3 \ + \ CH_3-\overset{\overset{\textstyle }{}}{\underset{\underset{O}{\|}}{C}}-\overset{\overset{\textstyle }{}}{\underset{\underset{O}{\|}}{C}}-CH_3 \ + \ CH_2=CH_2$$

$$+ \ (CH_3CH_2CH_2)_2 \ + \ \text{(1-methylcyclobutanol structure with OH and CH}_3\text{)}$$

$$+ \ \text{minor: } CO, CH_4, C_2H_4, CH_3CH=CH_2, C_3H_8, C_4H_{10}$$

[15,16]

Ethylene and 1-methylcyclobutanol are formed here in a type II reaction through a cyclic transition state. The formation of cyclic alcohols has been discussed in detail on page 63.

$$\text{(cyclic transition state structure)} \longrightarrow \begin{matrix} CH_2=CH_2 \\ + \\ CH_3-C=CH_2 \\ | \\ OH \end{matrix} \longrightarrow CH_3-C\overset{\overset{\textstyle O}{\diagup}}{\diagdown}CH_3$$

$$\text{(cyclic transition state structure)} \overset{?}{\longrightarrow} \begin{matrix} OH & \cdot CH_2 \\ | & | \\ CH_3-C\cdot & CH_2 \\ & \diagdown C \diagup \\ & H_2 \end{matrix} \longrightarrow \text{(1-methylcyclobutanol structure)}$$

[15]

In open-chain ketones hydrogen abstraction takes place from the same carbon atom, relative to the carbonyl group, as in cyclic ketones. The fact has been demonstrated in the photolysis of 2-hexanone-5,5-d_2.

[17]

The identification of the enol form of acetone in the vapor-phase photolysis of 2-pentanone provides further substantial evidence for the intermediacy of a six-membered ring.[18]

The introduction of a second oxygen atom in the cyclic intermediate has no effect on the reaction. Methoxyacetone is cleaved normally. Evi-

[17]

dence for the absence of a free-radical process is obtained from the noted insensitivity of the reaction to the addition of NO and to changes in the pressure of the system; nitric oxide being an excellent radical scavenger, free radicals are trapped by it. Decreasing quantum yields on the addition of oxygen are interpreted similarly as the trapping of long-lived free radicals and the quenching of triplet states. The influence of added oxygen on these systems varies; Srinivasan[17] has found that at higher temperature there is no effect on the photolysis of methoxyacetone and that at room temperature the quantum yield declines with increasing oxygen pressures. Oxygen has a moderate inhibiting effect in the photolysis of 2-pentanone, whereas it has a quite significant effect with 2-pentanone-4,5,5-d_3 both at room temperature and at 147°C.[15] It is possible that subtle differences in structure and deuterium content significantly alter the facility of free-radical formation or that the radicals in some cases are too short-lived to be trapped.

The liquid-phase photolysis of 4-methyl-4-methoxy-2-pentanone yields the products resulting from bond fission, as well as the cyclic alcohol. Hydrogen-abstraction steps through cyclic transition states again can account for the main products observed; however, if the mechanism is correct, it would be one of the few cases in which the intermediate involves a seven-membered ring.

[19]

b. Condensed-phase Reactions.

In the photolysis of saturated ketones in the condensed phase the choice of the solvent is often critical because it influences the reaction path. The first step in the reactions can be formally represented by the fission of a CO—C bond (*a*), generally on that side of the carbonyl group where the most substituted radical will be generated. (Such ground-state behavior is, of course, not automatically to be expected in excited-state chemistry.) The diradical species formed may then stabilize itself either by a hydrogen-transfer step *from* the carbon atom α to the carbonyl group (*b*) and form a ketene or by hydrogen transfer *to* the carbonyl group (*c*) and form an aldehyde. A third mode of reaction is the loss of carbon monoxide (*d*) in a sequence similar to that observed in gas-phase reactions. It appears that there are

instances when these steps are definitely consecutive, while other cases point to a concerted mechanism. There are two experimental facts that clearly show the reversibility of the fission step (*a*). First, the quantum yield is small, indicating that energy is "lost" in a repetition of the first step. More important, however, is the observed photochemical epimerization in compounds that bear centers of asymmetry adjacent to the carbonyl function.[21] Thus, 17-ketosteroids undergo facile photoepimerization, a fact that has been applied synthetically.[20,21] Since the same sys-

tems may also undergo hydrogen-transfer reactions, the two steps are, at least in this instance, not synchronous. The choice between path (*b*) and (*c*) as the hydrogen-transfer step depends on the presence of hydrogen at the appropriate centers, on the availability of nucleophiles capable of adding to the ketenes formed, and on the steric requirements for hydrogen abstraction in the transition state.

The intramolecularity of either of the hydrogen-abstraction steps is now well established,[6,25] and the actual intermediacy of the ketenes in these reactions has been demonstrated by spectroscopic methods.[22] In the reaction of fused five-membered ketones, the following three transition states can be visualized:

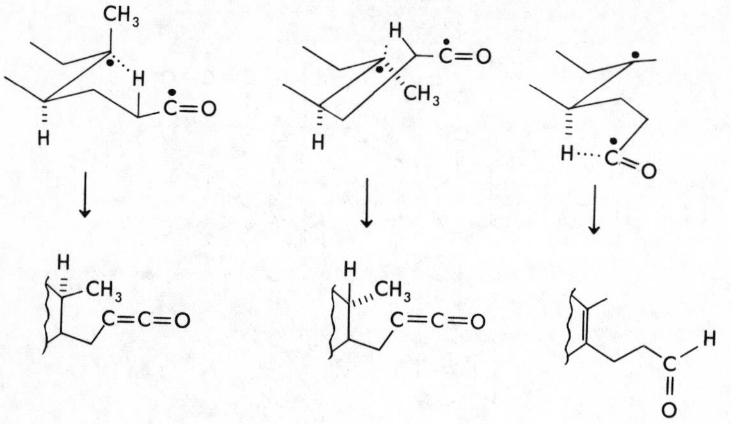

The relative energies of the two cyclic transition states leading to ketenes will generally determine the stereochemistry of the products, provided no racemization occurs in step (a). The examples shown below demonstrate the stereoselectivity that is often observed in the ring-opening reaction. It will be noted that products obtained through a six-membered transition state form in preference to those obtained through five-membered transition states. The ketenes formed react with water, alcohols, or amines present to yield carboxylic acids, esters, or amides.

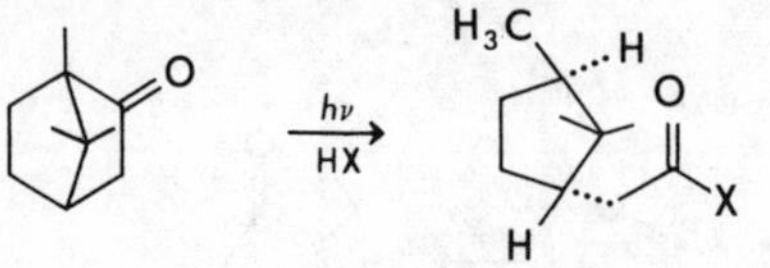

(1%, as amide; 5-membered transition state)

[20,23]

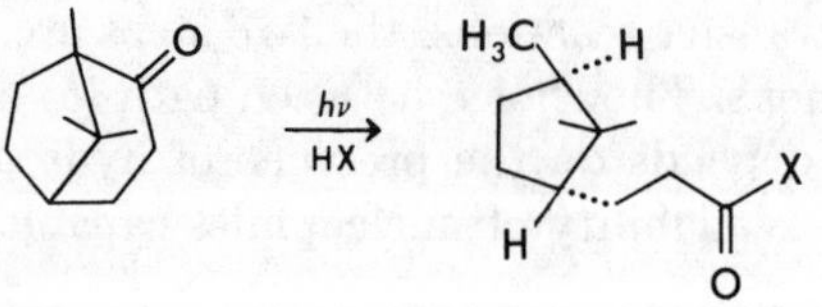

(17%, as amide; 6-membered transition state)

[20,23]

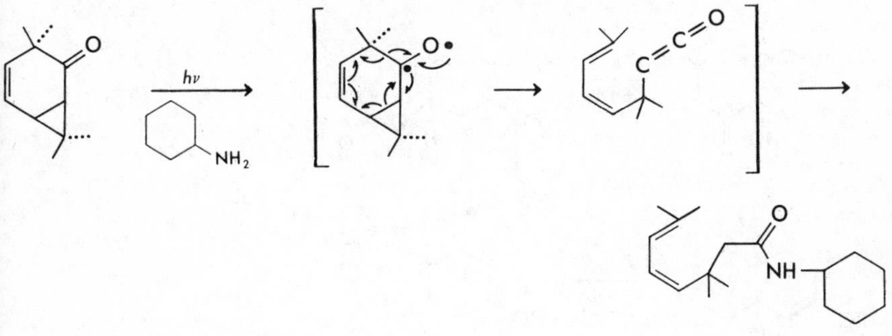

[24]

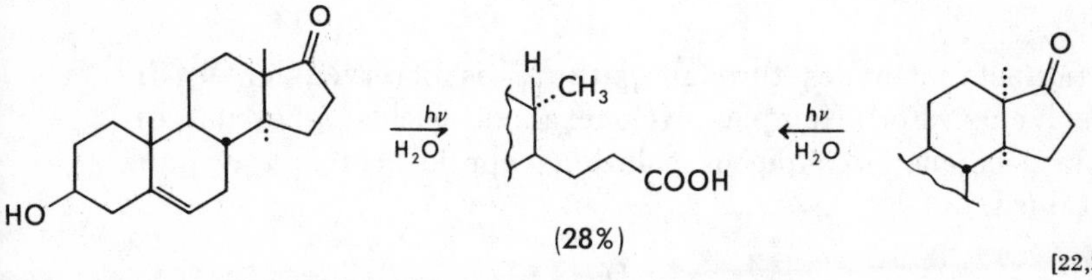

(28%)

[22,23,25]

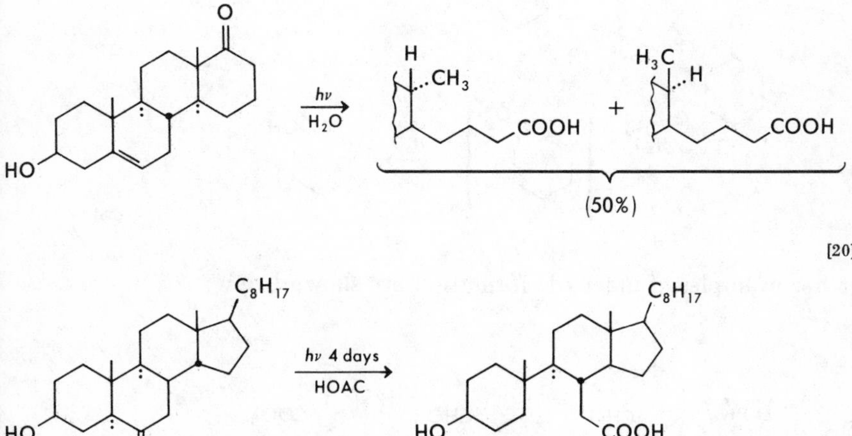

(50%)

[20]

(54%)

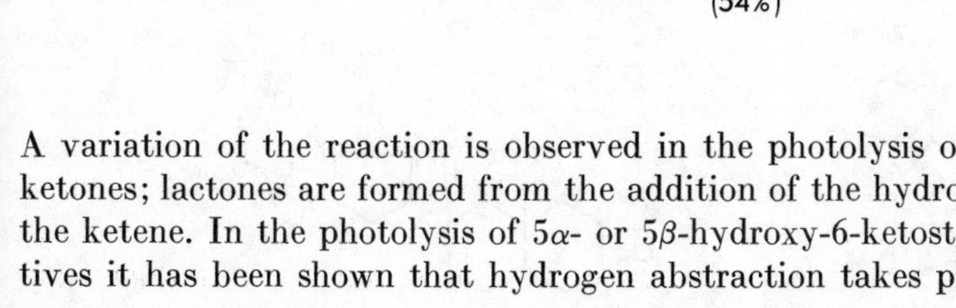

[25]

A variation of the reaction is observed in the photolysis of α-hydroxy-ketones; lactones are formed from the addition of the hydroxyl group to the ketene. In the photolysis of 5α- or 5β-hydroxy-6-ketosteroid deriva-tives it has been shown that hydrogen abstraction takes place from C_7

rather than from the hydroxyl group; reactions conducted in EtOD lead to no incorporation of deuterium:[26]

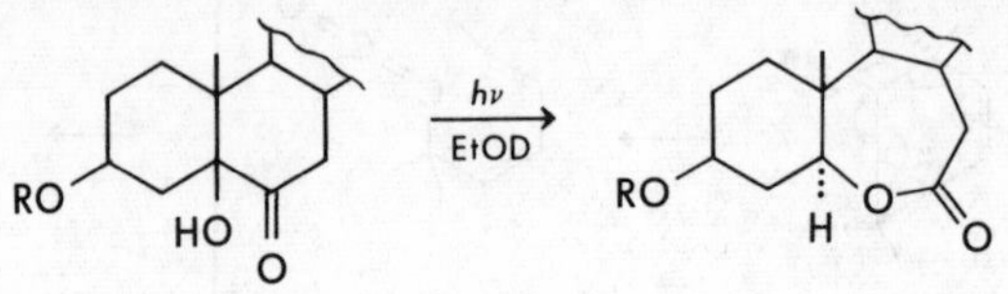

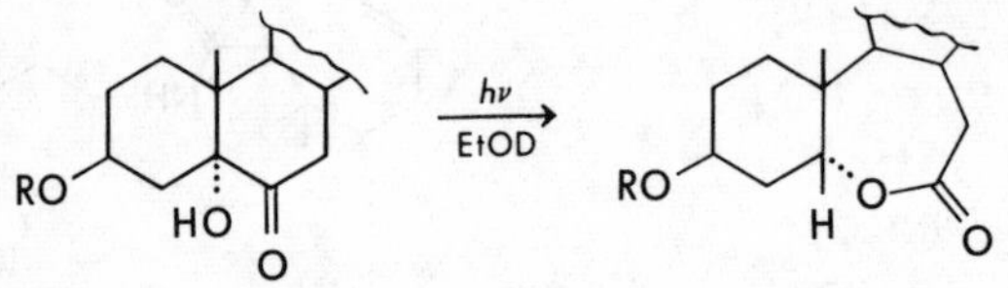

The formation of aldehydes through path (c) is observed largely in nonprotic solvents. For example, cyclohexanone yields 5-hexenal on photolysis in 1-octene; in aqueous solution caproic acid is the main product obtained.

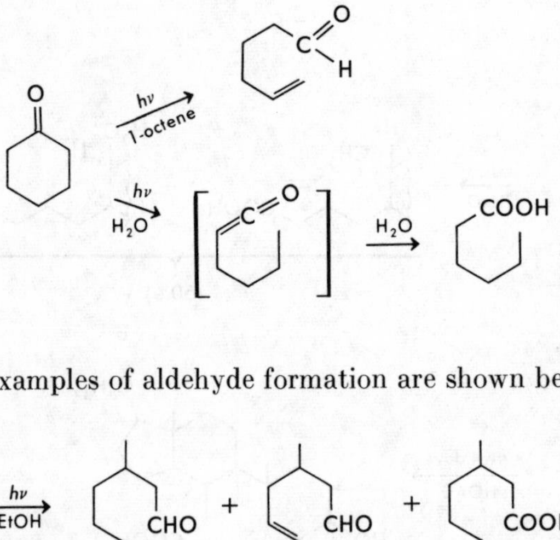

[27]

[28]

Two further examples of aldehyde formation are shown below:

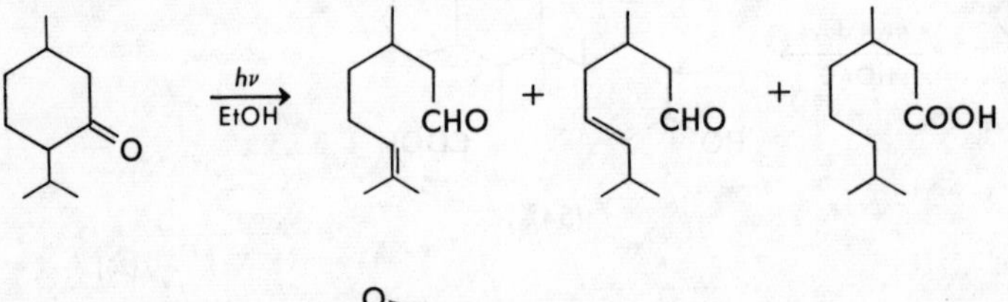

[29]

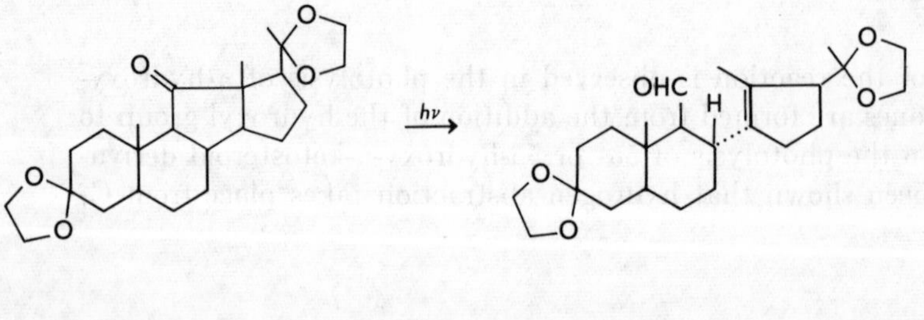

[30]

The liquid-phase photolysis of 2-alkylcyclopentanones and hexanones is reported to yield only *trans*-4-alkenals.[31] It would appear that the transfer of hydrogen from the β-carbon to the carbonyl carbon occurs here simultaneously with (or prior to) ring opening. However, these results are contrary to the findings of Pritchard[10] in the vapor-phase photolysis of the two 2,6-dimethylcyclohexanones. It is not known whether different mechanisms are operating under the two sets of conditions.

A minor product observed in the liquid-phase photolysis of cyclic ketones is the result of a ring contraction. Thus cyclohexanone yields 6% of 2-methylcyclopentanone, cycloheptanone yields 0.2% of 2-methylcyclohexanone, and cyclooctanone yields traces of 2-methyl-cycloheptanone as well as about 1.2% of 2-*n*-propylcyclopentanone.

[31]

Srinivasan[31] has shown with the photolysis of cyclohexanone-2,2,6,6-d_4 that hydrogen transfer takes place from the carbon β to the carbonyl group to that of the incipient methyl group (the α-carbon). The concomitant formation of unsaturated aldehydes decreases rapidly with time, while the rate of ring contraction is linear with time. It has been suggested that the two processes occur through different excited states.

Similar 1,2 shifts may account for the opening of the three-membered ring in the system shown here. The loss of carbon monoxide does not

[32]

occur as frequently in the liquid phase, where high vibrational energy levels are rapidly deactivated through collisional processes, as in the gas phase. The stability of the incipient radicals is directly related to the yields of the products from the decarbonylation reaction. This may be seen from the following series:[33]

$$R=R'=H \longrightarrow \quad \text{yield} < 10\%$$

$$R=C_6H_5; \; R'=H \longrightarrow \quad \text{yield} > 50\%$$

$$R=R'=C_6H_5 \longrightarrow \quad \text{(cis + trans)}$$

quantitative

Formation of the vicinal disubstituted dibenzocyclooctadienes as the main products from the radical-combination steps is peculiar. It suggests that the fission of the two CO—C bonds does not occur simultaneously and that bimolecular radical combination takes place prior to the loss of carbon monoxide.

The presence of free radicals in the decarbonylation step is most easily demonstrated with open-chain ketones containing radical-stabilizing groups. For example, the photolysis of mixtures of 1,3-diphenyl-2-propanone and 1,1,3,3-tetraphenyl-2-propanone leads to products resulting from mixed radical combinations:[33]

Benzoyldiphenylmethane similarly yields tetraphenylethane by radical combination, as well as benzaldehyde by hydrogen abstraction:[34]

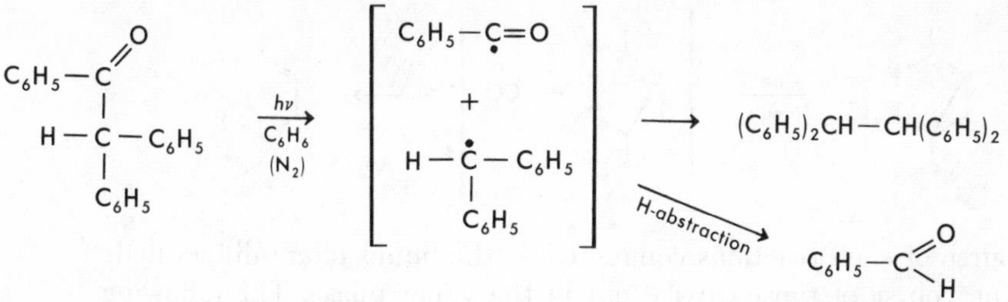

The presence of diradicals in cyclic systems is, as mentioned, not always demonstrable by the effect exerted by oxygen.

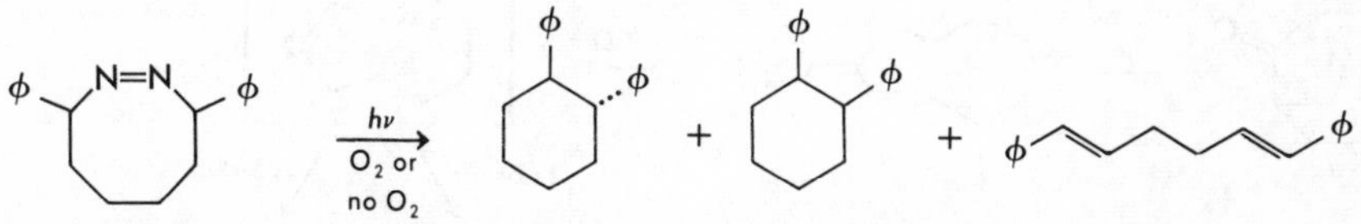

For example, the yield of the products obtained in the photolysis of the cyclic azo compound shown here is not affected by the presence of oxygen.[35]

Another example of decarbonylation, reported by Mislow, is the ready formation of 4,5-dimethyl-9,10-dihydrophenanthrene from a seven-membered cyclic ketone. The corresponding hydrocarbon undergoes racemization, apparently through internal conversion of the electronically excited state to a vibrationally excited ground state. (The

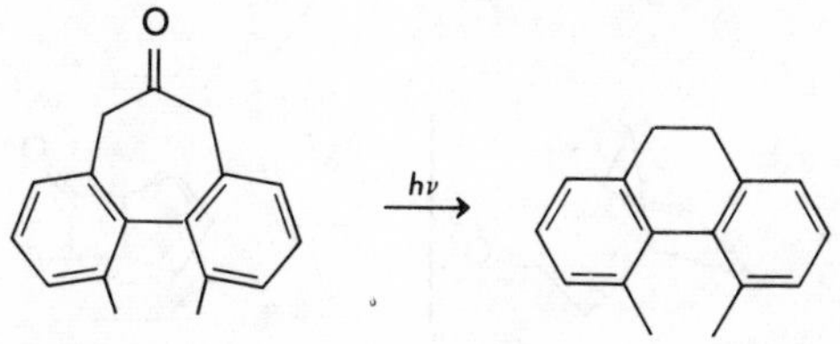

[36]

occurrence of molecular asymmetry in hindered biphenyl systems is due to interference of the *ortho,ortho′*-methyl groups, which prevents coplanarity of the two aromatic rings.) As mentioned before, carbon monoxide

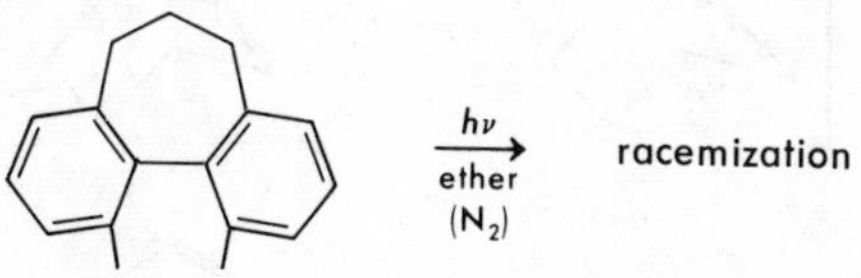

racemization

[36]

is eliminated less frequently in liquid-phase reactions than in gas-phase reactions. When it is eliminated, a relief of ring strain often appears to be the driving force, as, for example, in the decarbonylation of thujone:[37]

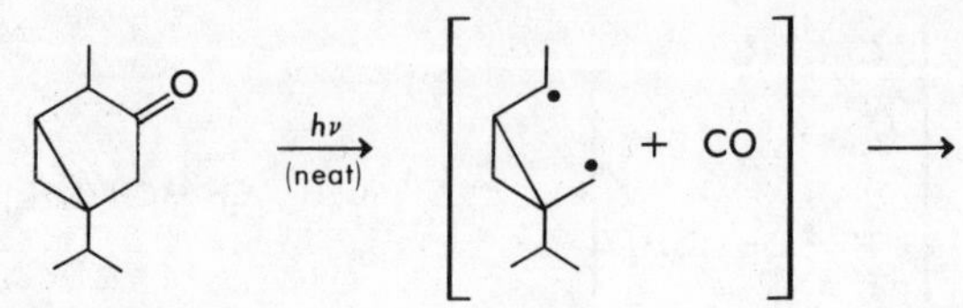

The course of such reactions conducted in the liquid phase differs little from the course of those carried out in the vapor phase. The following three examples demonstrate this.

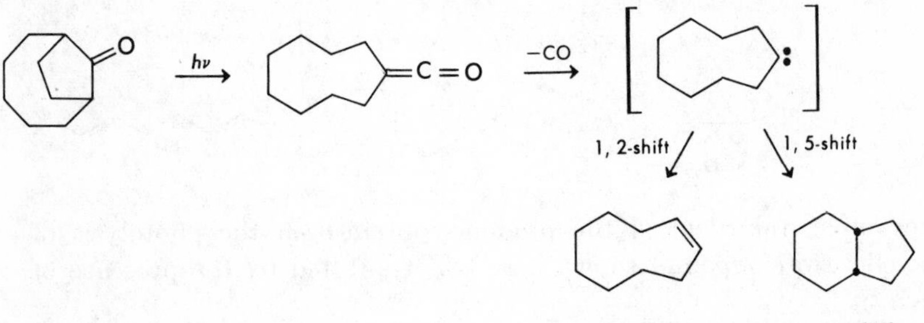

[38]

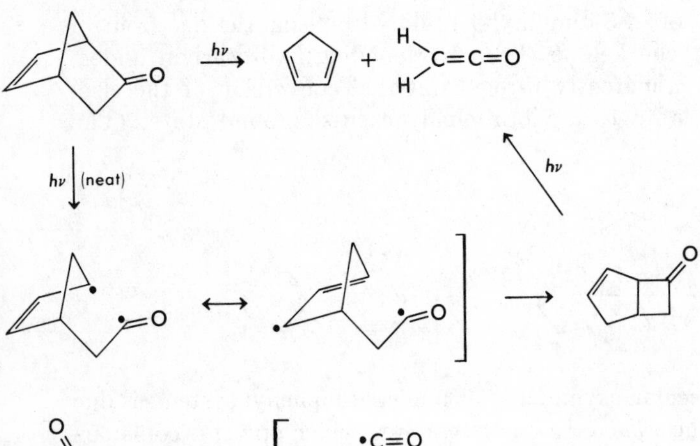

[39,40]

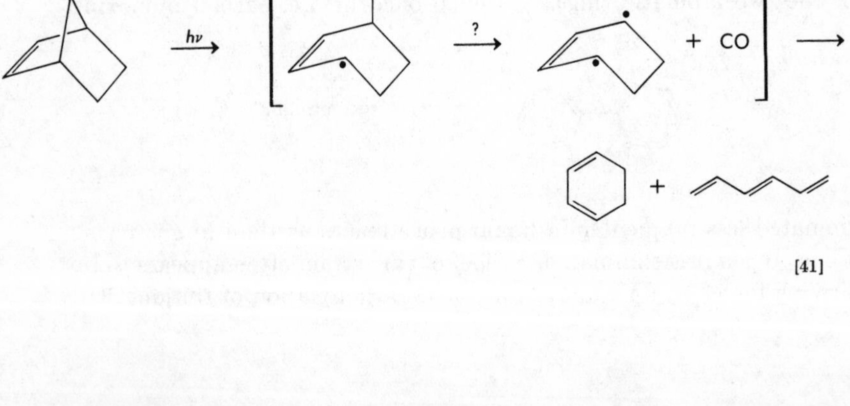

[41]

Frequently the solvent is found to assist during the photolysis. Thus, during the airfree photolysis of *dl*-camphor, the solvent acts as a "hydrogen-transfer agent." The quantum-yield ratio for the two products is solvent-dependent:

[42]

RH = diethyl ether, methanol, ethanol, n-heptane or 3-methylpentane

The photolysis of tetramethylcyclobutane-1,3-dione has received a great deal of attention[3,43-45] because changes in the experimental conditions of the photolysis cause appreciable variation in the type of product obtained. Photolyses conducted in inert solvents, such as pentane, show that more than one primary process takes place: dissociation to dimethylketene and the loss of 1 and 2 moles of carbon monoxide.[43]

The formation of both dimethylketene and tetramethylcyclopropanone has been demonstrated spectroscopically.[43,45] Further, the addition of trapping agents to pentane solutions of the moderately stable cyclopropanone has been shown to lead to the appropriate products:[3,43,44]

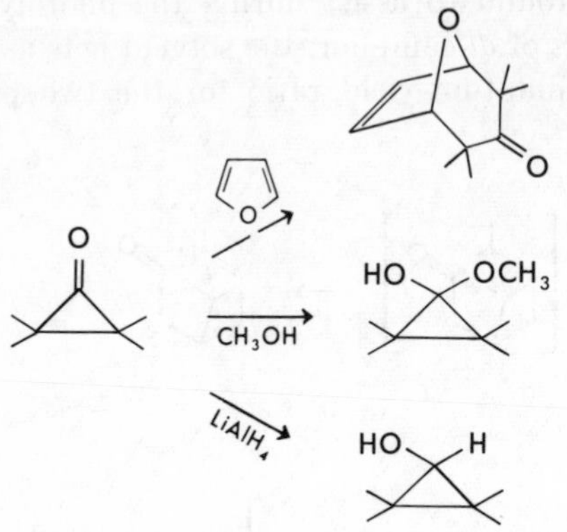

The reaction is complicated by the fact that the photolysis of dimethyl-ketene itself also can lead to the primary products by the sequence shown below and by the dimerization of the ketene to yield the starting material.[45]

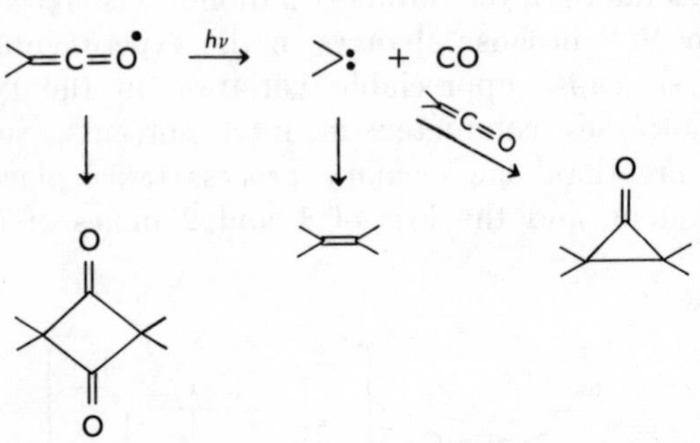

When the dione is irradiated in alcohols, the formation of tetramethyl-ethylene is suppressed and the only products observed are those result-ing from the addition of the solvent to dimethylketene and tetramethyl-cyclopropanone:

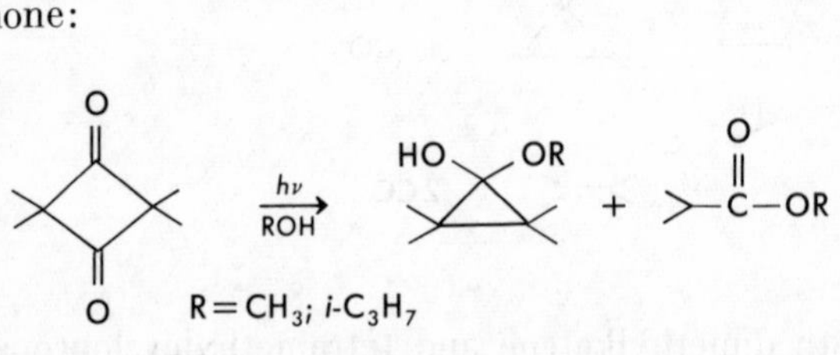

The presence of oxygen profoundly affects the course of the photolysis. When conducted in benzene and in the presence of oxygen, photolysis leads to the formation of acetone, carbon monoxide, carbon dioxide, and tetramethylethylene oxide. There is good indication that the sequence taking place is as shown below; tetramethylethylene is *not* a precursor in the formation of its oxide.[43]

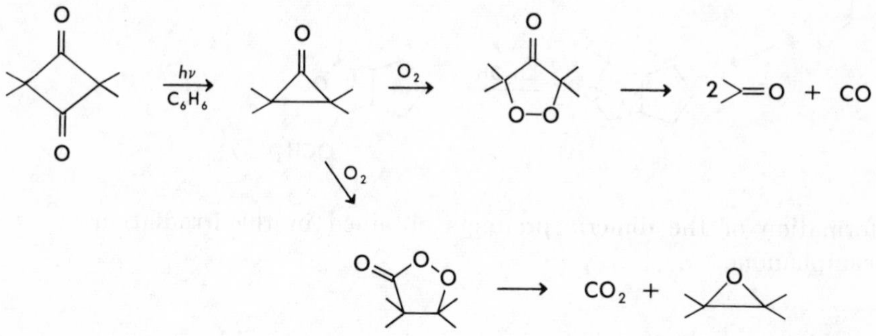

Similar results can apparently be obtained with other tetrasubstituted cyclobutadiones. The photolysis of dispiro[5.1.5.1]tetradecane-7,14-dione illustrates this.

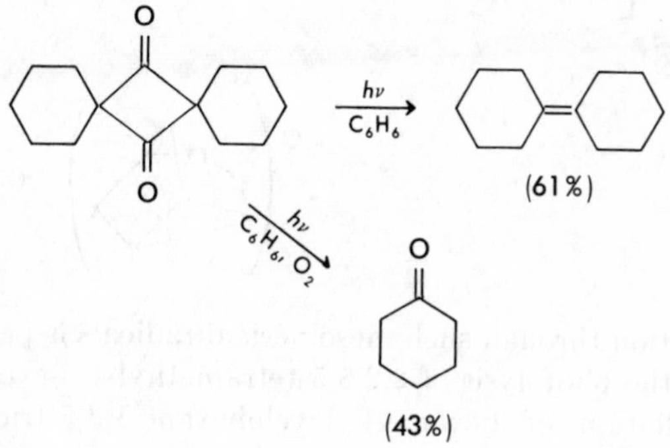

[43]

Diphenylcyclopropenone similarly loses carbon monoxide on photolysis:

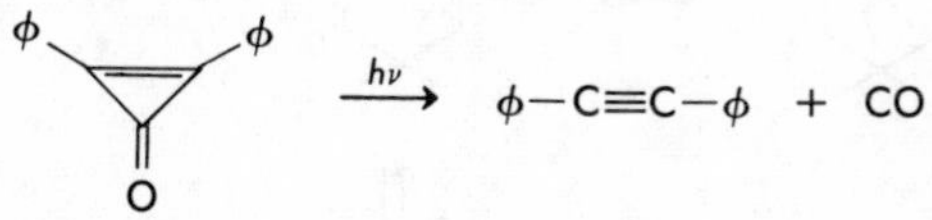

[33]

Several cases in which CO—C bond scission is followed by a "free-electron migration" prior to recombination have been reported. For example, 7,7-dimethylbicyclo[3.2.0]hept-2-en-6-one, upon photolysis, yields the methyl ester resulting from ketene-solvent addition, as well as the cyclic methyl acetal that results from such an electron migration.[47] Yates[48] has suggested that a similar acetal is the intermediate in the formation of the dimeric products obtained in the irradiation of cyclocamphanone.

Odd electron migration through such mesomeric diradicals is particularly well illustrated by the photolysis of 2,2,5,5-tetramethyl-1,3-cyclohexane-dione.[49] The irradiation of hexamethylcyclohexane-1,3,5-trione leads

to a combination of the foregoing two reaction types. The product mixture is composed of lactones, resulting from electron migration, and of several ketones, formed by successive decarbonylations.[46] In a similar fashion a variety of 2-disubstituted-indane-1,3-diones have been observed to rearrange (reversibly) to the corresponding alkylidene phthalides.[46a]

3-3 α-Dicarbonyl Compounds

The primary process in the photolysis of α-dicarbonyl systems is often the scission of the low-energy CO—CO bond.[50-52] The photolysis of pyruvates in benzene results in the formation of acetaldehyde, carbon monoxide, and the carbonyl derivative (ketone or aldehyde) corresponding to the O-alkyl group.[50] From the phosphorescence observed and from the fact that benzophenone is an effective sensitizer of the reaction it can be concluded that the excited state is a triplet.[52] That the transfer of hydrogen probably is not part of the primary process is indicated by the absence of a deuterium isotope effect.[50] The use of a solvent

facilitating hydrogen abstraction, such as 2-propanol, leads to the formation of pinacols, a photochemical reduction process discussed in detail in Sec. 7-2. While pyruvic acid yields mainly acetoin on photolysis in aqueous solution, benzaldehyde is the main product obtained from benzoylformic acid:[53]

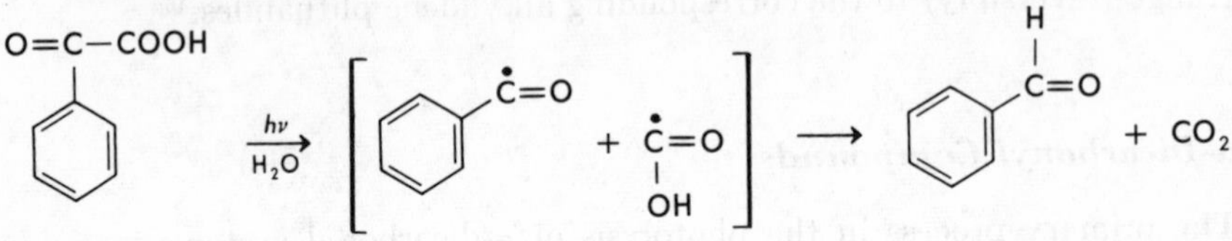

but:

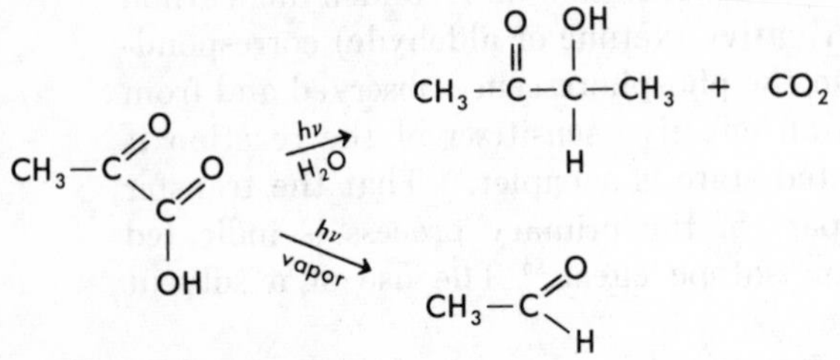

The reason for this variation is not clear; in both cases the excited state is presumed to be the triplet state resulting from n-π^* excitation.[53] In the gas phase pyruvic acid yields only acetaldehyde. The aldehyde formation can be visualized by a hydrogen-transfer step between a radical pair. The liquid-phase photolysis of triones is remarkable in that little carbon monoxide is produced, in contrast to the thermal behavior; the main reaction is a radical exchange:

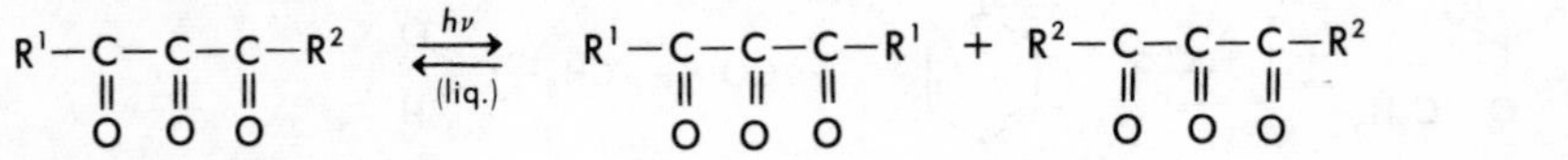

$R^1 = CH_3; R^2 = (CH_3)_3C$
$R^1 = C_2H_5; R^2 = (CH_3)_3C$

[54]

3-4 Unsaturated Ketones

Conjugated unsaturated ketones are extremely active photochemically. As we shall see later, they undergo a multitude of rearrangements as well as dimerizations. Fission processes occur also, and they are discussed here. The photochemistry of 2,4-cyclohexadienones is especially varied; frequently, fission adjacent to the carbonyl group may be observed. When ortho substituents are present, fission usually occurs on the side of the substituents.

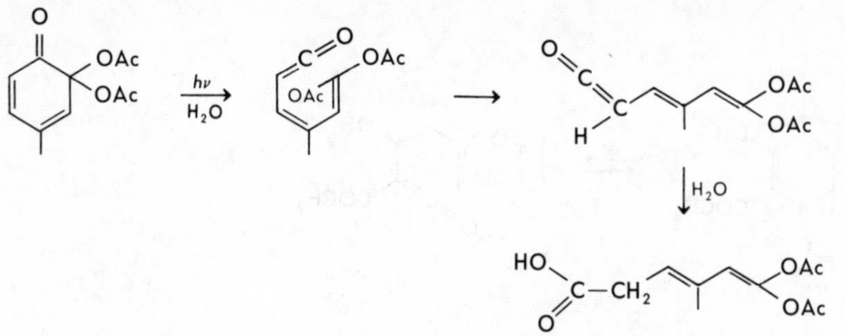

[55,56]

With acetoxy groups as substituents, migration and expulsion are observed occasionally:

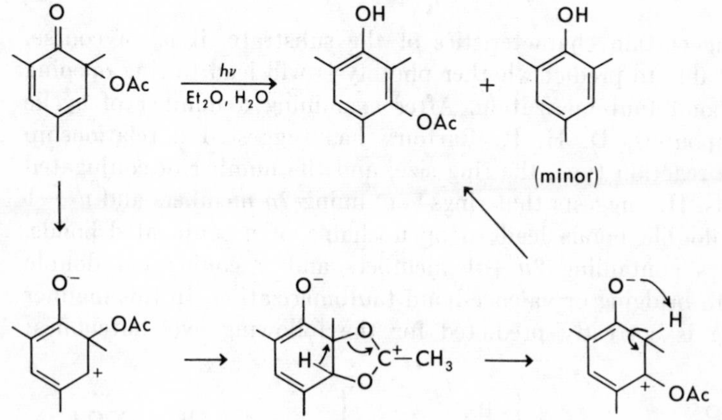

(minor)

[56]

[56,57]

One other example of a ring-opening reaction is given below. In a manner

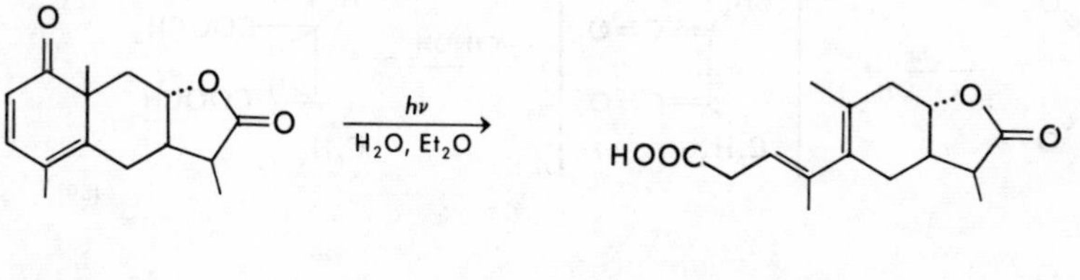

[55]

similar to the saturated ketones, the CO—C bond-fission step is reversible in dienone systems. This fact is illustrated by the easy racemization of the material shown below:

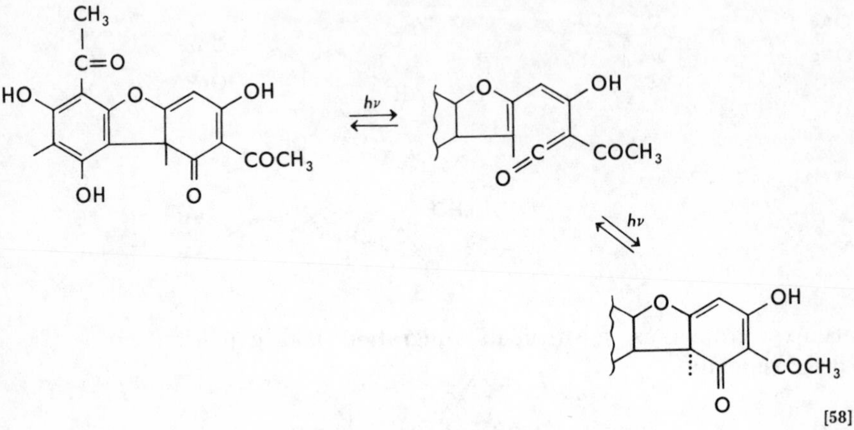

[58]

Knowing certain characteristics of the substrate, it is, of course, useful to be able to predict whether photolysis will lead to ring opening or valence-bond tautomerization. After examining a number of cyclic olefinic compounds, D. H. R. Barton[57] has suggested a relationship between the reaction type, the ring size, and the number of conjugated double bonds. He suggests that rings containing $2n$ members and $n-1$ conjugated double bonds lead to open chains of n conjugated bonds, whereas rings containing $2n+1$ members and n conjugated double bonds lead to bridging or valence-bond tautomerization. In this manner ring opening is correctly predicted for the following cyclobutenones:

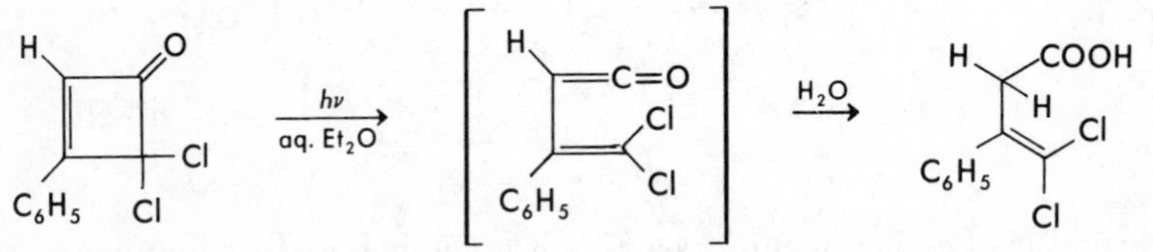

[57]

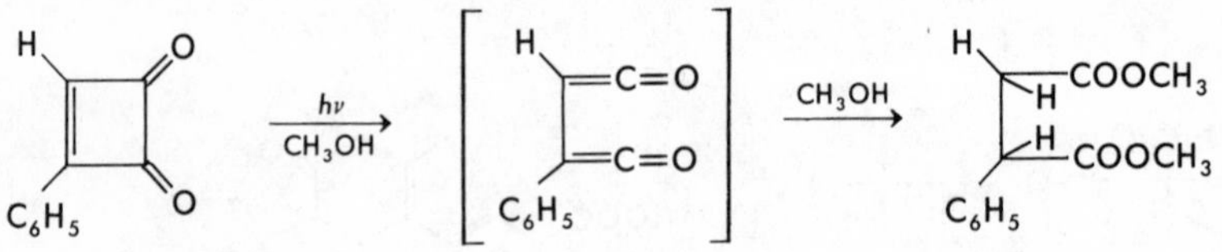

[59]

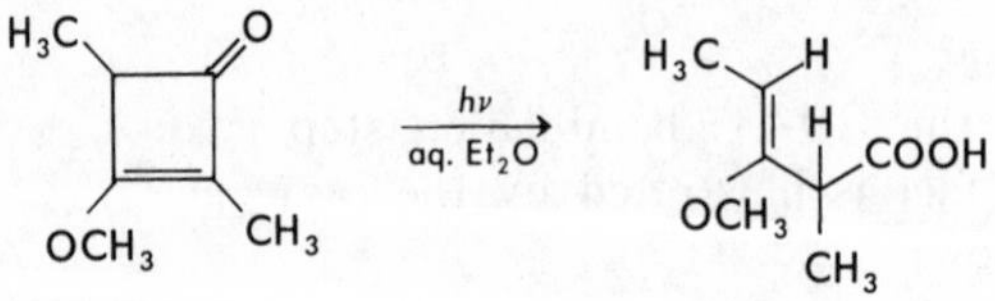

[57]

Similarly, one can predict the ring opening of the diacetate illustrated below:

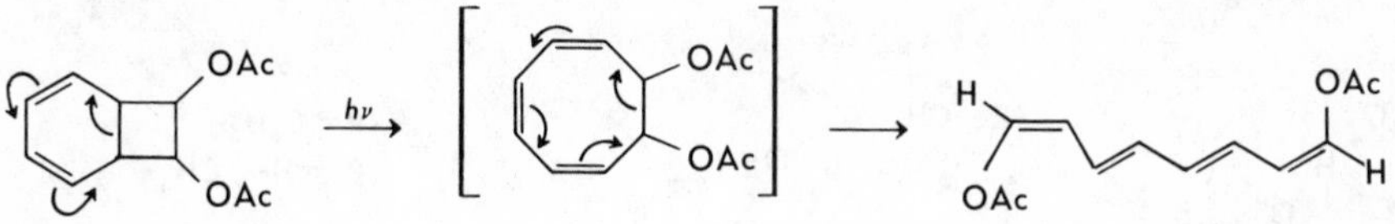

[57]

Reactions of seven-membered ring systems, leading mostly to bridging, are discussed in Sec. 2-3. (For exceptions to Barton's rules, see below.)

3-5 Fission of C—S Bonds and Related Reactions

Because of the superior ability of sulfur to stabilize free electrons, the fission of CO—S and S—S bonds occurs readily on photolysis. The loss of carbon monoxide in the example shown below is one of several cases of such fissions:

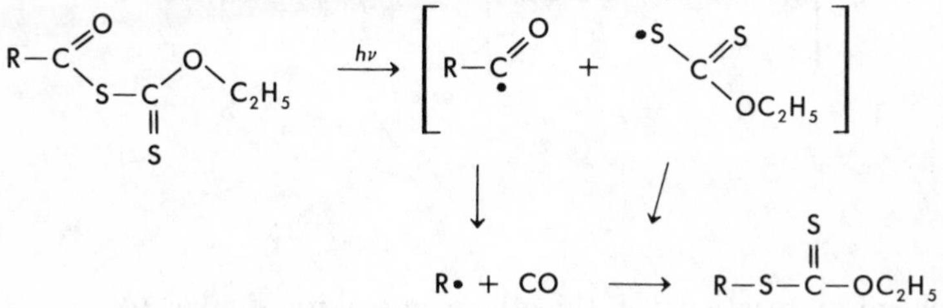

[60]

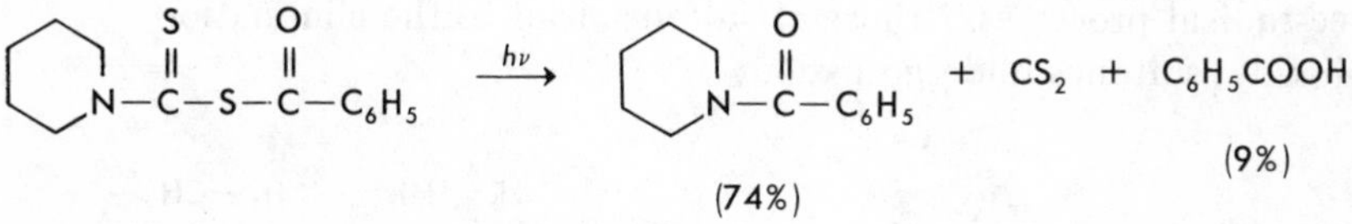

(74%)

(9%)

[61]

Recombination of the carbonyl fractions has also been observed with the formation of 1,2-cyclopentadione.

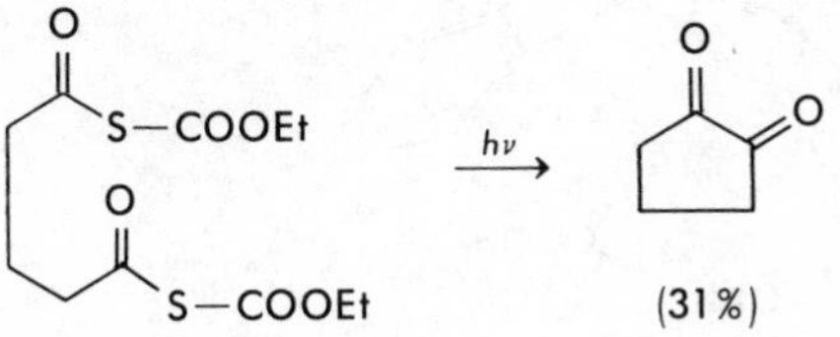

(31%)

[60]

In the rearrangement of sulfoxonium ylides C—S bond fission takes place in a process reminiscent of the Arndt-Eistert reaction.

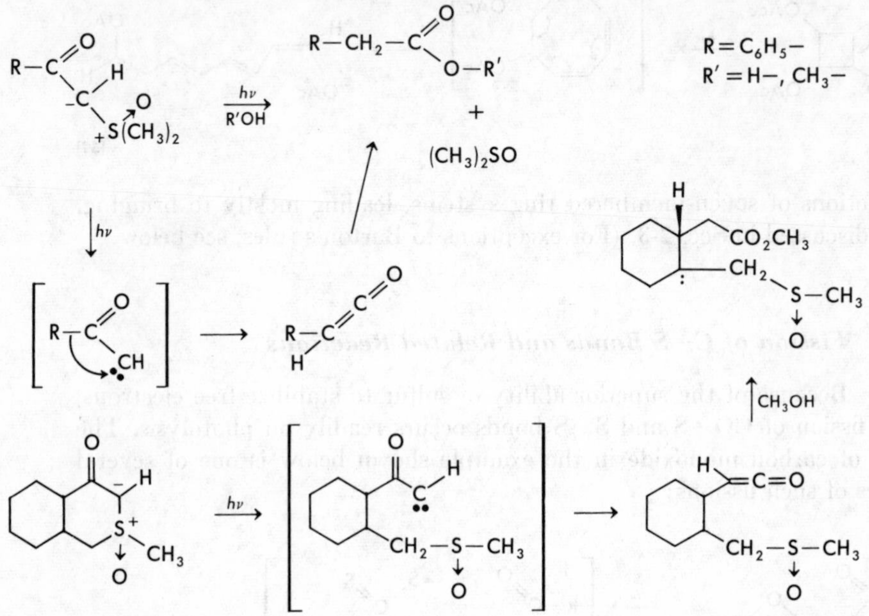

[62]

While the photochemical reactions of thioethers are quite similar to thermal free-radical processes,[63] those of sulfones lead to the elimination of sulfur dioxide; sultones undergo fission:

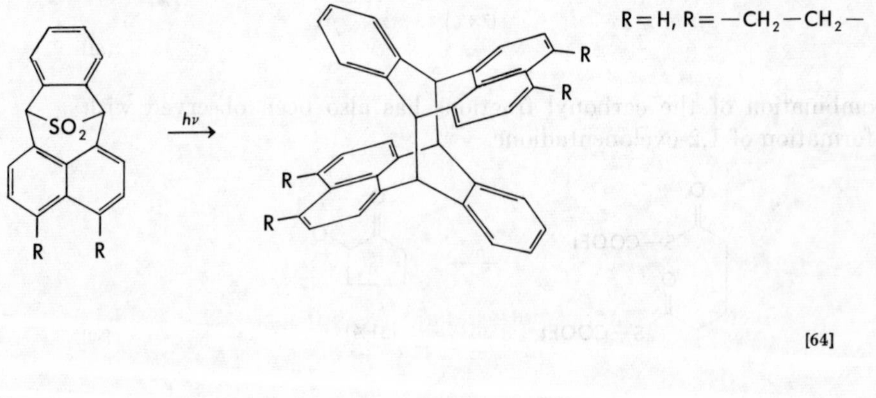

[64]

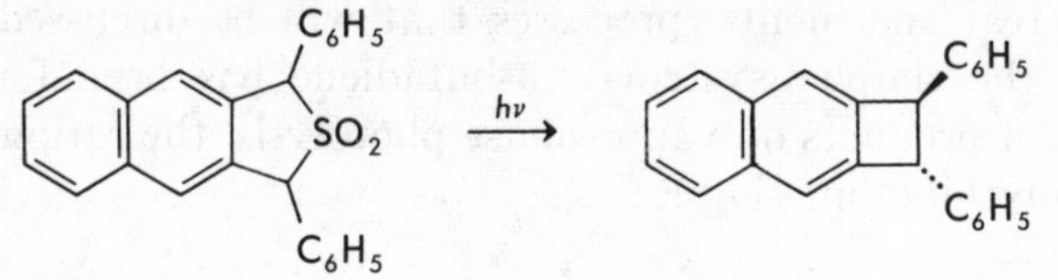

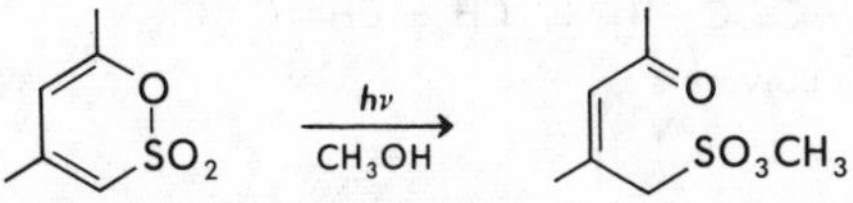

None of the sulfones decomposes in the absence of sensitizers on irradiation above 3200 Å, so that the excited state is likely to be a triplet. The possibility exists that intersystem crossing to the vibrationally excited ground state occurs prior to bond breakage, but no concrete evidence is available on this point.[64] The last reaction mentioned is similar to the fission claimed to occur in α-pyrone. It is unusual in that the same

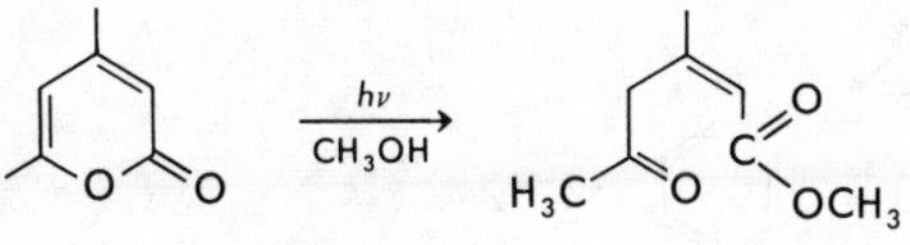

system has been observed to undergo bridging and dimerization reactions. A final example is the fission of acetals leading to the formation of esters:

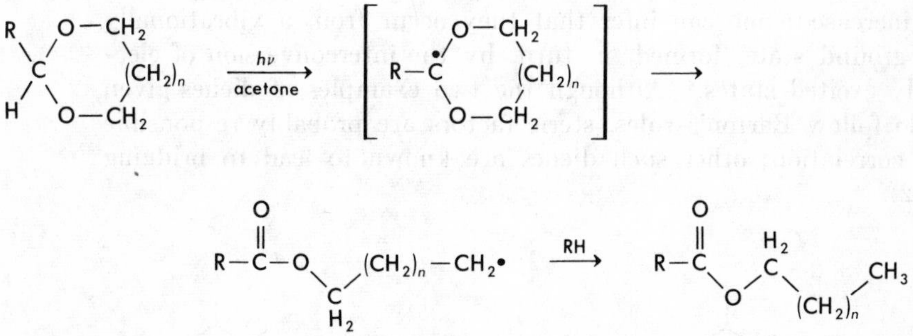

3-6 Conjugated Olefins

Cyclic olefins are the only other major group susceptible to bond breakage on photolysis. Most of the more complex systems undergo isomerizations and rearrangements, processes that will be discussed in other chapters. Of the simpler systems 1,3-butadiene has been found to yield a profusion of products on vapor-phase photolysis, the rationalization of which is anything but simple:

$$\xrightarrow{h\nu} \begin{array}{l} H-C\equiv C-H \ + \ H_2 \ + \ CH_2=CH_2 \ + \ CH_4 \\ + \ CH_3-CH_2-C\equiv C-H \ + \ CH_3-CH=C=CH_2 \\ + \ dimers \ + \ polymers \end{array}$$

[68]

Barton's rules fail in predicting the type of product observed on photolysis of 1,3-cyclohexadiene; both the open triene and the bridged bicyclic system are obtained. In the vapor phase, aromatization and secondary bond fission may occur:

[69]

[68]

$$+ \ CH_3CH=C=CH-CH_2-CH_3$$
$$+ \ H-C\equiv C-H \ + \ CH_2=C=CH_2$$

There exists as yet little theoretical foundation for such a variety of processes. The reactions leading to fission products decrease as the pressure is increased; one can infer that they occur from a vibrationally excited ground state, formed, in turn, by the interconversion of electronically excited states.[68] Although the two examples of dienes given below do follow Barton's rules, steric factors are probably responsible for the correlation; other such dienes are known to lead to bridging (Chap. 2).

[70]

There is one final item. It has been reported that flash photolysis of a variety of substituted benzenes (anilines, phenols, thiophenols, nitrobenzenes, and their halogen derivatives) causes elimination of a carbon atom with the formation of cyclopentadienyl.[72]

References

1. C. H. Bamford and R. G. W. Norrish, *J. Chem. Soc.*, **1935**, 1504; R. G. W. Norrish and R. P. Wayne, *Proc. Roy. Soc. (London)*, Ser. A, **284**, 1 (1965); J. N. Pitts, Jr., L. D. Hess, E. J. Baum, E. A. Schuck, and J. K. S. Wan, *Photochem. & Photobiol.*, **4**, 305 (1965).

1a. J. K. S. Wan, R. N. McCormick, E. J. Baum, and J. N. Pitts, Jr., *J. Am. Chem. Soc.*, **87**, 4409 (1965) and references cited therein.

2. R. Srinivasan, in "Advances in Photochemistry," vol. I, p. 83, W. A. Noyes, Jr., G. S. Hammond, J. N. Pitts, Jr. (eds.), Interscience, New York, 1963.

3. R. C. Cookson, M. J. Nye, and G. Subrahamanyam, *Proc. Chem. Soc.*, **1964**, 144.

4. F. E. Blacet and A. Miller, *J. Am. Chem. Soc.*, **79**, 4327 (1957); M. C. Flowers and H. M. Frey, *J. Chem. Soc.*, **1960**, 2758.

5. S. W. Benson and G. B. Kistiakowsky, *J. Am. Chem. Soc.*, **64**, 80 (1942).

6. R. Srinivasan, *J. Am. Chem. Soc.*, **81**, 1546 (1959).

7. R. Srinivasan, *J. Am. Chem. Soc.*, **81**, 2601 (1959).

8. R. Srinivasan, *J. Am. Chem. Soc.*, **81**, 5541 (1959).

9. R. Srinivasan, *J. Am. Chem. Soc.*, **83**, 4344 (1961).

10. B. Rickborn, R. L. Alumbaugh, and S. O. Pritchard, *Chem. Ind. (London)*, **1964**, 1951.

11. R. Srinivasan, *J. Am. Chem. Soc.*, **83**, 4348 (1961).

12. R. Srinivasan, *J. Am. Chem. Soc.*, **83**, 4923 (1961).

13. S. E. Cremer and R. Srinivasan, *Tetrahedron Letters*, nos. 21, 24 (1960).

14. R. Srinivasan, *J. Am. Chem. Soc.*, **83**, 2590 (1961).
15. P. Ausloos and R. E. Rebbert, *J. Am. Chem. Soc.*, **83**, 4897 (1961); R. P. Borkowski and P. Ausloos, *J. Phys. Chem.*, **65**, 2257 (1961).
16. P. Ausloos and E. Murad, *J. Am. Chem. Soc.*, **80**, 5929 (1958).
17. R. Srinivasan, *J. Am. Chem. Soc.*, **81**, 5061 (1959), **84**, 2475 (1962).
18. G. R. McMillan, J. G. Calvert, and J. N. Pitts, Jr., *J. Am. Chem. Soc.*, **86**, 3602 (1964).
19. D. J. Coyle, R. V. Peterson, and J. Heicklen, *J. Am. Chem. Soc.*, **86**, 3850 (1964).
20. G. Quinkert, *Angew. Chem.*, **77**, 229 (1965), and references cited therein.
21. H. Wehrli and K. Schaffner, *Helv. Chim. Acta*, **45**, 385 (1962).
22. G. Quinkert, E. Blanke, and F. Homburg, *Ber.*, **97**, 1799 (1964).
23. G. Quinkert, B. Wegemund, and E. Blanke, *Tetrahedron Letters*, **1962**, 221.
24. A. J. Bellamy and G. H. Whitham, *J. Chem. Soc.*, **1964**, 4035.
25. G. Quinkert, B. Wegemund, F. Homburg, and G. Cimbollek, *Ber.*, **97**, 958 (1964); D. Arigoni, D. H. R. Barton, R. Barnasconi, C. Djerassi, J. S. Mills, and R. E. Wolff, *Proc. Chem. Soc.*, **1959**, 306; *J. Chem. Soc.*, **1960**, 1900; G. Quinkert, *Angew. Chem.*, **74**, 218 (1962).
26. R. P. Ghandi, unpublished results; see R. C. Cookson, *Pure Appl. Chem.*, **9**, 575 (1964).
27. M. S. Kharasch, J. Kuderna, and W. Nudenberg, *J. Org. Chem.*, **18**, 1225 (1953).
28. G. Ciamician and P. Silber, *Ber.*, **46**, 3077 (1913).
29. G. Ciamician and P. Silber, *Ber.*, **40**, 2415 (1907).
30. J. Iriarte, K. Schaffner, and O. Jeger, *Helv. Chim. Acta*, **47**, 1255 (1964).
31. S. E. Cremer and R. Srinivasan, *J. Am. Chem. Soc.*, **86**, 4197 (1964); R. Srinivasan and S. E. Cremer, *J. Am. Chem. Soc.*, **87**, 1647 (1965).
32. O. L. Chapman, A. I. Dutton, P. Fitton, and T. A. Rettig, unpublished results.
33. G. Quinkert, K. Opitz, W. W. Wiersdorff, and J. Weinlich, *Tetrahedron Letters*, **1963**, 1863; G. Quinkert, *Pure Appl. Chem.*, **9**, 607 (1964).
34. A. Schönberg, A. K. Fateen, and S. M. A. R. Omran, *J. Am. Chem. Soc.*, **78**, 1224 (1956).
35. C. G. Overberger and J. Tashlik, *J. Am. Chem. Soc.*, **81**, 217 (1959); C. G. Overberger and J. P. Anselme, *J. Am. Chem. Soc.*, **86**, 658 (1964).
36. K. Mislow and A. J. Gordon, *J. Am. Chem. Soc.*, **85**, 3521 (1963).
37. R. H. Eastman, J. E. Starr, R. St. Martin, and M. K. Sakata, *J. Org. Chem.*, **28**, 2162 (1963).
38. C. D. Gutsche and J. W. Baum, *Tetrahedron Letters*, **1965**, 2301.
39. G. O. Schenck and R. Steinmetz, *Ber.*, **96**, 520 (1963).
40. D. I. Schuster, M. Axelrod, and J. Auerbach, *Tetrahedron Letters*, **1963**, 1911.
41. D. I. Schuster, F. T. H. Lee, A. Padwa, and P. G. Gassman, *J. Org. Chem.* **30**, 2262 (1965).
42. R. Srinivasan, *J. Am. Chem. Soc.*, **81**, 2604 (1959).
43. N. J. Turro, P. A. Leermakers, H. R. Wilson, D. C. Neckers, G. W. Byers, and G. F. Vesley, *J. Am. Chem. Soc.*, **87**, 2613 (1965); N. J. Turro, W. B. Hammond, and P. A. Leermakers, *J. Am. Chem. Soc.*, **87**, 2774 (1965).
44. H. G. Richey, Jr., M. J. Richey, and D. C. Clagett, *J. Am. Chem. Soc.*, **86**, 3906 (1964).
45. I. Haller and R. Srinivasan, *J. Am. Chem. Soc.*, **87**, 1144 (1965).
46. H. U. Hostettler, *Tetrahedron Letters*, **1965**, 1941.
46a. J. Rigaudy and P. Derible, *Bull. Soc. Chim. France*, **1965**, 3047, 3055, 3061.
47. H. U. Hostettler, *Tetrahedron Letters*, **1965**, 687.
48. P. Yates and L. Kilmurry, *Tetrahedron Letters*, **1964**, 1739.
49. H. Nozaki, Z. Yamaguti, and R. Noyori, *Tetrahedron Letters*, **1965**, 37; R. C.

Cookson, A. G. Edwards, J. Hudec, and M. Kingsland, *Chem. Commun.*, **1965,** 98.

50. P. A. Leermakers, P. C. Warren, and G. F. Vesley, *J. Am. Chem. Soc.*, **86,** 1768 (1964).

51. N. C. Yang and A. Morduchowitz, *J. Org. Chem.*, **29,** 1654 (1964).

52. G. S. Hammond, P. A. Leermakers, and N. J. Turro, *J. Am. Chem. Soc.*, **83,** 2395 (1961).

53. P. A. Leermakers and G. F. Vesley, *J. Am. Chem. Soc.*, **85,** 3776 (1963).

54. W. H. Urry, M. H. Pai, and C. Y. Chen, *J. Am. Chem. Soc.*, **86,** 5342 (1964).

55. W. G. Dauben, D. A. Lightner, and W. K. Hayes, *J. Org. Chem.*, **27,** 1897 (1962).

56. D. H. R. Barton and G. Quinkert, *J. Chem. Soc.*, **1960,** 1.

57. D. H. R. Barton, *Helv. Chim. Acta*, **42,** 2604 (1959).

58. G. Stork, *Chem. Ind. (London)*, **1955,** 915; S. Mackenzie, *J. Am. Chem. Soc.*, **77,** 2214 (1955); D. H. R. Barton and G. Quinkert, *J. Chem. Soc.*, **1960,** 1.

59. F. B. Mallory and J. D. Roberts, *J. Am. Chem. Soc.*, **83,** 393 (1961), footnote 6.

60. D. H. R. Barton, M. V. George, and M. Tomoeda, *J. Chem. Soc.*, **1962,** 1967.

61. E. H. Hoffmeister and D. S. Tarbell, *Tetrahedron*, **21,** 35, 2857, 2865 (1965).

62. E. J. Corey and M. Chaykovsky, *J. Am. Chem. Soc.*, **86,** 1640 (1964).

63. L. Horner and J. Dörges, *Tetrahedron Letters*, **1963,** 757.

64. M. P. Cava, R. H. Schlessinger, and J. P. VanMeter, *J. Am. Chem. Soc.*, **86,** 3173 (1964).

65. J. F. King, P. de Mayo, E. Morkved, A. B. M. A. Sattar, and A. Stoessl, *Can. J. Chem.*, **41,** 100 (1963); Y. Odaira, K. Yamaji, and S. Tsutsumi, *Bull. Chem. Soc. Japan*, **37,** 1410 (1964).

66. J. G. Esterle, P. M. Girling, P. de Mayo, and R. H. Wiley, unpublished observations; see P. de Mayo, in "Advances in Org. Chem.," vol. 2, p. 394, R. A. Raphael, E. C. Taylor, H. Wynberg (eds.), Interscience, New York, 1960.

67. D. Elad and R. D. Youssefyeh, *Tetrahedron Letters*, **1963,** 2189.

68. R. Srinivasan, *J. Am. Chem. Soc.*, **82,** 5063 (1960).

69. W. G. Dauben and R. L. Cargill, *J. Org. Chem.*, **27,** 1910 (1962).

70. R. L. Autrey, D. H. R. Barton, A. K. Ganguli, and W. H. Reusch, *J. Chem. Soc.*, **1961,** 3313.

71. Chap. 2, ref. 47.

72. G. Porter and B. Ward, *Proc. Chem. Soc.*, **1964,** 288.

Rearrangements

4-1 Enones and Dienones

Photochemical rearrangements probably constitute the most profound series of structural changes observed in "single-step" chemical reactions. Their mechanisms must, however, be represented by a series of many steps that occur either consecutively, as witness the occasional observation of the appropriate intermediates, or else in a concerted fashion. Whether these steps are best represented by polar structures or nonpolar, free-radical types of structure has been the subject of considerable discussion, and it is certain that some rearrangements are better represented by one of the two treatments than are others. Consider, for example, the rearrangement of 4,4-diphenylcyclohexadienone:

The excitation involved in this reaction is probably that of the n-π^* type, and the phosphorescence observed indicates a triplet.[1] Treatment of such an excited state as a dipolar system has been adopted by Chapman[2] as a working hypothesis, and it is commonly referred to as the "polar-state concept." This treatment demonstrates the fact that excitation of the α,β-unsaturated ketone moiety of a molecule involves electron redistribution which renders the molecule more polarizable, if not more polar, than the ground state. How this polarity must be represented depends on the type of excitation; π-π^* (triplet) excitations really involve a depletion of electronic charge from the π system, so that positive character would be localized in the conjugated system of the molecule and negative charge would be localized on oxygen. The opposite polarity should be obtained with n-π^* (triplet) excitations, for here an electron that is usually localized on oxygen is "withdrawn."[3] Many of the photochemical rearrangements observed are highly reminiscent of carbonium-ion processes, even though they are usually assumed to be associated with n-π^* excitations. Thus one can represent the excited state of 4,4-diphenylcyclohexadienone by either of the following two "structures":

The second of these two is somewhat misleading in that it places a positive charge on oxygen. We feel that it is useful merely in pointing out that the normal polarization of the carbonyl group has been reduced; in other words, oxygen in the excited state bears less negative charge than in the ground state. Excitation or not, however, oxygen is negatively polarized with respect to carbon,[4] and those structures implying the opposite probably contribute little, if anything, to the resonance hybrid, even though evidence on this point is still lacking.

When one considers the first of the two polar states, it can be written in several ways, and subsequent processes might occur from any of these representations as the starting point:

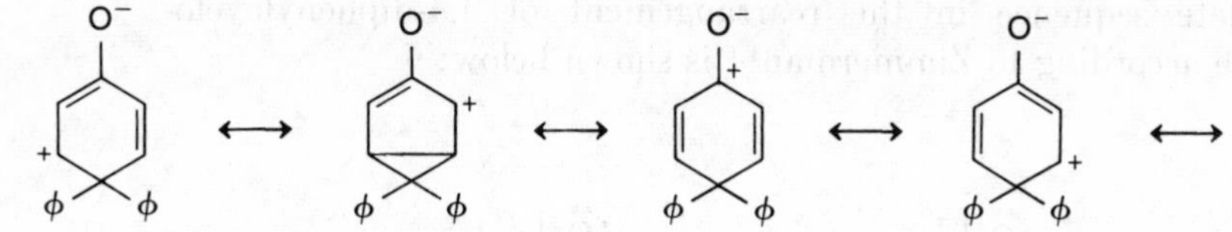

I   II

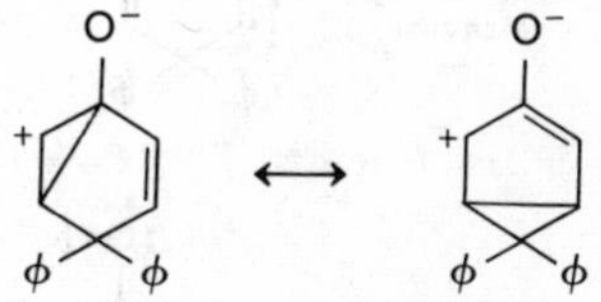

Further examination will show that the product of the rearrangement, which is chemically equivalent to III, can easily be obtained by the following bond migration in I:

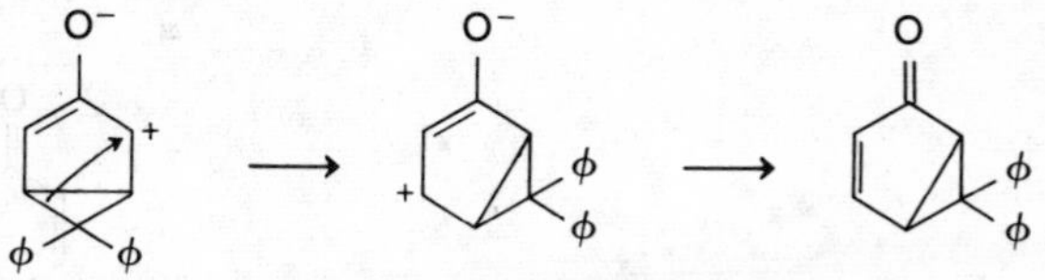

I   III

A second school of thought has been advanced by Zimmerman and coworkers,[4,5] who consider the excited state as one in which continuous electron redistribution takes place (for which they employ the terms "rebonding" and "bond alteration"). Only after intersystem crossing of the lowest n-π^* triplet to the singlet state and deactivation (termed "demotion") to the ground state do they consider polar structures realistic representations. The polar state obtained on demotion can then undergo further electron redistribution similar to the rearrangement steps shown in the polar-state mechanism. Thus, the excited state may be represented as shown here:

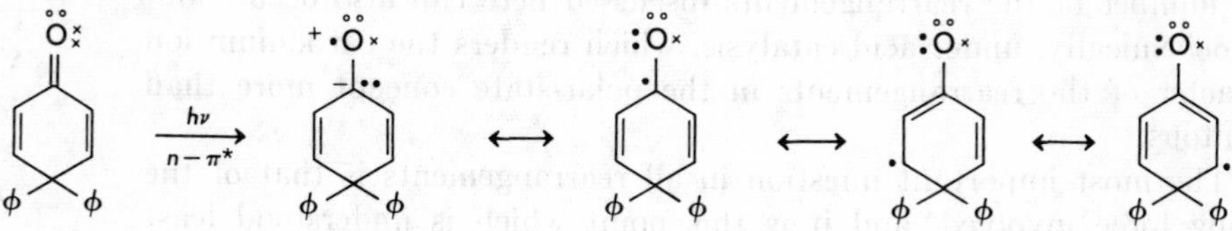

The complete sequence in the rearrangement of 4,4-diphenylcyclo-hexadienone according to Zimmerman[1,5] is shown below:

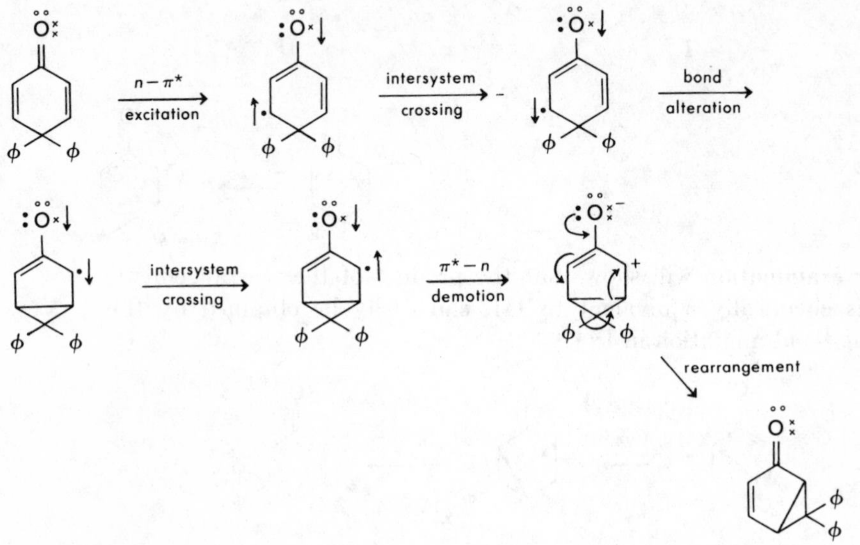

It may be seen from this sequence that certain events, such as exci-tation, intersystem crossings, and demotion, which were not spelled out in detail in the Chapman polar-state mechanism, are here given in detail. The actual rearrangement steps involving bond migrations remain essentially unaltered, although their timing in the overall process is now defined. We choose to employ the polar-state concept throughout most of the discussion, mainly because it provides a fairly lucid method of visualizing the formation of most products observed and also because, even if it is only a hypothesis and a simplification of the real train of events, it emphasizes the actual rearrangement steps. Moreover, a signifi-cant number of the rearrangements discussed here can also occur non-photochemically, under acid catalysis, which renders the carbonium-ion character of the rearrangements in the polar-state concept more than fortuitous.

The most important question in all rearrangements is that of the driving force involved, and it is this point which is understood least satisfactorily. Models shed little light on the problem and the factors weighed in ground-state chemistry seem to have little bearing, because one of the requirements of ground-state chemistry—the one specifying that transition states and intermediates of lowest energy must be involved—seems to have been removed. As indicated in Chap. 1, the absorption of a quantum of a certain energy will in theory allow to occur all processes that require no more than the amount of energy absorbed. In many photochemical reactions the various "resonance structures" and valence-bond tautomers are of very similar energy, and the independent or consecutive rearrangements of the compound written as any one of these structures seem to be almost isoenergetic. Thus, many products are obtained (see, for example, the santonin case described later), and the type and relative amount of the products are determined by secondary factors, such as the solvent polarity, and the presence or absence of substituents in certain strategic locations. However, since the lowest excited states are still populated preferentially, calculations of the relative electron distribution in those states may be a guide in predicting subsequent reactions. Although some success has been obtained with this method,[1] especially in connection with photochemical solvolytic displacement reactions (Sec. 8-4), the calculations are complex and the identity of the excited state is by no means certain in all cases.

Returning now to the example under discussion, we see that the product of the rearrangement can itself react further, since it is still endowed with a chromophore capable of undergoing $n\text{-}\pi^*$ excitation. The following six structures represent the various states of electron distribution:

Among these, III and IV were proposed to be precursors in the formation of the starting material itself and they should not lead to new products; V and VI each can undergo phenyl migration leading respectively to 2,3- and 3,4-diphenylphenol. (The latter can also form from II in the first rearrangement.) Both of the phenols have been isolated.[5,6]

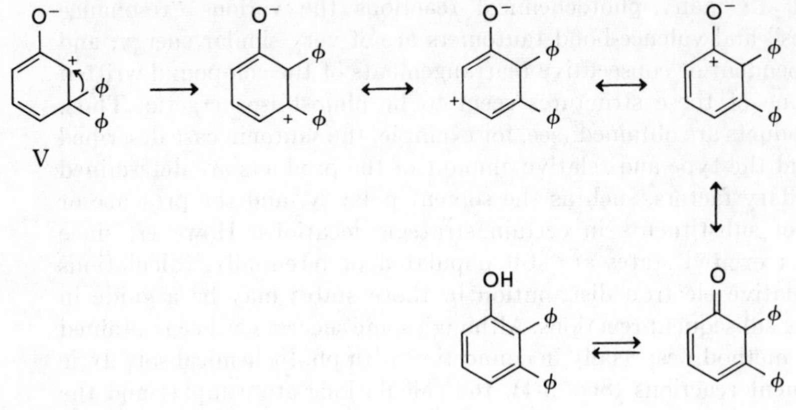

V

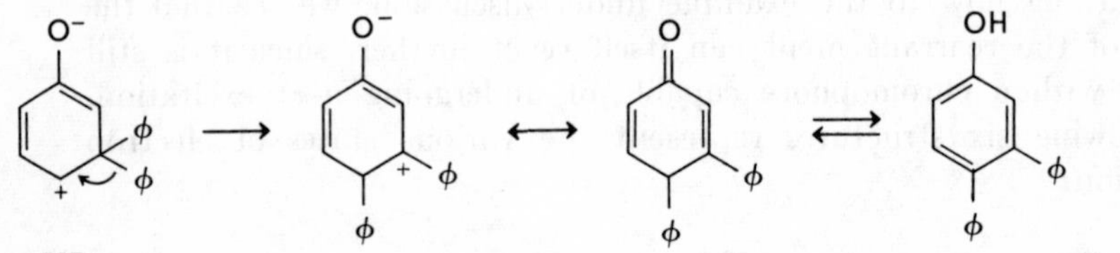

VI

3,4-Diphenylphenol is obtained in only small amounts when the photolysis is conducted in aqueous dioxane but in an amount equal to that of the 2,3 isomer when the photolysis is conducted in aqueous acetic acid. One possible reason for this difference is the better electron delocalization with V than with VI in the dioxane reactions.[6]

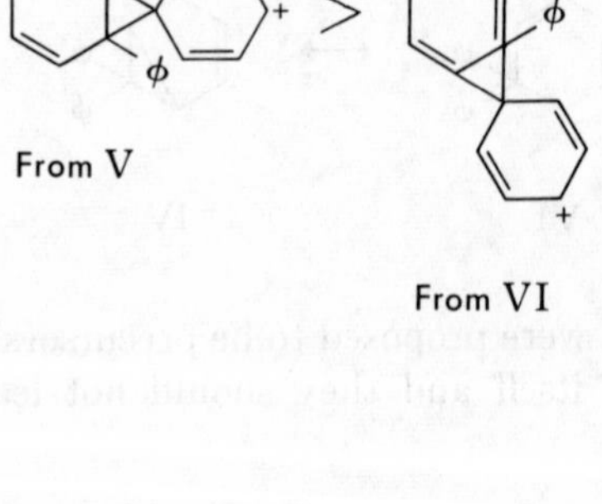

From V   >   From VI

In acetic acid, protonation on oxygen occurs and delocalization is a less significant factor. Of the remaining structures, VII can rearrange to a ketene and form an acid in aqueous media but VIII cannot; it has little means of stabilizing itself other than by a return to starting material. The acid resulting from the rearrangement of VII has indeed been isolated.[7]

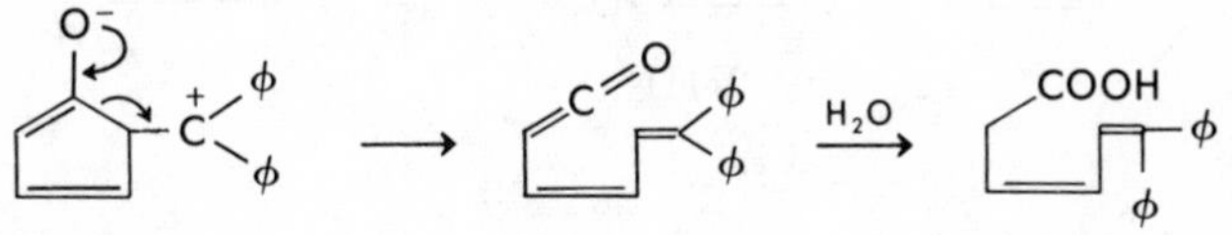

In terms of the Zimmerman mechanism these various steps can be represented as shown below.[3,5]

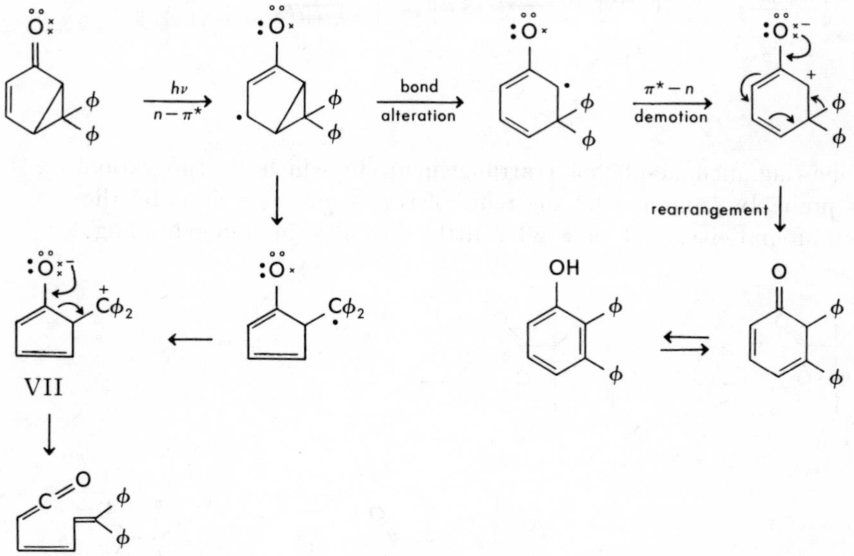

In the presence of protic solvents proton migration can take place through abstraction and donation. For example, by analogy with the reaction of 4,4-dimethylcyclohexenone, discussed later, one might expect the two products shown to form; but even though these compounds

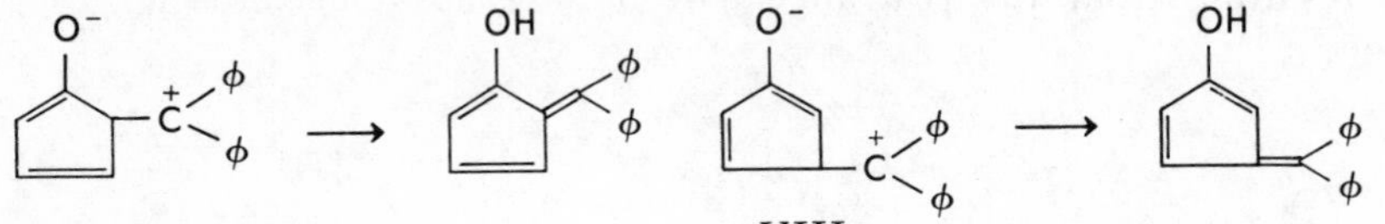

VII   VIII

would have sufficient stability, they have not as yet been encountered, probably because the other, competing processes occur at a faster rate. Such solvent participation is observed, however, in the photolysis of umbellone;[8] here the aromaticity of the product is undoubtedly the driving force:

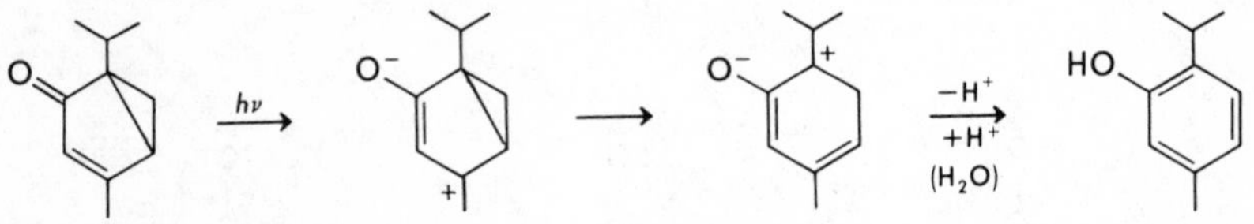

The following dienone-phenol rearrangement, in which the migration step is probably promoted by the relief of ring strain as well as by the product aromaticity, will now offer little difficulty in understanding:

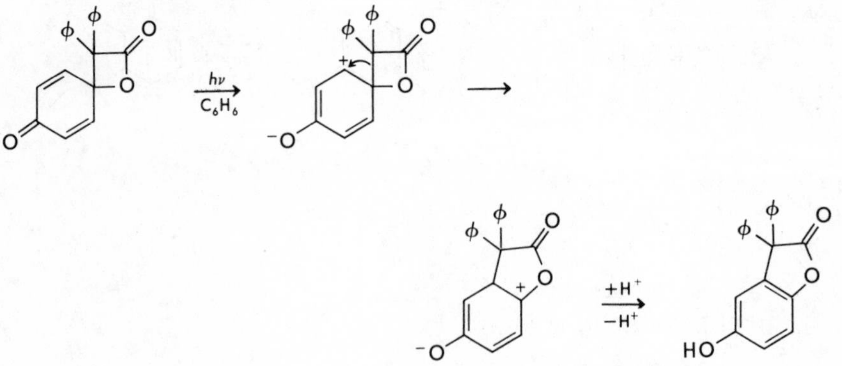

[9]

When hydroxyl replaces a phenyl group, an alternate course, namely, ring opening, is available, and phenyl migration is not observed:

[13]

Some recent studies[84] of migration aptitudes in the related rearrangement of 4,4-disubstituted-1-naphthalenones have produced interesting results. The reaction, which involves only the migration of one of the 4-substituents to the 3 position (and no skeletal rearrangement, as shown by labeling studies), has been demonstrated to involve the triplet state. Photolysis of 4-methyl-4-phenyl-1(4H)-naphthalenone in methanol yields 55% of 3-phenyl-4-methyl-1-naphthol, while the corresponding 4-(*p*-cyanophenyl)-4-phenyl derivative yields mixtures in which the product from *p*-cyanophenyl migration predominates in ratios of 3:2 or 2:1, depending on the solvent employed. The significance of the second

$$R = CH_3; \ R' = C_6H_5$$

$$\text{or} \begin{cases} R = p\text{-}CNC_6H_4; \ R' = C_6H_5 \\ R = C_6H_5; \ R' = p\text{-}CNC_6H_5 \end{cases}$$

result lies in its implication that the carbon β to the carbonyl group is *not* electron deficient and that the customarily written polarization is not a correct representation of the excited state in this case. It should be noted that this same rearrangement proceeds in the dark on acid catalysis to yield only the product resulting from phenyl migration.

A second type of rearrangement of cyclohexadienones, one in which the 2-carbon, rather than the 4-carbon, becomes C_5 of the bicyclo-[3.1.0]hexane system, has been discovered by Hart.[81] Labeling experiments have shown that methyl migration does not occur, so that of the three paths indicated below, only the first two are possible.

Even more surprising is the fact that the corresponding exocyclic methylene derivative undergoes the same kind of rearrangement in the absence of a sensitizer! The type of rearrangements that 4,4-disubstituted

α,β-unsaturated ketones undergo is unexpected. In view of the products obtained it is very likely that a carbonium-ion type of mechanism is involved here.[10]

However, the corresponding phenyl derivative rearranges with migration of a phenyl group[11] to yield two isomeric products:

The last two are photochemically interconvertible, a logical result if the last step is reversible. One might ask why 4,4-diphenyl-cyclohexadienone gives rise to a bicyclic product resulting from C_4 migration, 4,4-dimethylcyclohexenone yields monocyclic products as well as the bicyclic one, and 4,4-diphenylcyclohexenone undergoes only phenyl migration; such disparity casts in doubt the necessity of the "bond-alteration" step in dienone rearrangements.[12] One must assume that C_3—C_5 bonding is a faster and more favorable process for 4,4-diphenylcyclohexadienone than the fission step through IX–X–XI. The latter path is, of course, also open in the photolysis of diphenylcyclohexenone, but here the more modest increase in electron density, on excitation, at carbons 3 and 5, cannot compete with phenyl migration. It in turn takes place with much greater facility, through the phenonium ion, than would a similar methyl migration. Quantum yields show that the dialkylcyclohexenone rearrangement is the least efficient of those considered here,[82] and Zimmerman[11] has further observed that the dienones rearrange faster than the enones.

Zimmerman and coworkers[11] have reported that even though such enone triplets can rearrange in a fashion similar to the dienone triplets (see p. 107) the reactions are much slower and much less efficient. They suggest that such rearrangements therefore take place by a different mechanism, perhaps similar to that shown here for the photolysis of 4a-methyl-4,4a,9,10-tetrahydro-2(3H)phenanthrone:

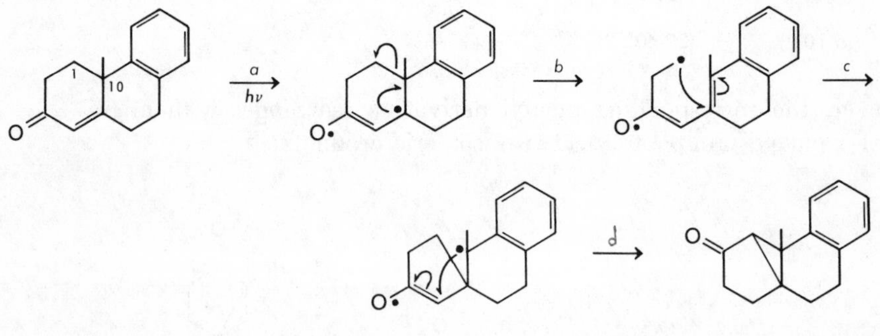

Chapman, Sieja, and Welstead,[11a] on studying the same reaction, have found, however, that the asymmetry at C_{10} is retained to the extent of 95 per cent during the rearrangement, so that, for the mechanism presented above to have validity, steps *c* and *d* must take place in a concerted fashion that does not involve complete fission of the 1,10 bond. It is clear that more work is needed before a distinction between the mechanistic details of enone and dienone reactions can be made.

Rearrangement of cross-conjugated dienones that are part of the A ring of multicyclic systems can be readily explained in terms of the previously discussed systems. Four main routes can generally be distinguished[14-18]:

a. The formation of a bicyclo[3.1.0]hexane system analogous to that observed in monocyclic dienones;

b. The rearrangements of ring B with or without participation of the solvent;

c. Secondary rearrangements of products formed in the previous two paths;

d. Rearrangements involving solvent attack at the A-B ring junction.

a. The formation of a bicyclo[3.1.0]hexane system is frequently observed, and the product can often be isolated, although it may undergo a secondary photolysis via route (*c*):

Route (a)

The product obtained by route (*a*) is often indicated by the prefix lumi-, because it first gained recognition in the santonin-lumisantonin conversion.

b. Rearrangements of ring B can best be seen to originate from structure XII:

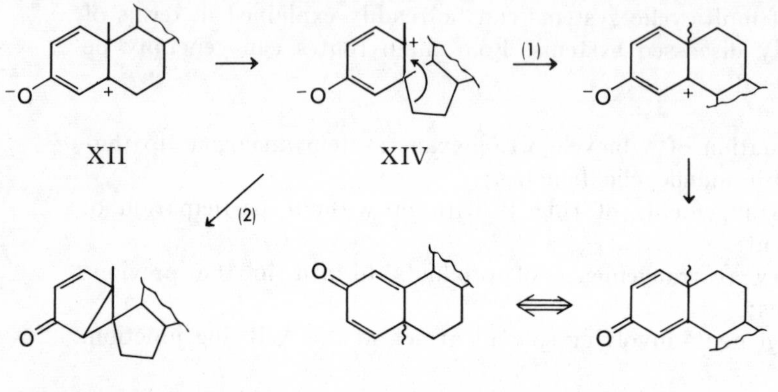

Protonation of XIV by the solvent can lead to a phenol, but there is little evidence for such a sequence. Route (*c*) is a more likely route leading to phenols.

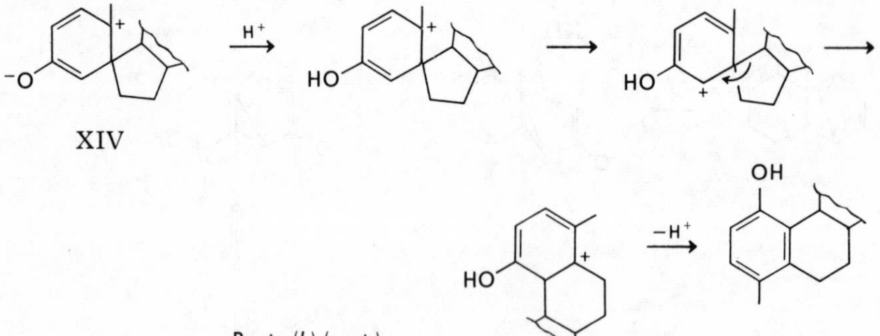

Route (*b*) (cont.)

c. Rearrangements of the "lumi-products" account for the formation of most of the phenols observed. Participation of the solvent can conceivably take place, but the path indicated below is more consistent with the intermediates that have been isolated in some of the reactions. The sequences shown should be considered rationalizations rather than well-documented mechanisms.

Route (c)

Route (c) (cont.)

d. Attack of the solvent at the A-B junction (C$_{10}$, using steroid numbering) gives rise to two types of products:

XII

XV

Route (d)

In fact, both are observed in the photolysis of dienones that carry no substituents at either side of the carbonyl group (when the irradiation is conducted, of course, in an appropriate solvent such as aqueous acetic acid). The presence of a methyl group at C$_2$ will stabilize XV, however, presumably because of an inductive effect, and in agreement 2-methyl-substituted dienones yield only the spiro compounds and no perhydro-azulene derivatives. Conversely, a methyl group at C$_4$ will stabilize XVI; here only perhydroazulenes are obtained.[19] It may be pointed out once again that several of these reactions, such as the dienone-phenol rearrangement, can be carried out nonphotochemically.

By using the four main paths outlined above, it is now possible to consider specific examples of rearrangements of cross-conjugated dienones and to understand the formation of the multitude of products that are often observed. For example, androsta-1,4-dien-3-one-17β-ol acetate gives *at least* ten products upon irradiation in acetic acid.[15]

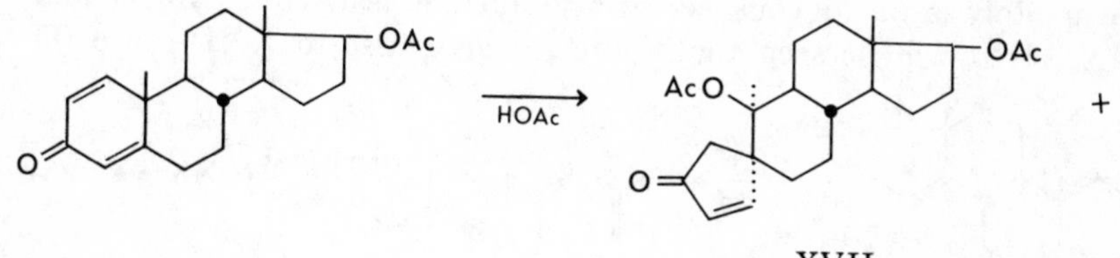

XVII

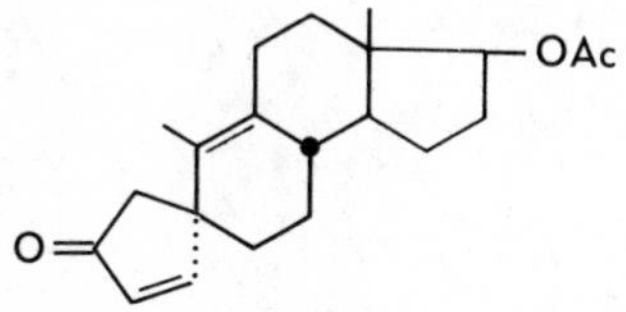

XVIII

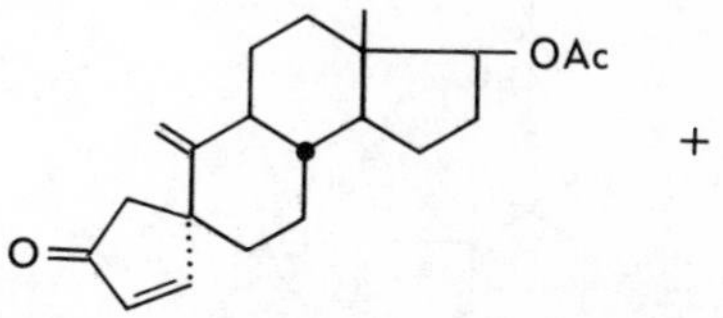

XIX

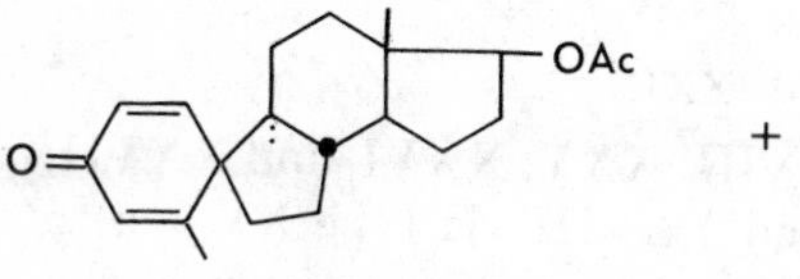

XX

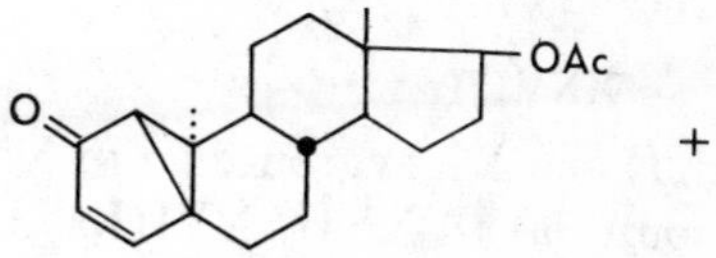

XXI

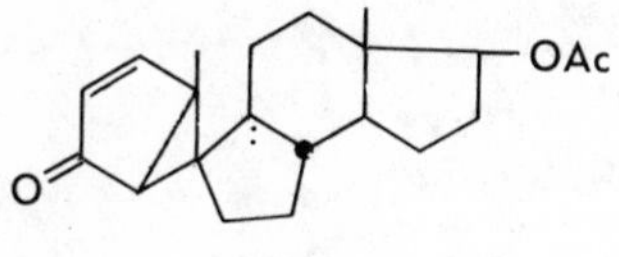

XXII

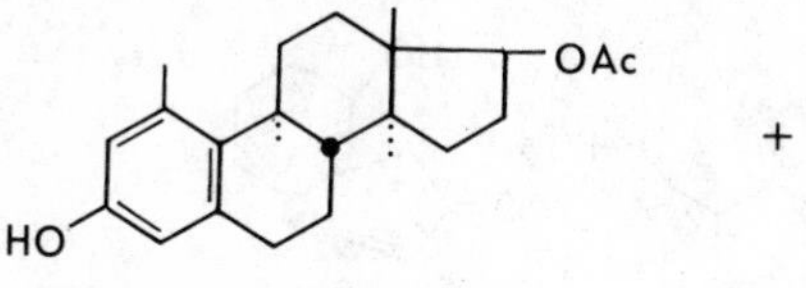

XXIII

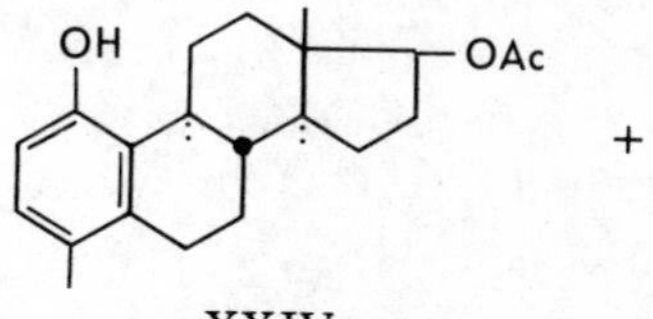

XXIV

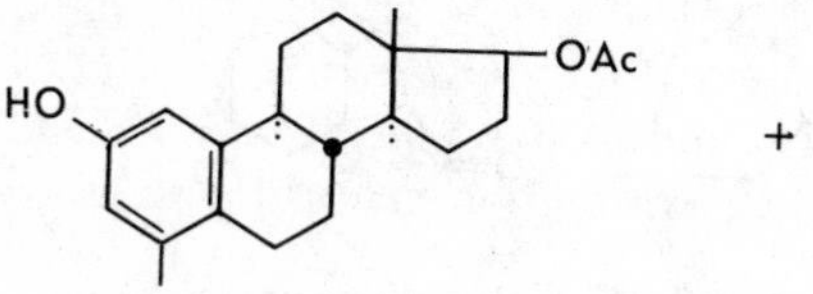

XXV

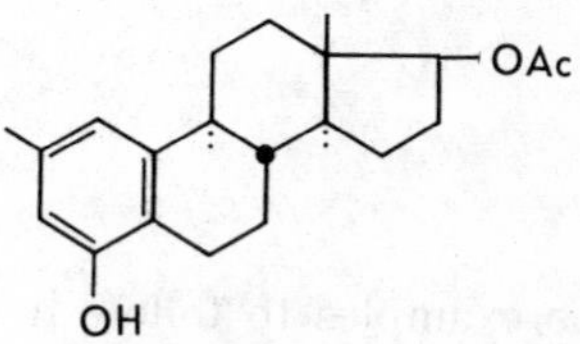

XXVI

In aqueous dioxane XXVII is obtained in addition to XX–XXVI,[14,20,21] while photolysis in aqueous acetic acid further leads to XXVIII and XXIX.[15,17] It will be seen that route (*a*) gives rise to XXI, route (*b*)

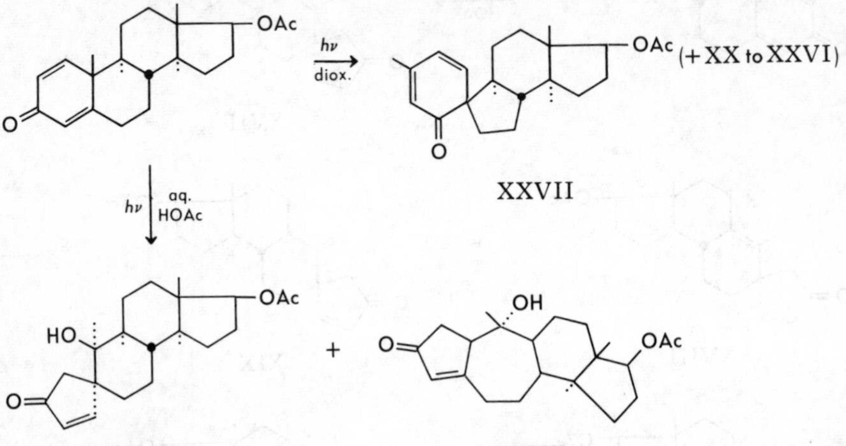

XXVII

XXVIII XXIX

to XXII and XXIV, route (*c*) to XX, XXIII, XXV, XXVI, and XXVII, and route (*d*) to XVII, XVIII, XIX, and XXVIII via type XV and to XXIX through the structure of type XVI. The photochemistry of the simple bicyclic ketones is quite similar, as demonstrated by the example shown below.[17,18]

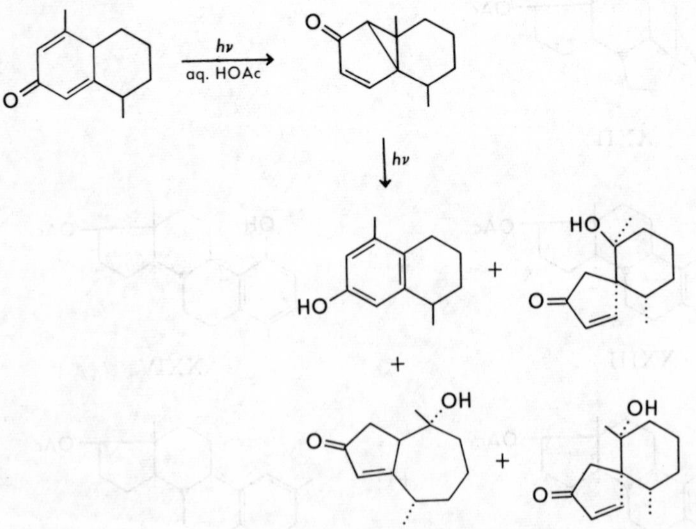

From the examples to follow it may be seen that the dienone systems follow the same general scheme.[22–25] Those bearing substituents in the

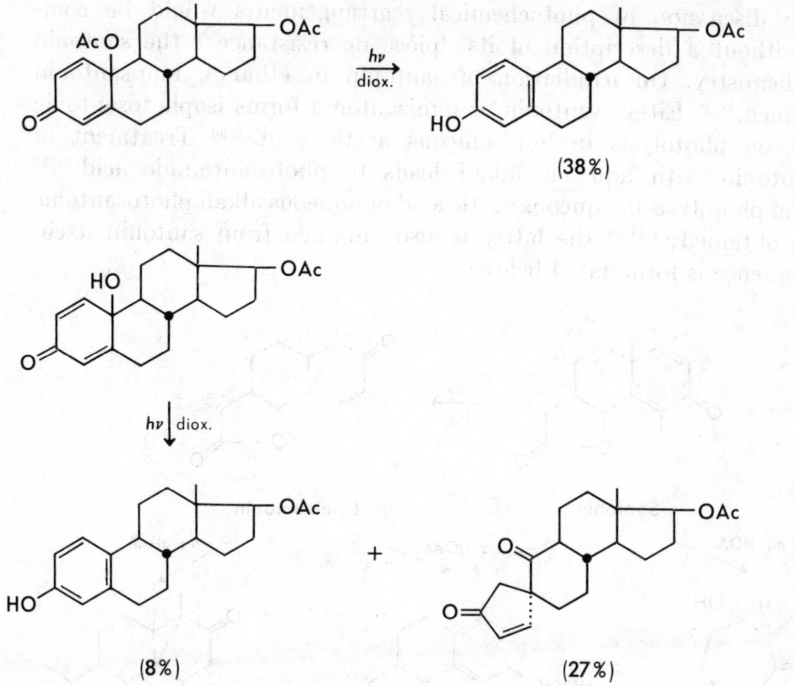

2 position are shown below in additional examples. It may be noted that
no perhydroazulenes are formed.[19,26,27]

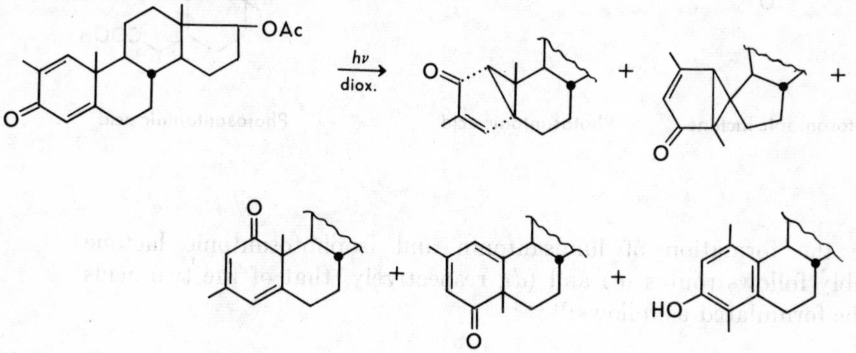

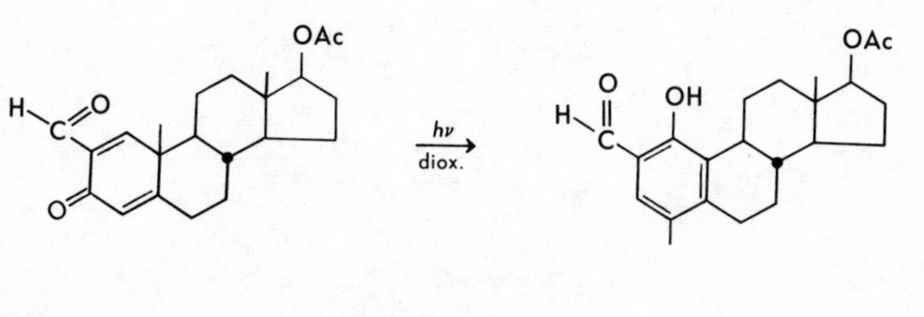

No discussion of photochemical rearrangements would be complete without a description of its "pièce de résistance": the santonin photochemistry. On irradiation of santonin in ethanol, lumisantonin is obtained.[28,29] Either santonin or lumisantonin forms isophotosantonic lactone on photolysis in hot aqueous acetic acid.[28,30] Treatment of lumisantonin with aqueous alkali leads to photosantoninic acid,[31,32] while on photolysis in aqueous acetic acid or aqueous alkali photosantonic acid is obtained;[29,33,34] the latter is also obtained from santonin itself. The sequence is formulated below:

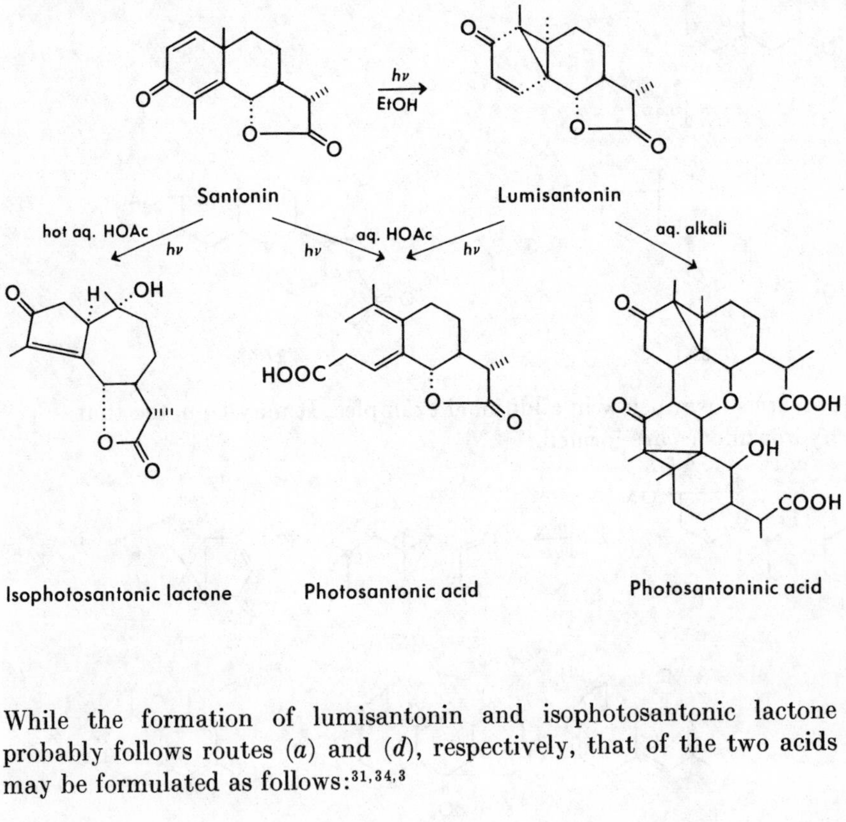

While the formation of lumisantonin and isophotosantonic lactone probably follows routes (*a*) and (*d*), respectively, that of the two acids may be formulated as follows:[31,34,3]

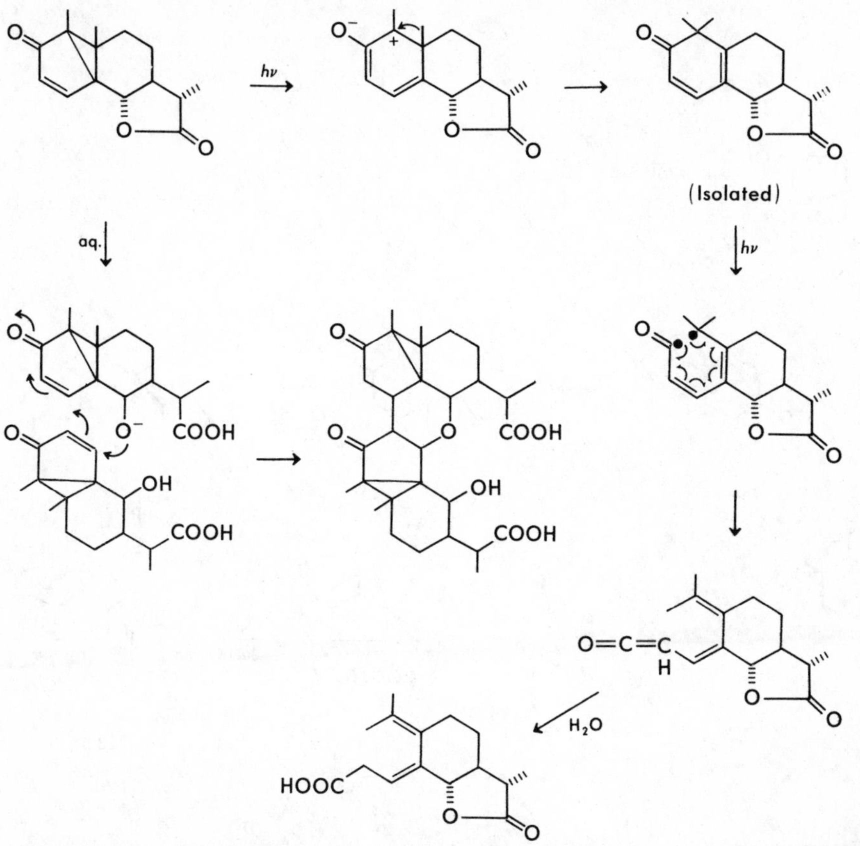

$h\nu$

(Isolated)

$h\nu$

aq.

O⁻ COOH

COOH

OH

COOH

O

COOH

OH

COOH

O=C=C⟨H

H_2O

HOOC

In this series of transformations the mechanism has received considerable attention. It has been described in terms of both the Chapman
and the Zimmerman conventions.[3]

The variety of products obtained from the analogous mono-enones
can be visualized to form in a similar fashion, as indicated in the examples
given below. It will be seen that nonconjugated dienones show analo-

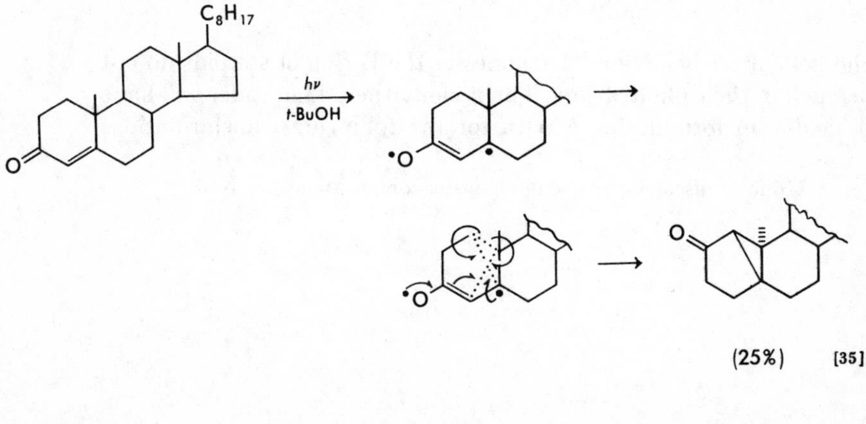

C_8H_{17}

$h\nu$
t-BuOH

(25%)   [35]

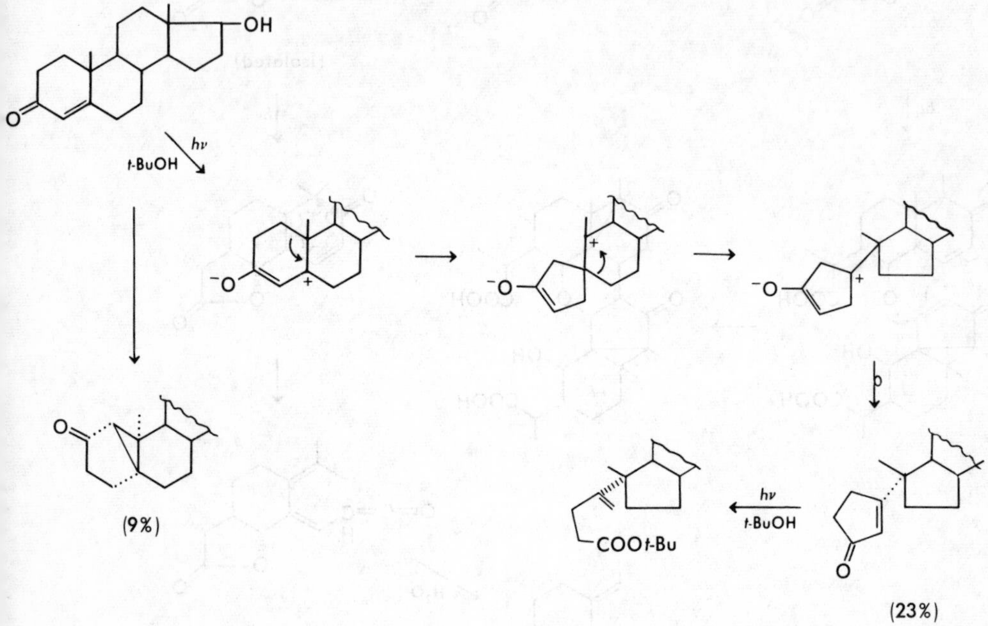

(9%)

(23%)

[36]

(23%)   (6%)

(+ stereoisomers)

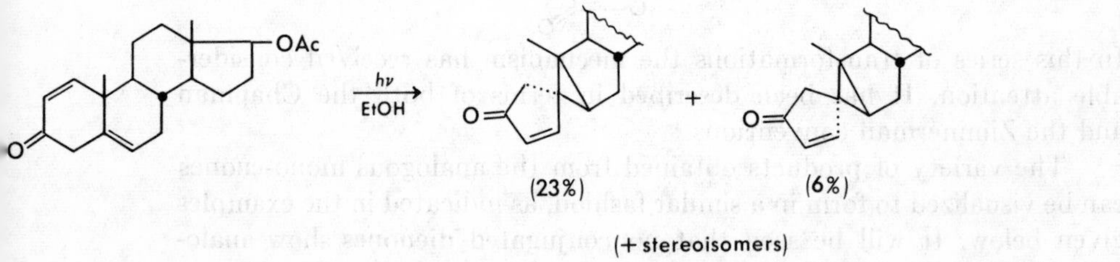

[36]

gous photochemical behavior.† Dienones in the B ring of steroids do not deviate much in their photochemical behavior either. The reader will have little difficulty in formulating a path for the following transformation:

† See p. 116 for a discussion of the mechanistic complications involved.

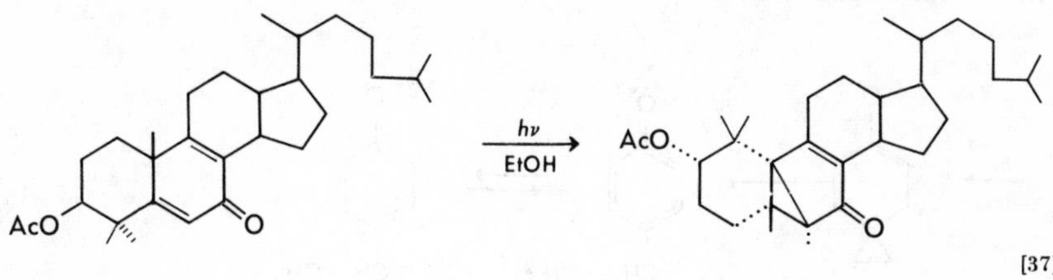

[37]

Thus far, the nature of these reactions has been pictured as being dipolar or ionic, involving carbonium-ion and allylic rearrangements and proton abstractions and additions. It is clear that, on the basis of the numerous ground-state analogies, the type of products obtained seems to justify such treatment.

At times, unusual products that may be interpreted to reinforce or weaken such assumptions are obtained. For example, in the conversion shown below it is noteworthy that a carbethoxy group migrates, a step that is usually not even observed with methyl groups in such rearrangements. The migration seems to point to the existence of a dipolar intermediate. Further, the bicyclo[3.1.0]hexane derivative forms almost exclusively under conditions that usually lead to solvent attack (45% acetic acid); this may be due to interaction between the solvent and the carbethoxy group or to steric hindrance against attack at the angular position.

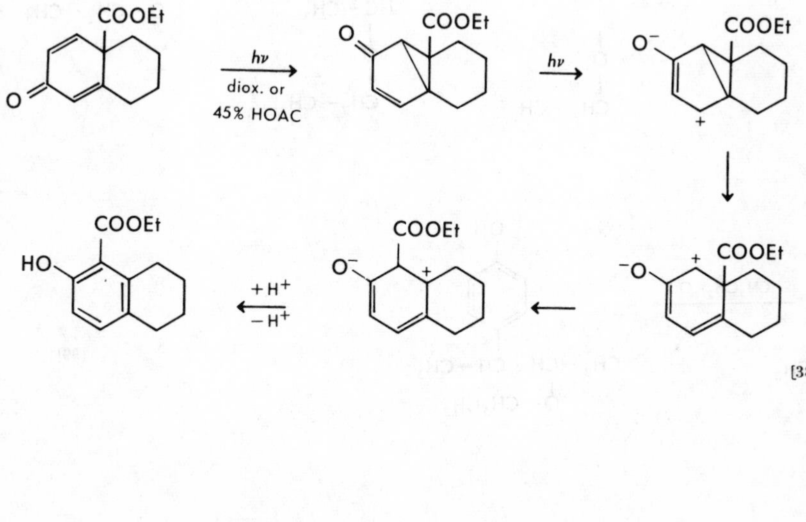

[38]

A free-radical intermediate is, however, more consistent with the products formed in the following transformations:

[39]

The last example shown is somewhat similar to that of *p*-hydroxyphenacyl halides:

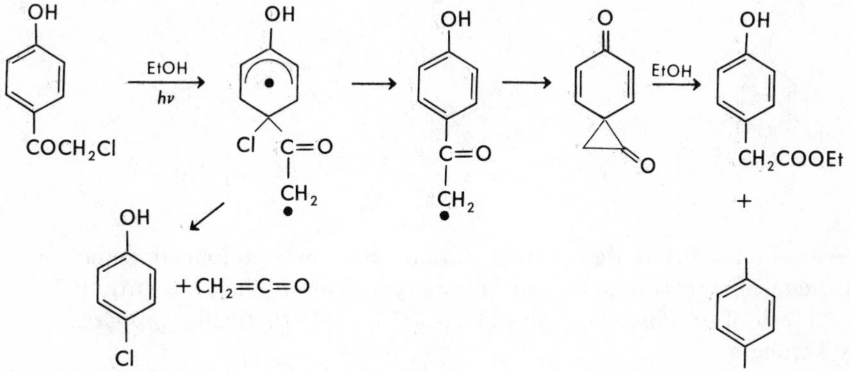

[40]

Loss of halogen from haloalkyl groups is a normal feature in photolytic reactions. It also occurs in the photolysis of the chloroalkyldienone shown below:

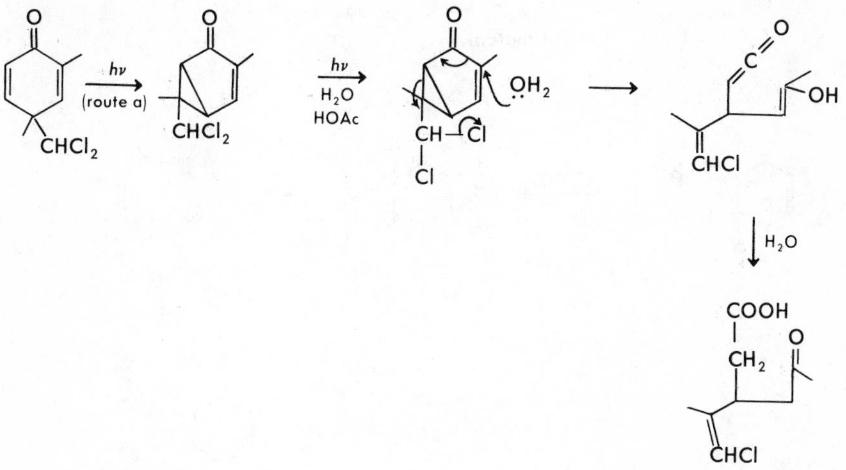

[41]

4-2 *Epoxy Ketones*

The rearrangements encountered on photolysis of epoxy ketones have been studied in detail. One of these studies concerns the formation of furfural derivatives on photolysis of 2,6-disubstituted γ-pyrones. It had been postulated initially that the sequence should involve an intermediate epoxy ketone:

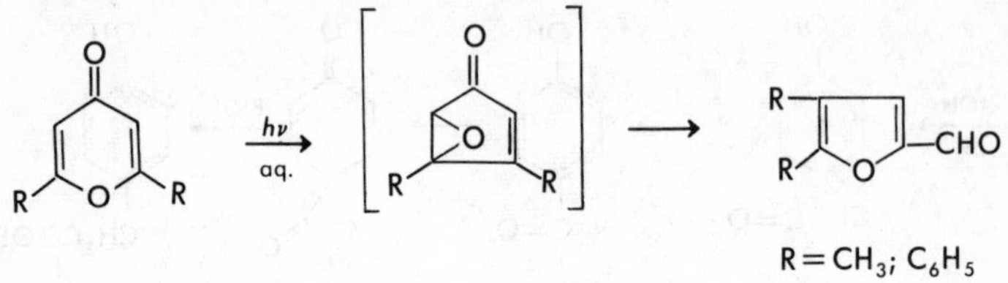

$$R = CH_3; C_6H_5$$

[42]

However, Padwa[43] has demonstrated that the epoxy ketone does not photochemically rearrange to the furaldehyde. He obtained an entirely different set of products on photolysis of the synthetically prepared epoxy ketone:

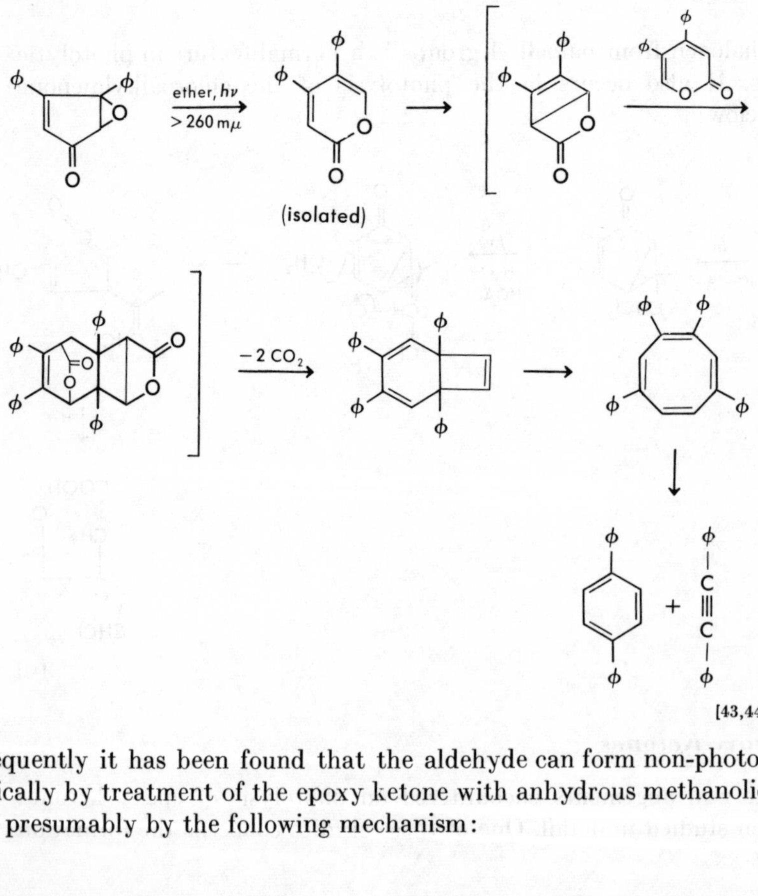

(isolated)

[43,44]

Subsequently it has been found that the aldehyde can form non-photochemically by treatment of the epoxy ketone with anhydrous methanolic HCl, presumably by the following mechanism:

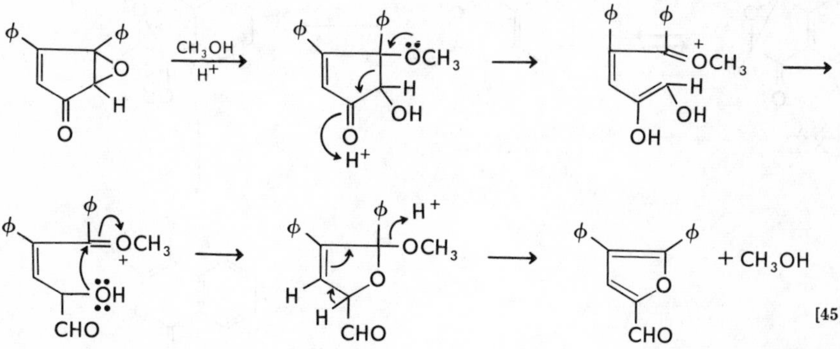

[45]

The formation of 4,5-diphenyl-2-pyrone in the photochemical rearrange-ment of this epoxyketone is not unique. Thus, 2,3-diphenylindenone oxide, on irradiation in benzene or ethanol, yields besides two stereo-isomeric solvent adducts and a dimer, the diphenyl isocoumarin also:

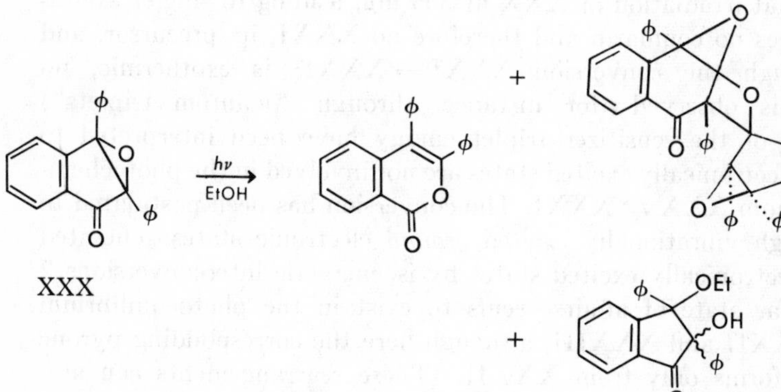

[46–48]

However, 2,3-diphenylindenone oxide (XXX) exists in thermal as well as photochemical equilibrium with its pyrilium oxide (XXXI),[49] and good evidence is available[47] that it is exclusively the latter that rearranges to the isocoumarin and the solvent adducts:

The photochemical equilibrium between XXX and XXXI is unusual. The photostationary state is very dependent on the presence of sensitizers (XXXI/XXX = 0.097 unsensitized and 0.35 in the presence of benzophenone, both in deoxygenated benzene). A slight decrease in the sensitizer triplet energy (for example, from benzophenone, 68.5 kcal, to fluorene, 67.6 kcal) brings an abrupt end to the formation of XXXI. The facts that irradiation of XXX at 365 mμ, leading to singlet excitation, produces no coumarin and therefore no XXXI, its precursor, and that, although the conversion $XXX^T \rightarrow XXXI^T$ is exothermic, no conversion is observed (for instance, through "phantom triplets") on lowering of the sensitizer triplet energy have been interpreted to mean that electronically excited states are not involved in the photochemical equilibrium XXX $\rightleftarrows$ XXXI. The conversion has been postulated to occur through vibrationally excited *ground* electronic states generated from the electronically excited states by isoenergetic interconversions.[47]

A similar state of affairs seems to exist in the photoequilibrium between XXXII and XXXIII, although here the corresponding pyrone apparently forms only from XXXII. (These rearrangements can also be effected under non-photochemical conditions by acid catalysis.)

$h\nu$

$(R=H; C_6H_5)$

[50]

The formation of the solvent adducts from XXXI may be rationalized by the following sequence:

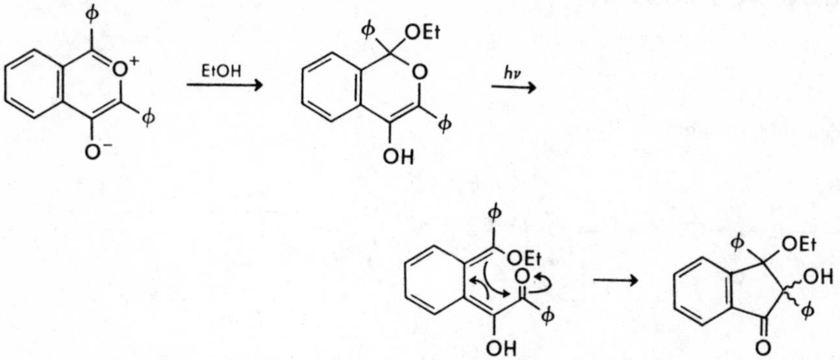

A fourth example of epoxy ketone–to–α-pyrone conversion, that of 2-methyl-3-phenylindenone oxide, has been reported by Zimmerman.[51] It is not known whether the pyrilium oxide is involved here also:

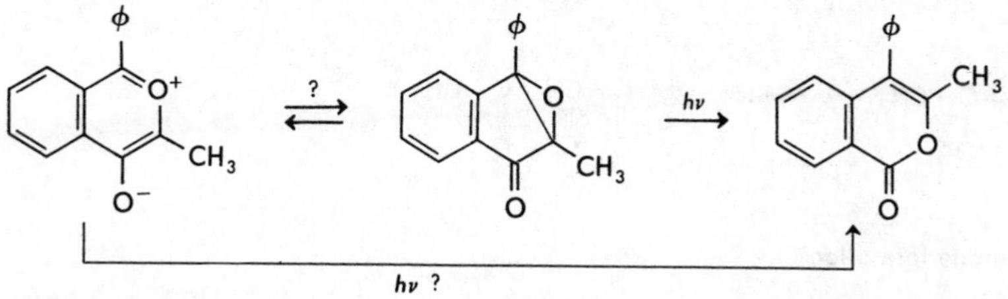

The photochemical reactions of linear and aliphatic α, β-epoxy ketones follow an entirely different course; they lead to 1,3-diketones and α-hydroxyketones through migration of methyl and hydrogen, respectively:

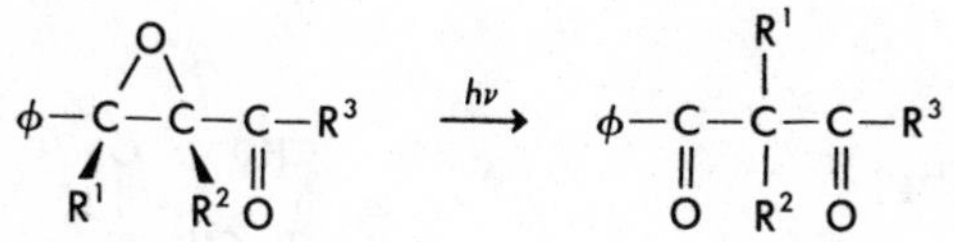

$$(R_1 = H; R_2 = R_3 = C_6H_5;$$
$$R_1 = CH_3, R_2 = H, R_3 = CH_3)$$ [52–54]

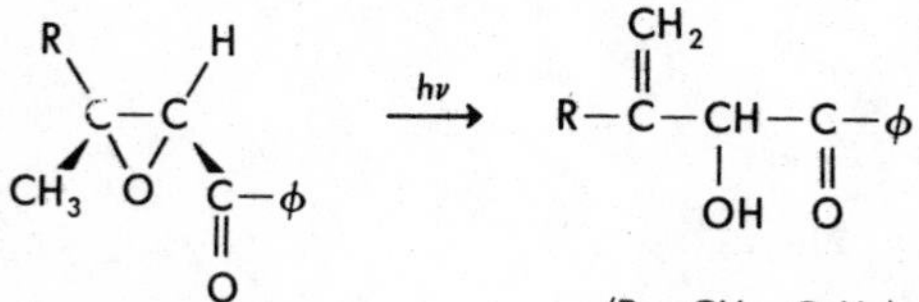

$$(R = CH_3, C_6H_5)$$ [52]

Although little is known about the nature of the intermediates involved, the mechanism proposed by Zimmerman is quite satisfactory in accounting for the process observed:[52]

1, 3-Diketone formation:

$$\phi-\overset{\overset{\displaystyle CH_3}{|}}{\underset{\underset{\displaystyle O}{\diagdown}}{C}}-\overset{\overset{\displaystyle H}{|}}{C}-\overset{\displaystyle C}{\underset{\underset{\displaystyle O^x}{\|}}{}}-CH_3 \quad \xrightarrow[n-\pi^*]{h\nu} \quad \phi-\overset{\overset{\displaystyle CH_3}{|}}{C}-\overset{\overset{\displaystyle H}{|}}{C}\cdot\cdot\overset{\displaystyle \cdot}{C}-CH_3 \quad \xrightarrow[\text{alteration}]{\text{bond}}$$

$$\phi-\overset{\overset{\displaystyle CH_3}{|}}{\underset{\underset{\displaystyle :O\cdot}{}}{C}}-\overset{\overset{\displaystyle H}{|}}{C}=C-CH_3 \quad \xrightarrow{\text{demotion}} \quad \phi-\overset{\overset{\displaystyle CH_3}{|}}{\underset{\underset{\displaystyle :O\cdot}{}}{C}}-\overset{\displaystyle C}{}=C-CH_3 \quad \xrightarrow{\text{rearrangement}}$$

XXXIV

$$\phi-\overset{\displaystyle C}{\underset{\underset{\displaystyle O}{\|}}{}}-CH=C-CH_3 \quad \longrightarrow \quad \phi-\overset{\displaystyle C}{\underset{\underset{\displaystyle O}{\|}}{}}-CH-\overset{\displaystyle C}{\underset{\underset{\displaystyle O}{\|}}{}}-CH_3$$

α-Hydroxyketone formation:

$$R-\overset{\overset{\displaystyle H_2C}{\diagup}}{\underset{\underset{\displaystyle O}{\diagdown}}{C}}\overset{\overset{\displaystyle O}{\|}}{\underset{\displaystyle CH}{\diagup}}C-\phi \quad \xrightarrow{h\nu} \quad R-\overset{\overset{\displaystyle H_2C}{\diagup}}{\underset{\underset{\displaystyle O}{\diagdown}}{C}}\overset{\overset{\displaystyle :O:}{\diagup}}{\underset{\displaystyle CH}{\diagup}}C-\phi \quad \longrightarrow$$

$$R-\overset{\overset{\displaystyle CH_2}{\diagup}}{\underset{\underset{\displaystyle :O:}{\diagdown}}{C}}\overset{\overset{\displaystyle OH}{|}}{\underset{\displaystyle CH}{\diagup}}\overset{\cdot}{C}-\phi \quad \longrightarrow \quad R-\overset{\overset{\displaystyle CH_2}{\|}}{\underset{\underset{\displaystyle H}{\diagdown}}{C}}-CH-\overset{\displaystyle C}{\underset{\underset{\displaystyle O:}{}}{}}-\phi \quad \longrightarrow \quad R-\overset{\overset{\displaystyle CH_2}{\|}}{C}-\overset{\overset{}{}}{\underset{\underset{\displaystyle OH}{}}{CH}}-\overset{\displaystyle C}{\underset{\underset{\displaystyle O}{\|}}{}}-\phi$$

Several points of interest can be observed. First, the steps leading to XXXIV should be reversible; XXXIV (or its ionic equivalent) must be the common intermediate formed from both stereoisomeric epoxides in order to account for the cis-trans isomerizations shown below:

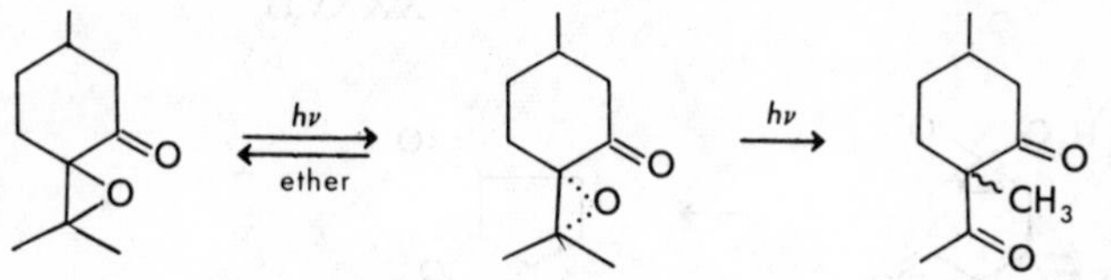

[55,56]

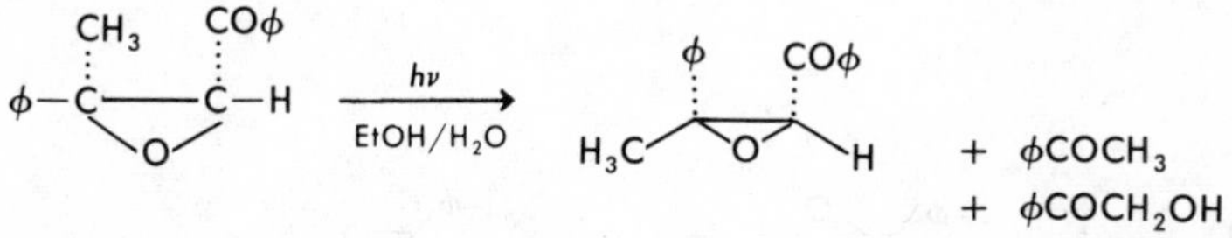

[54]

A solvent adduct such as XXXV could conceivably be involved in the second example but not in the first, where ether is the solvent employed.

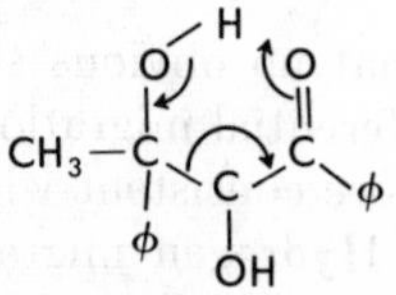

XXXV

Second, the cis relationship between methyl and benzoyl in α-hydroxy-ketone formation is a requirement; the corresponding trans isomer is unreactive.[52] Third, the formation of the 1,3-diketones by migration of methyl or hydrogen in preference to phenyl is unusual in ground-state reactions, but it is quite regularly observed in photochemical reactions. For example, isophorone oxide on photolysis in a variety of solvents gives a 9 to 10% yield of XXXVI and XXXVII in a 9:1 ratio, but 3-phenyl-5,5-dimethyl-2,3-epoxycyclohexanone yields *only* 2-benzoyl-4,4-dimethylcyclopentanone (XXXVIII, 15% yield) and no isomer corresponding to XXXVII, which would have involved phenyl migration.[56]

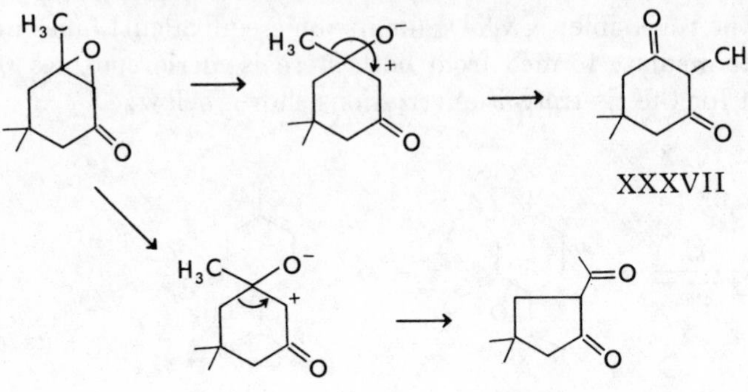

XXXVII

XXXVI

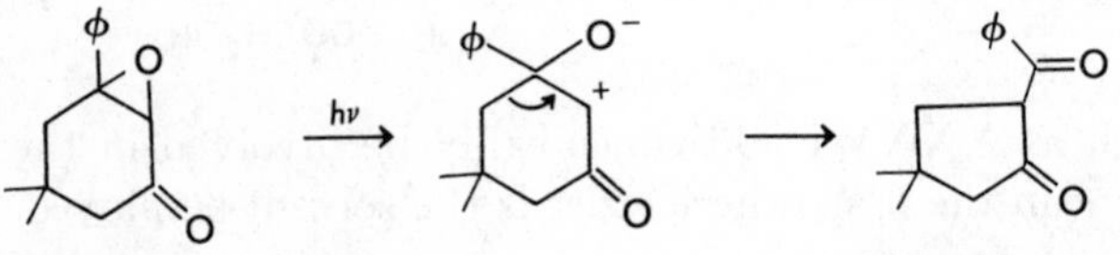

XXXVIII

Examination of models indicates that no obvious steric factors can be invoked in the latter case;[56] the preferential migration of alkyl or hydrogen over phenyl observed here is more consistent with a diradical intermediate than with a dipolar one. Hydrogen migration might also be thought to occur in the rearrangement of 1,2,3,4,5-pentaphenyl-1,3-cyclohexadiene on its photolysis in the absence of oxygen.[57] It is more likely, however, that a valence bond tautomerization is involved.

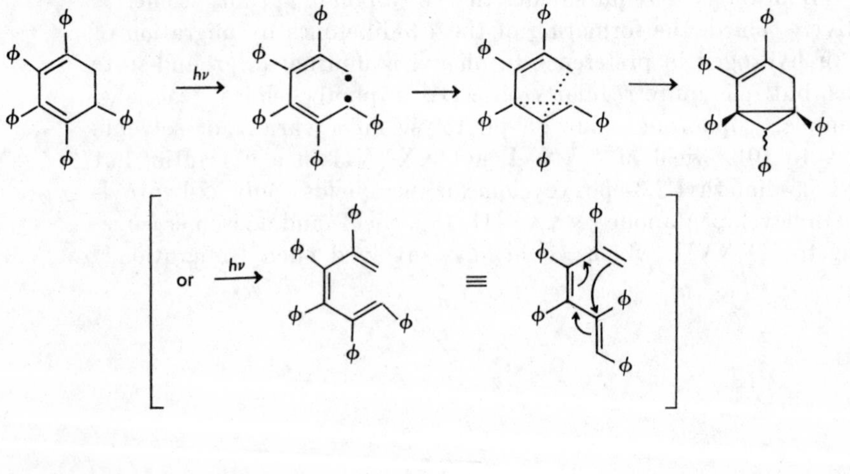

The alkyl shifts in epoxy ketones are invariably from C_β to C_α. In the case of 4,5-epoxy-3-ketosteroids the migration leads to the formation of the same 5-7 ring system regardless of whether the α- or β-epoxide is employed.[55,58] However, whether the mechanism involved in these

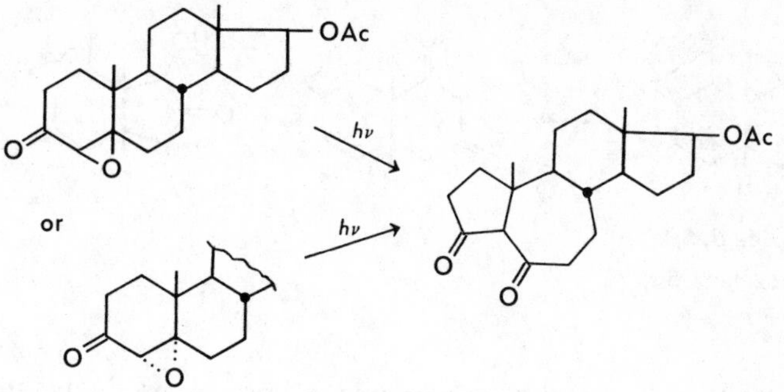

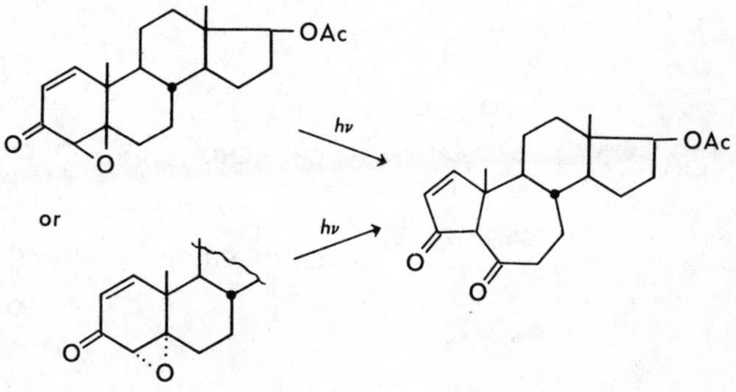

reactions is ionic or free radical in nature, the bond-migration and carbonyl-formation steps must be synchronous; the spatial properties of methyl groups at C_4 are conserved with complete stereospecificity in the products which are formed.

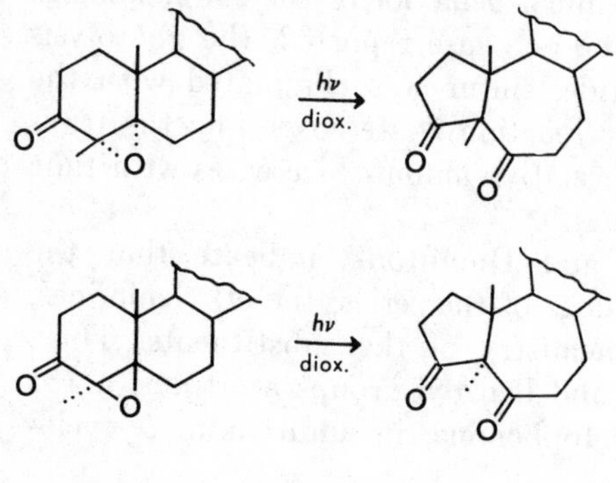

Stereochemistry
tentatively
identified

[55]

Similar rearrangements involving either 1,2 hydrogen shifts or migration of C_{10} take place with retention of configuration of the C_{19} methyl group. Several other such cases are described in ref. 55. In the absence

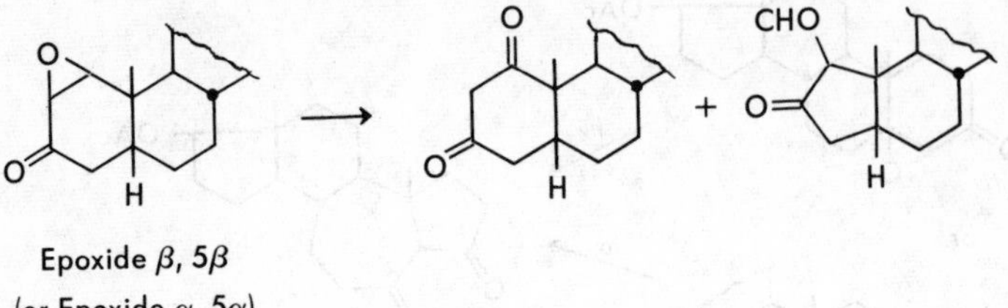

Epoxide β, 5β
(or Epoxide α, 5α)

[55]

of any radical- or ion-stabilizing groups a host of products, many of them obtained from secondary processes, can be observed:

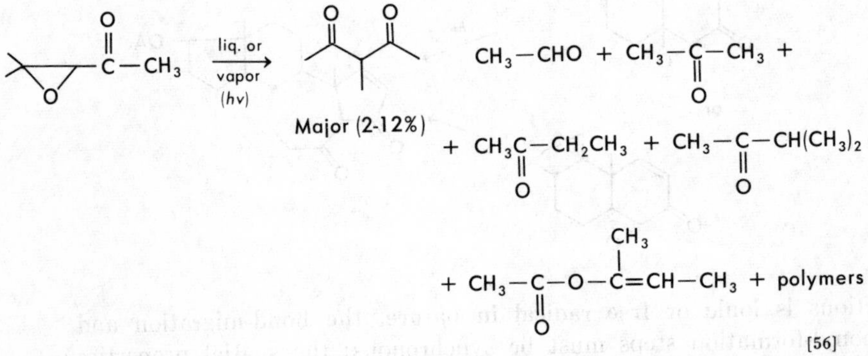

Major (2-12%)

$$CH_3-CHO + CH_3-\underset{\underset{O}{\|}}{C}-CH_3 +$$

$$+ CH_3\underset{\underset{O}{\|}}{C}-CH_2CH_3 + CH_3-\underset{\underset{O}{\|}}{C}-CH(CH_3)_2$$

$$+ CH_3-\underset{\underset{O}{\|}}{C}-O-\overset{\overset{CH_3}{|}}{C}=CH-CH_3 + polymers$$

[56]

Little is known about the photochemical behavior of the sulfur analogs of epoxides, the episulfoxides. In the one case reported, the photolysis of *trans*-dibenzoylstilbene episulfoxide, sulfur was eliminated with the formation of dibenzoylstilbene. The reaction is stereospecific; the trans isomer is the main product, but its relative amount decreases with time as more trans-cis isomerization occurs.[59a]

Results obtained by Padwa and Hamilton[59] indicate that the photochemistry of the nitrogen analogs of the series, the ethylenimines, depends markedly on the stereochemistry of the substituents. Thus, as shown below, when the phenyl and benzoyl groups are trans, a 1:1 mixture of *cis*- and *trans*-benzalacetophenone, in addition to *N*-cyclohexylhydroxylamine, is formed on photolysis in 95% ethanol. When the two groups are cis, no benzalacetophenone is formed at all, but the corresponding imine is observed instead:

$$\phi-C-CH=CH\phi + C_6H_{11}-NHOH$$

$$\phi-CH=N-C_6H_{11} + \phi CHO + \phi COCH_3$$
$$(25\%) \qquad (6\%) \qquad (8\%)$$

[59]

It is probable that the relative positions of the substituents influence the mode of ring opening and the stability of the intermediate diradical.

Recently the study of these systems has been extended by Padwa[85] to include β,γ-epoxyketones, and rather surprising results have been obtained. From the epoxide of 1,4-diphenyl-3-butene-1-one, *two primary photoproducts* have been obtained, one being an epoxycyclobutanol and the other being identified as 1,2-dibenzoyl ethane:

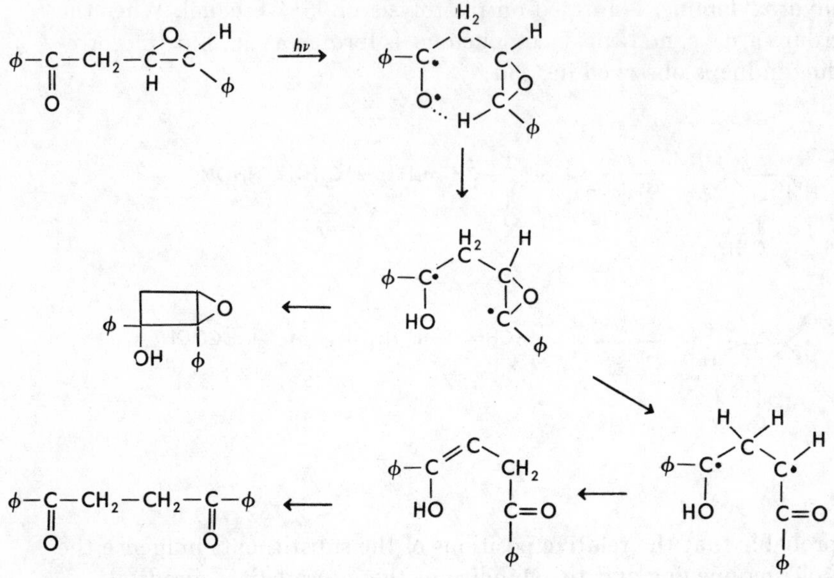

The isolation of the diketone as a primary photoproduct is significant because it is clear that hydrogen transfer must have occurred here in a separate step, followed by epoxide opening and a hydrogen shift. This example provides concrete evidence that Norrish type II processes, as discussed in Secs. 2-4 and 3-1, do not necessarily occur in a concerted fashion. The possibility that the carbonyl group in this system acts merely as intramolecular sensitizer has been discounted by the fruitless attempts[85] to produce acetophenone or phenyl acetaldehyde from the photolysis of mixtures of benzophenone and styrene oxide:

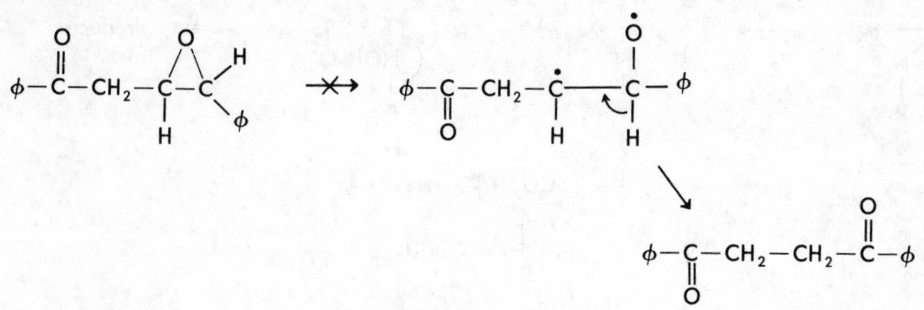

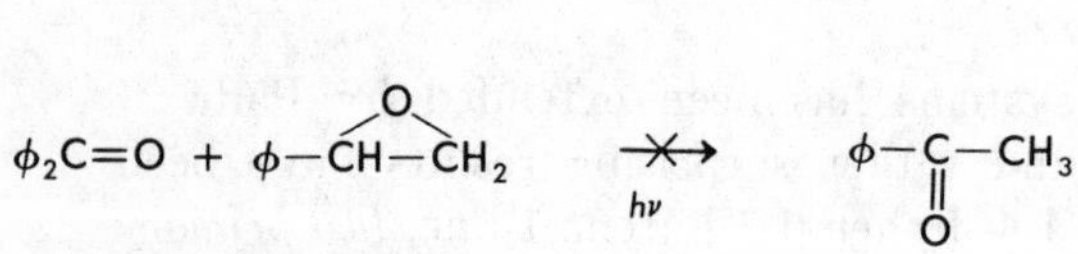

4-3   *Enol Esters*

The formation of β-diketones from enol esters is a rather general photochemical rearrangement.

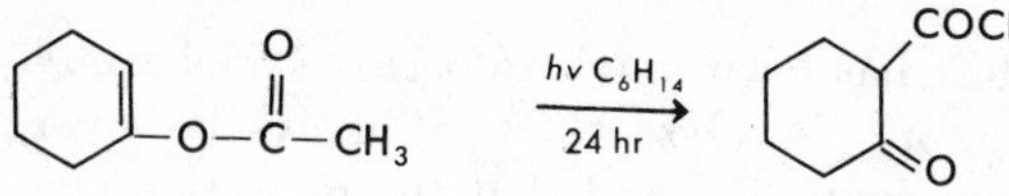

[60–62]

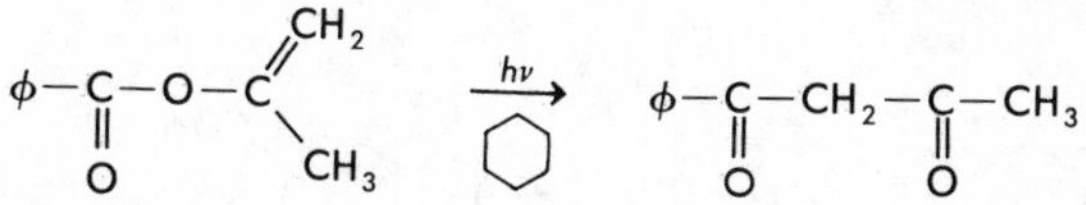

[62]

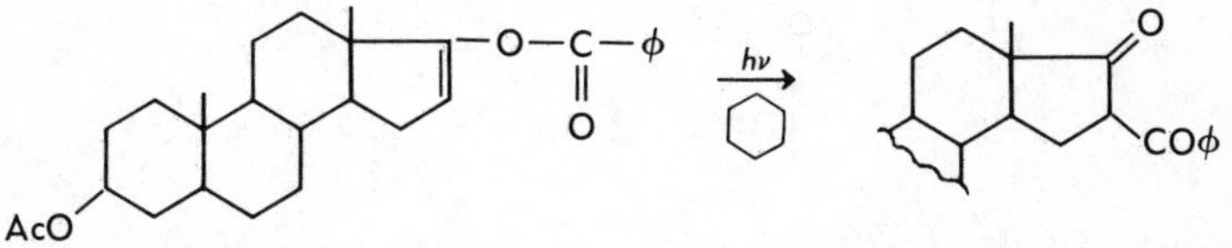

[60]

Its mechanism probably involves a radical dissociation-recombination step:

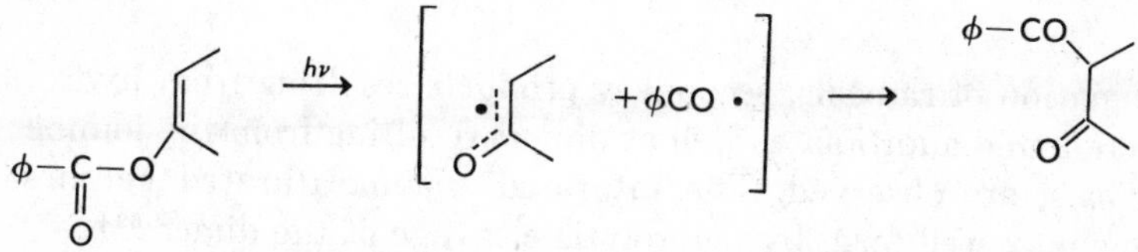

The possibility of a four-centered reaction mechanism has been discounted by the observed migration of the acetyl group to C_6 in conjugated steroidal enol acetates. Nevertheless, the stereoselectivity observed renders complete separation of the radicals improbable; more likely, a cage mechanism in which the solvent participates is operative. The intramolecularity of the reaction has been demonstrated with mixed deuterated and non-deuterated esters.[60]

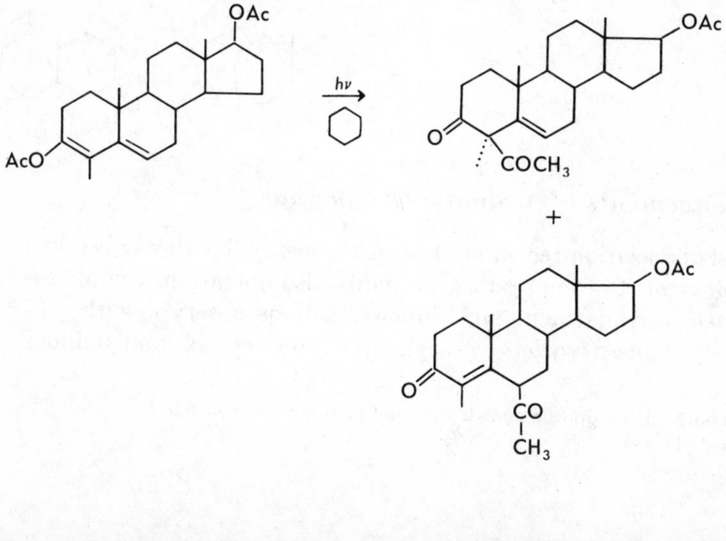

[61]

In one instance a hydrogen shift has been found to occur; cyclohexenyl benzoate suffers ring opening on photolysis.[60] It is likely, however, that the normal rearrangement occurs first and that the migration step takes place in a secondary process. When steric or other reasons prevent

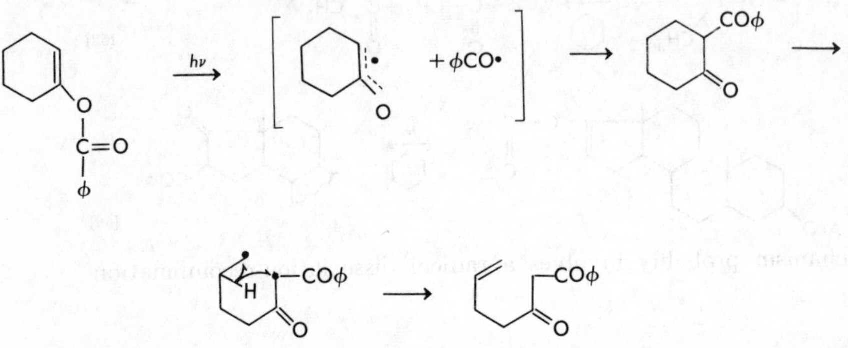

the recombination of radicals, secondary products resulting from hydrogen abstraction and addition, as well as dimers resulting from the joining of like radicals, are observed. The saturated and unsaturated ketones shown below may well form by heterolytic cleavage of the dimer:[62]†

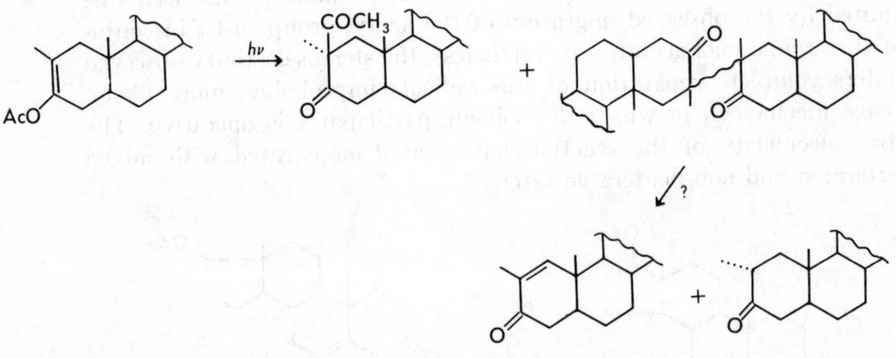

4-4   Rearrangements of Aromatic Compounds

Radical dissociation-recombination mechanisms, like those observed in the rearrangement of enol esters, probably also operate in the photochemical Fries rearrangement and similar reactions observed with aromatic systems. Thus a variety of aryl esters, aryl ethers, and anilides

† For a report on the photochemistry of enol lactones, see ref. 62*a*.

undergo migration of acyl and alkyl groups to the ortho and para positions on photolysis:

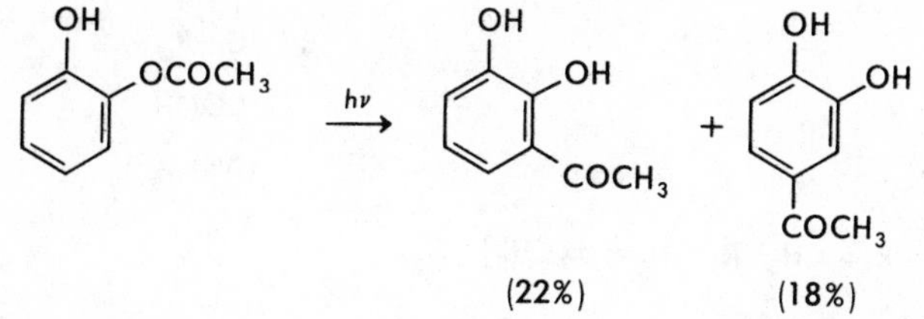

(22%)   (18%)   [63]

Notwithstanding the rather modest yields obtained in the photochemical Fries rearrangement, the reaction is synthetically quite useful because it can be applied to reagents that, under the normal conditions in the presence of a Friedel-Crafts catalyst, suffer extensive dealkylation and carbonium ion rearrangements. The examples listed illustrate this point.

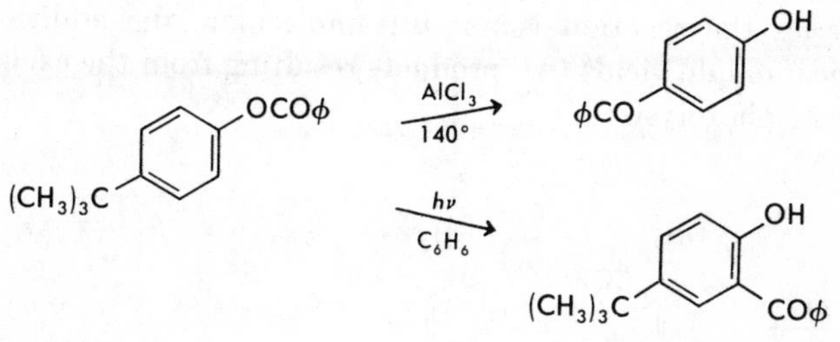

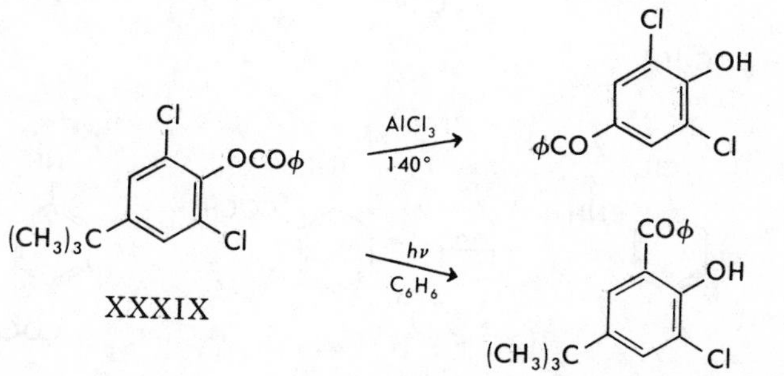

XXXIX

[64]

The radicals probably exist in solvent cages in which most of the pairs recombine; that a certain percentage escapes follows from the constant presence of phenol, formed by hydrogen abstraction of the radicals, as shown in the following series:

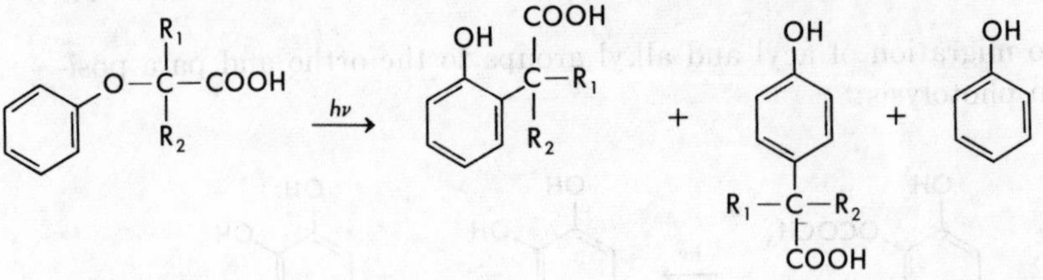

(18%)   (10%)   (Trace)

$[R_1 = R_2 = H; \ R_1 = R_2 = CH_3; \ R_1 = H; \ R_2 = CH_3]$

[65]

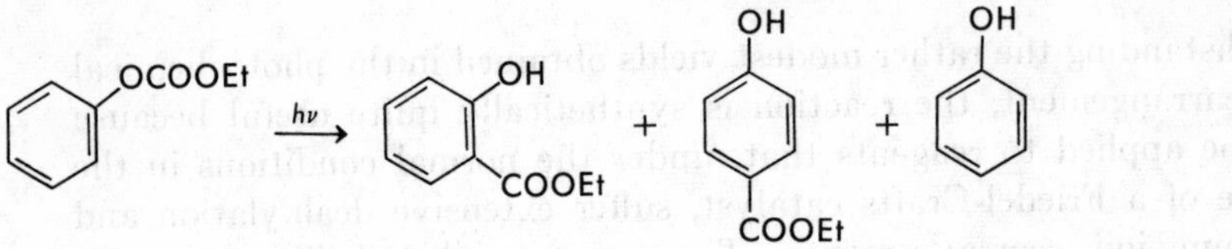

(16%)   (25%)   (7-8%)   [66]

N-Acyl anilines rearrange similarly. However, it has been clearly shown that in this series the reaction is not intramolecular; the addition of *o*-toluidine to acetanilide yields two products resulting from the exchange of radicals during photolysis:

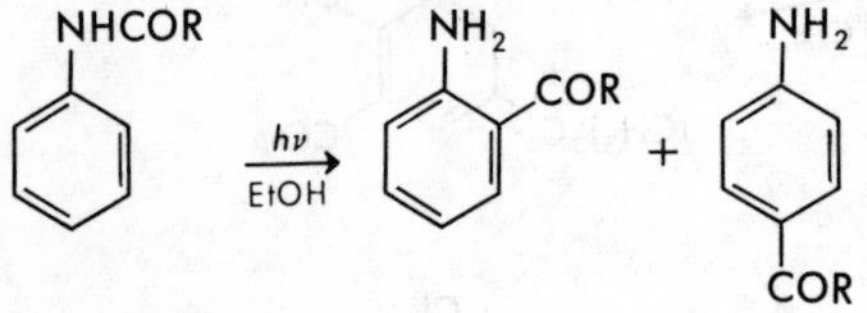

$[R = CH_3; \ C_2H_5; \ n\text{-}C_3H_7]$

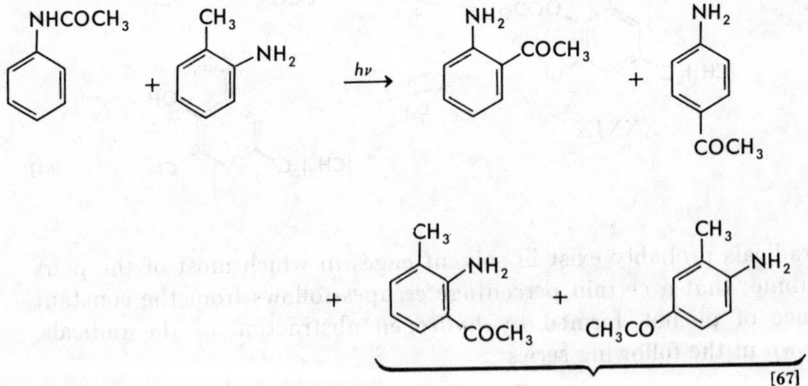

Minor

[67]

The orientation pattern in these rearrangements is not clearly defined. As a rule, when both the ortho and para positions are available, substitution will take place at either, sometimes even displacing other substituents, as seen in the case of 2,6-dichloro-4-*t*-butylphenylbenzoate (XXXIX). However, Kharasch and coworkers have reported that the rearrangement of benzylphenyl ether, allylphenyl ether, and diphenyl ether in isopropanol leads exclusively to phenol and para-substituted phenols.[68]

That more direct involvement of the aromatic ring occurs is evident from the rather varied photochemistry of dibenzoyl ethylene (see also page 28). In the presence of sensitizers, hydrogen abstraction to dibenzoyl ethane takes place; on photolysis in alcohols, rearrangement with addition of the solvent occurs:

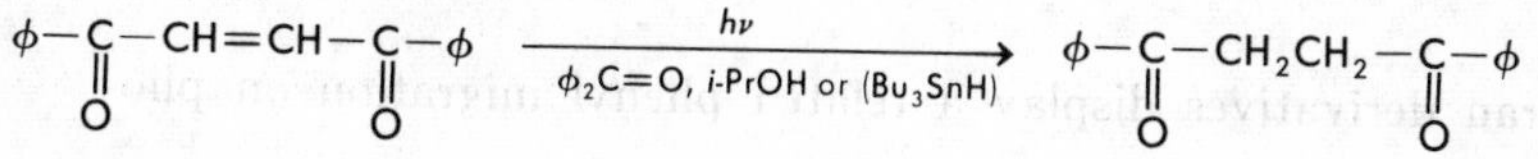

[69]

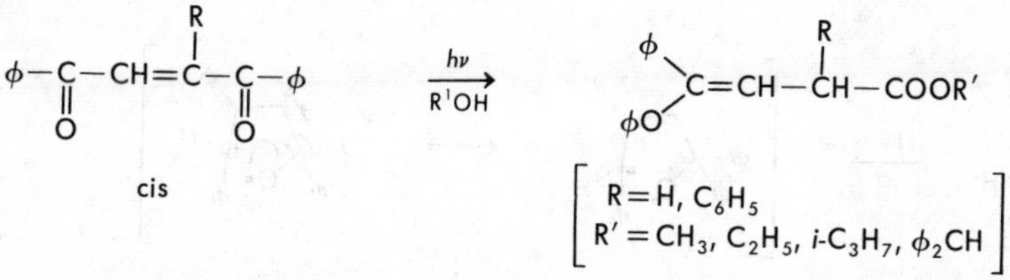

[69,70]

The rearrangement is facilitated by the delocalization of charge over the participating aromatic ring.

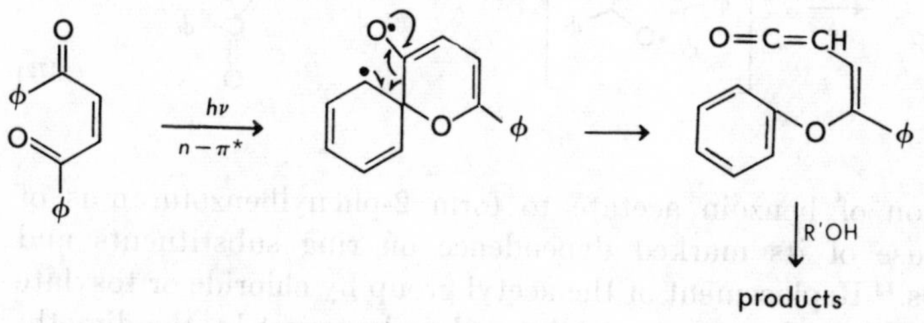

[69,70]

Phenyl migration is also involved in the rearrangement of tetrabenzoyl ethylene.[71] The mechanism is probably similar to that of the dibenzoyl ethylene rearrangement:

Dihydrofuran derivatives display a related phenyl migration on photolysis:

[72]

The cyclization of benzoin acetate to form 2-phenylbenzofuran is of interest because of its marked dependence on ring substituents and leaving groups.[73] Replacement of the acetyl group by chloride or tosylate inhibits the reaction almost completely, and replacement by the dimethylammonium chloride group raises the yield from 10 to 15% to 55 to 65%. The yield from 4,4'-dimethoxybenzoin acetate is very small (1%), while the 3,3'-dimethoxy analog gives a 48% yield of the corresponding furan mixture. The success of the reaction seems to depend on overlap between the π system of the free phenyl group and the nonbonded oxygen electrons, as shown by the greatly enhanced intensity of the n-π^* band. The poor yields observed from the 4,4'-dimethoxy isomer have been attributed[73] to the occurrence of charge-transfer states, the importance of which is greatly increased by the presence of the 4,4'-dimethoxy groups because they promote the migration of charge density from donor to acceptor group in the molecule. This charge-transfer band is dominant in the ultraviolet spectrum and masks the much weaker n-π^* band; absorption by the charge-transfer state leads to no acetate departure. (See Sec. 7-2 for a more detailed discussion of similar substituent effects.)

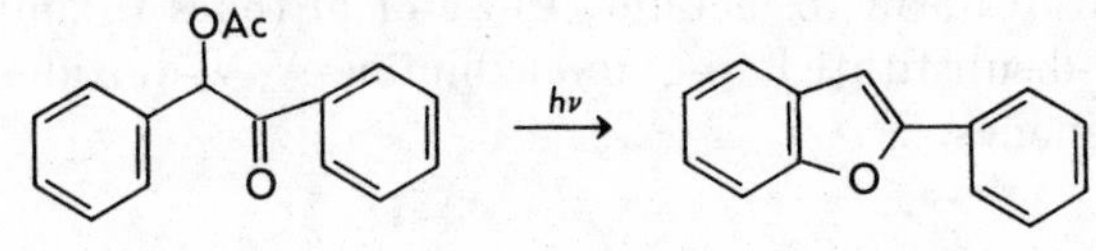

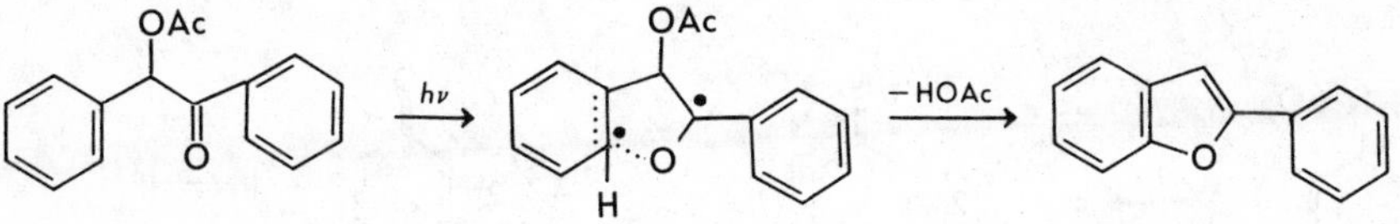

Charge transfer:

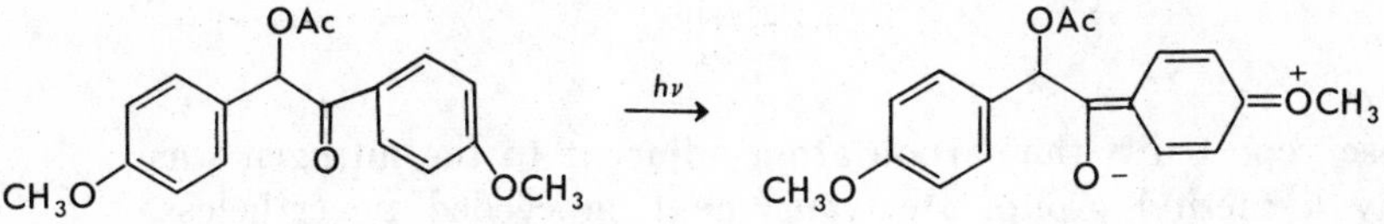

4-5   N-Oxides and Nitrocompounds

Photolysis of *N*-oxides usually leads to the transfer of oxygen from nitrogen to carbon. The rearrangement is almost certain to proceed through the oxazirane ring; several of these have been isolated:[74,75]

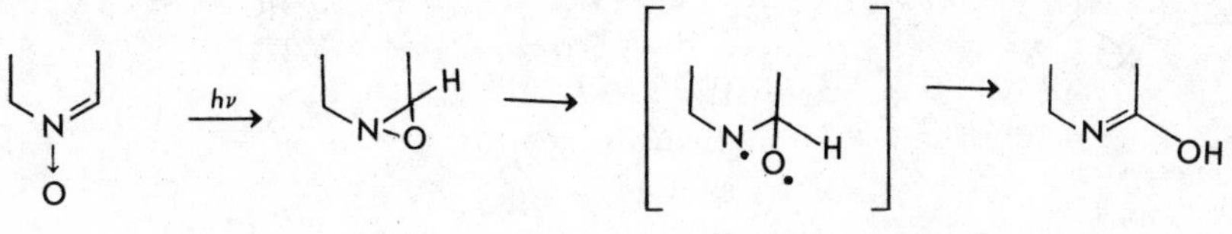

The reactions of *N*-oxides lead to lactams, those of nitrones to amides, and those of *N,N'*-disubstituted *p*-quinonediimine-*N,N'*-dioxides to the corresponding quinones:

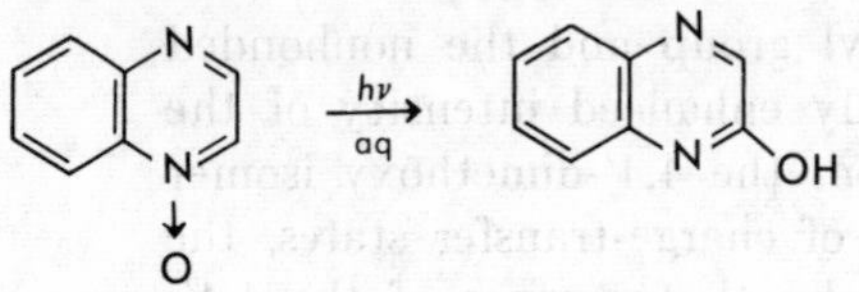

[76]

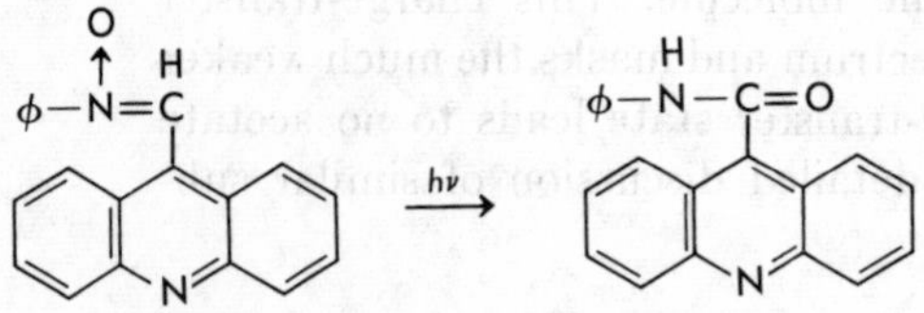

[77]

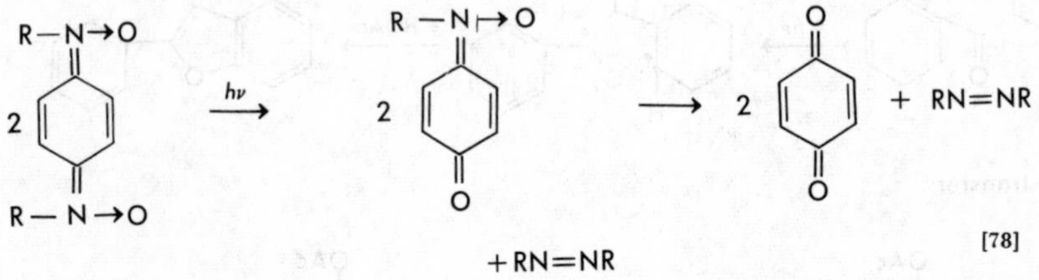

[78]

In one case reported[76a] the carbon atom adjacent to the nitrogen was blocked by a methyl group. Rearrangement proceeded nevertheless, although in low yield, with concomitant migration of the methyl group; 2-methylquinoline-*N*-oxide rearranged in solution to 3-methylcarbostyril.

Azoxy derivatives also undergo oxygen transfer in what appears to be an intramolecular process:

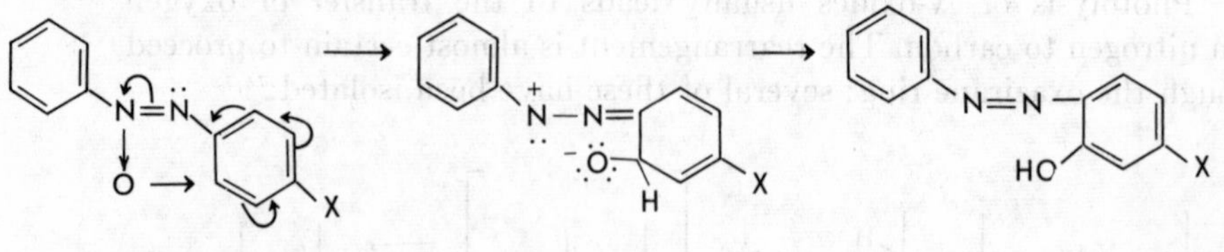

[79]

The formation of amides from aryl aldoximes[80] can follow a similar course or might be a radical-chain reaction.

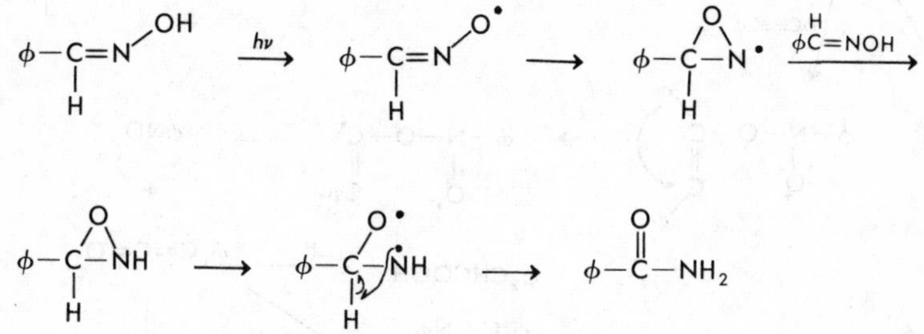

An oxazirane ring is also involved in the formation of phenanthridone on photolysis of the *p*-chlorophenyl anil of *o*-nitro-*o*′-formylbiphenyl; the *N*-oxide itself yields the same amide on irradiation:

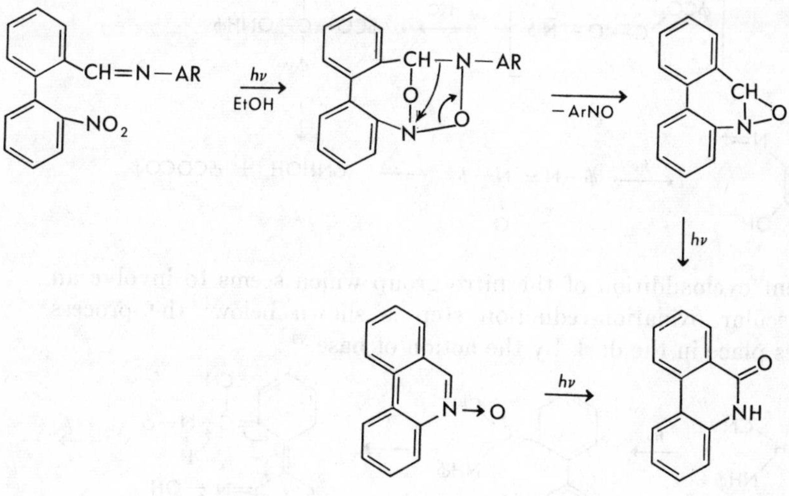

There exists precedence for this mode of addition of the nitro group to double bonds. One example, shown below, is the photochemical reaction of nitrobenzene with tolan.[83] It will be seen that the reaction is quite complex (see also Sec. 7-1).

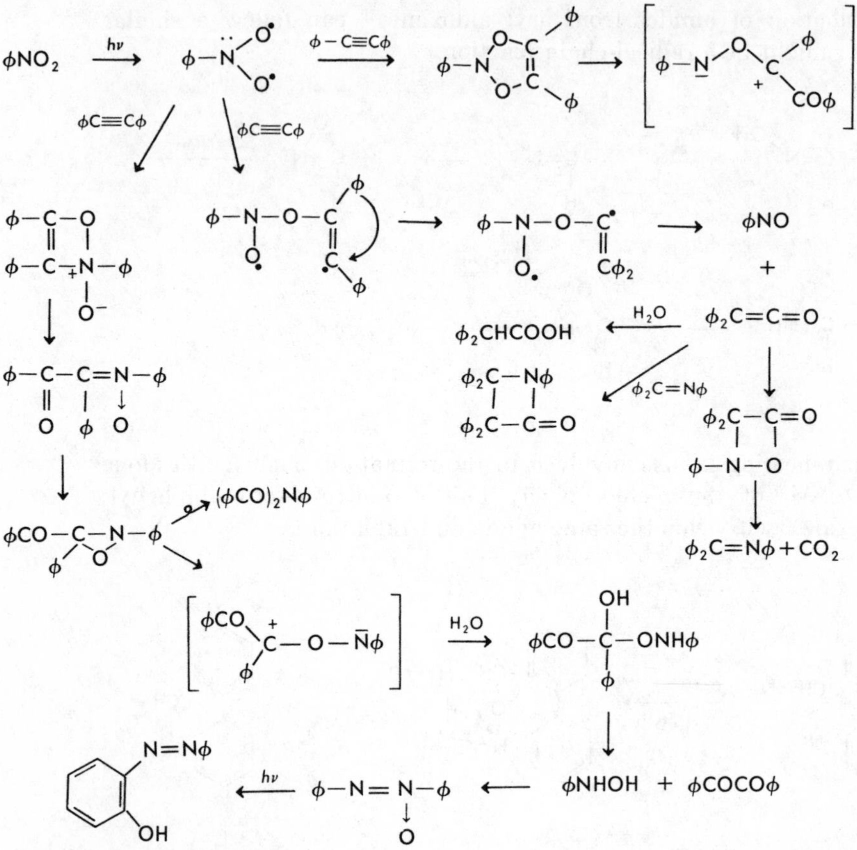

$\phi NO_2 \xrightarrow{h\nu} \phi - \overset{\cdot\cdot}{\underset{\displaystyle O^{\bullet}}{N}} \overset{O^{\bullet}}{\diagup} \xrightarrow{\phi - C \equiv C\phi} \phi - N \diagdown \overset{O - C}{\underset{O - C}{|}} \overset{\phi}{\diagdown}_\phi \longrightarrow \left[\phi - N \overset{O}{\diagdown} \overset{\phi}{\underset{+}{\diagup}} \overset{\diagup \phi}{\underset{CO\phi}{\diagup}} \right]$

$\downarrow \phi C \equiv C\phi \qquad \downarrow \phi C \equiv C\phi$

$\phi - C - O$
$\phi - C \overset{+}{-} N - \phi$
$\qquad \overset{|}{O^-}$

$\phi - N - O - C \overset{\diagup \phi}{\underset{\diagdown}{\parallel}} \longrightarrow \phi - N - O - C^{\bullet} \longrightarrow \phi NO$
$\quad \overset{|}{O^{\bullet}} \qquad C \overset{\phi}{\diagdown} \qquad\qquad \overset{|}{O_{\bullet}} \quad C\phi_2 \qquad\qquad +$

$\downarrow$

$\phi - C - C = N - \phi$
$\quad \parallel \quad | \quad \downarrow$
$\quad O \quad \phi \quad O$

$\phi_2 CHCOOH \xleftarrow{H_2O} \phi_2 C = C = O$

$\phi_2 C - N\phi$
$\quad | \qquad | \qquad \xleftarrow{\phi_2 C = N\phi}$
$\phi_2 C - C = O$

$\phi_2 C - C = O$
$\quad | \qquad |$
$\quad \phi - N - O$

$\downarrow$

$\downarrow$

$\phi CO - C - N - \phi \xrightarrow{} (\phi CO)_2 N\phi$
$\quad \overset{|}{\phi} \overset{|}{O}$

$\phi_2 C = N\phi + CO_2$

$\left[\overset{\phi CO}{\underset{\phi}{\diagdown}} \overset{+}{C} - O - \bar{N}\phi \right] \xrightarrow{H_2O} \phi CO - \overset{\displaystyle OH}{\underset{\displaystyle \phi}{\overset{|}{\underset{|}{C}}}} - ONH\phi$

$\downarrow$

$\xleftarrow{h\nu} \phi - N = N - \phi \xleftarrow{} \phi NHOH + \phi COCO\phi$
$\qquad\qquad\quad \downarrow$
$\qquad\qquad\quad O$

A different cycloaddition of the nitro group which seems to involve an intramolecular oxidation-reduction step is shown below; the process also takes place in the dark by the action of base.[89]

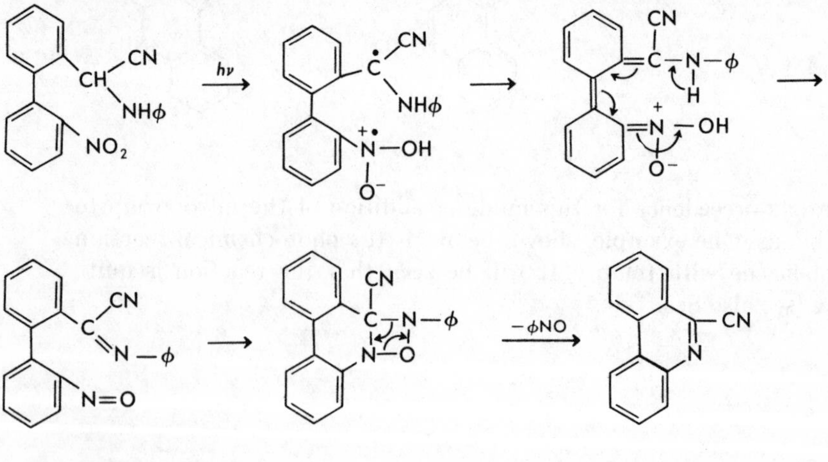

(48%)

4-6   Miscellaneous Rearrangements

Many isolated photochemical rearrangements are known; some of them can be readily understood, while others must occur through a complex series of steps about which little is known. The rearrangement of steroidal dienes probably involves intramolecular diradical cleavage and recombination, while the "no-mechanism" rearrangements shown in the last three examples will undoubtedly provide a challenge to the reader in his effort to supply the mechanistic details.

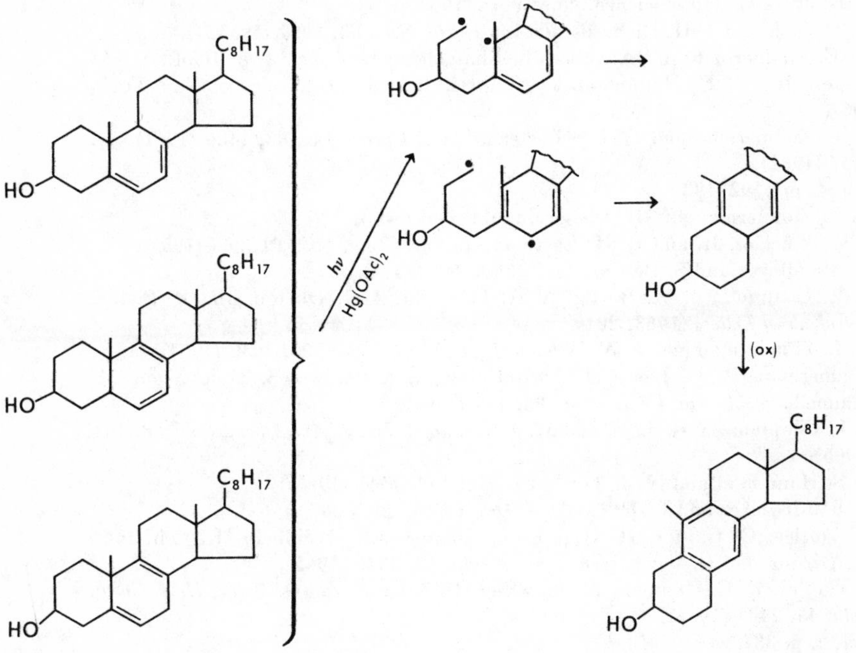

[86]

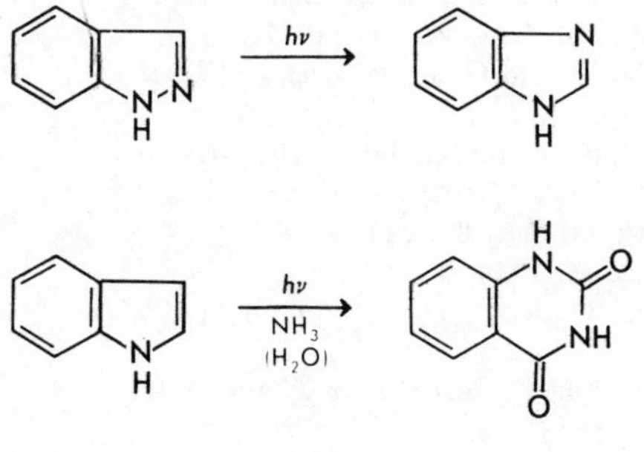

[87]

$$\phi \underset{R}{\overset{\phi}{\bigvee}} \phi \quad \xrightarrow[NH_3]{h\nu} \quad \underset{N}{\overset{\phi}{\bigvee}} \quad + \phi CH_2NH_2 + RNH_2 \qquad [88]$$

References

1. H. E. Zimmerman and J. S. Swenton, *J. Am. Chem. Soc.*, **86**, 1436 (1964).
2. O. L. Chapman and L. Englert, unpublished work; see O. L. Chapman, in "Advances in Photochemistry," vol. I, W. A. Noyes, Jr., G. S. Hammond, J. N. Pitts, Jr. (eds.), Interscience, New York, 1963, p. 335.
3. H. H. Fish and J. H. Richards, *J. Am. Chem. Soc.*, **85**, 3029 (1963).
4. H. E. Zimmerman, in "Advances in Photochemistry," vol. I, p. 183ff., W. A. Noyes, Jr., G. S. Hammond, J. N. Pitts, Jr. (ed.), Interscience, New York, 1963.
5. H. E. Zimmerman and D. I. Schuster, *J. Am. Chem. Soc.*, **83**, 4486 (1961); **84**, 4527 (1962).
6. Ref. 4, pp. 192, 193.
7. H. E. Zimmerman and R. Keese, unpublished results.
8. J. W. Wheeler, Jr. and R. H. Eastman, *J. Am. Chem. Soc.*, **81**, 236 (1959).
9. H. Staudinger and S. Bereza, *Ann.*, **380**, 243 (1911).
10. O. L. Chapman, T. A. Rettig, A. A. Griswold, A. I. Dutton, and P. Fitton, *Tetrahedron Letters*, **1963**, 2049.
11. H. E. Zimmerman and J. W. Wilson, *J. Am. Chem. Soc.*, **86**, 4036 (1964). H. E. Zimmerman, R. G. Lewis, J. J. McCullough, A. Padwa, S. Staley, and M. Semmelhack, *J. Am. Chem. Soc.*, **88**, 159 (1966).
11a. O. L. Chapman, S. B. Sieja, and W. J. Welstead, Jr., *J. Am. Chem. Soc.*, **88**, 161 (1966).
12. G. S. Hammond and N. J. Turro, *Science*, **142**, 1541 (1963).
13. E. R. Altwicker and C. D. Cook, *J. Org. Chem.*, **29**, 3087 (1964).
14. H. Dutler, C. Ganter, H. Ryf, E. C. Utzinger, K. Weinberg, K. Schaffner, D. Arigoni, and O. Jeger, *Helv. Chim. Acta*, **45**, 2346 (1962).
15. C. Ganter, E. C. Utzinger, K. Schaffner, D. Arigoni, and O. Jeger, *Helv. Chim. Acta*, **45**, 2403 (1962).
16. Ref. 2, p. 337.
17. P. J. Kropp and W. F. Erman, *J. Am. Chem. Soc.*, **85**, 2456 (1963).
18. P. J. Kropp and W. F. Erman, *Tetrahedron Letters*, **1963**, 21.
19. P. J. Kropp, *J. Am. Chem. Soc.*, **86**, 4053 (1964); *Tetrahedron*, **21**, 2183 (1965).
20. H. Dutler, H. Bosshard, and O. Jeger, *Helv. Chim. Acta*, **40**, 494 (1957).
21. E. Utzinger, H. Dutler, K. Weinberg, D. Arigoni, and O. Jeger, *Angew. Chem.*, **71**, 80 (1959).
22. C. Ganter, R. Warszawski, H. Wehrli, K. Schaffner, and O. Jeger, *Helv. Chim. Acta*, **46**, 320 (1963).
23. D. H. R. Barton and W. C. Taylor, *J. Am. Chem. Soc.*, **80**, 244 (1958).
24. D. H. R. Barton and W. C. Taylor, *J. Chem. Soc.*, **1958**, 2500.
25. K. Weinberg, E. C. Utzinger, D. Arigoni, and O. Jeger, *Helv. Chim. Acta*, **43**, 236 (1960).
26. C. Ganter, F. Greuter, D. Kägi, K. Schaffner, and O. Jeger, *Helv. Chim. Acta*, **47**, 627 (1964).
27. E. Altenburger, H. Wehrli, and K. Schaffner, *Helv. Chim. Acta*, **46**, 2753 (1963).

28. D. H. R. Barton and P. T. Gilham, *J. Chem. Soc.*, **1960,** 4596.
29. D. H. R. Barton, P. de Mayo, and M. Shafiq, *J. Chem. Soc.*, **1958,** 140.
30. D. H. R. Barton, P. de Mayo, and M. Shafiq, *J. Chem. Soc.*, **1957,** 929.
31. I. Satoda and E. Yoshii, *Tetrahedron Letters*, **1962,** 331.
32. E. Schott, D. Arigoni, and O. Jeger, *Helv. Chim. Acta*, **46,** 307 (1963).
33. D. H. R. Barton, P. de Mayo, and M. Shafiq, *J. Chem. Soc.*, **1958,** 3314.
34. O. L. Chapman and L. F. Englert, *J. Am. Chem. Soc.*, **85,** 3028 (1963).
35. W. W. Kwie, B. A. Shoulders, and P. D. Gardner, *J. Am. Chem. Soc.*, **84,** 2268 (1962); See also B. A. Shoulders, W. W. Kwie, W. Klyne, P. D. Gardner, *Tetrahedron Le*, **21,** 2973 (1965).
36. B. Nann, D. Gravel, R. Shorta, H. Wehrli, K. Schaffner, and O. Jeger, *Helv. Chim. Acta.* **46,** 2473 (1963); B. Nann, H. Wehrli, K. Schaffner, O. Jeger, *ibid*, **48,** 1680 (1965).
37. D. H. R. Barton, J. F. McGhie, and M. Rosenberger, *J. Chem. Soc.*, **1961,** 1215.
38. P. J. Kropp, *Tetrahedron Letters*, **1964,** 3647.
39. D. I. Schuster and C. J. Polowczyk, *J. Am. Chem. Soc.*, **86,** 4502 (1964).
40. J. C. Anderson and C. B. Reese, *Tetrahedron Letters*, **1962,** 1.
41. E. E. van Tamelen, K. Kirk, and G. Brieger, *Tetrahedron Letters*, **1962,** 939; See also J. King and D. Leaver, *Chem. Commun.*, 539 (1965).
42. P. Yates and I. W. J. Still, *J. Am. Chem. Soc.*, **85,** 1208 (1963).
43. A. Padwa and R. Hartman, *J. Am. Chem. Soc.*, **86,** 4212 (1964).
44. A. Padwa, *Tetrahedron Letters*, **1964,** 813.
45. A. Padwa, *Tetrahedron Letters*, **1965,** 1049.
46. E. F. Ullman, *J. Am. Chem. Soc.*, **85,** 3529 (1963).
47. E. F. Ullman and W. A. Henderson, Jr., *J. Am. Chem. Soc.*, **86,** 5050 (1964).
48. E. F. Ullman and J. E. Milks, *J. Am. Chem. Soc.*, **84,** 1315 (1962).
49. E. F. Ullman and J. E. Milks, *J. Am. Chem. Soc.*, **86,** 3814 (1964).
50. J. M. Dunston and P. Yates, *Tetrahedron Letters*, **1964,** 505.
51. H. E. Zimmerman and R. D. Simkin, *Tetrahedron Letters*, **1964,** 1847.
52. H. E. Zimmerman, B. R. Cowley, C. Y. Tseng, and J. W. Wilson, *J. Am. Chem. Soc.*, **86,** 947 (1964).
53. S. Bodforss, *Ber.*, **51,** 214 (1918).
54. H. E. Zimmerman, *Abstract of Papers*, 17th *National Org. Chem. Symp.*, *Am. Chem. Soc.*, *Bloomington, Ind.*, June, 1961, p. 31.
55. H. Wehrli, C. Lehmann, K. Schaffner, and O. Jeger, *Helv. Chim. Acta*, **47,** 1336 (1964); O. Jeger, K. Schaffner, and H. Wehrli, *Pure Appl. Chem.*, **9,** 555 (1964).
56. C. K. Johnson, B. Dominy, and W. Reusch, *J. Am. Chem. Soc.*, **85,** 3894 (1963).
57. G. R. Evanega, W. Bergmann, and J. English, Jr., *J. Org. Chem.*, **27,** 13 (1962).
58. C. Lehmann, K. Schaffner, and O. Jeger, *Helv. Chim. Acta*, **45,** 1031 (1962).
59. A Padwa and L. Hamilton, *J. Am. Chem. Soc.*, **87,** 1821 (1965).
59a. A. Padwa, D. Crumrine, *Chem. Commun.*, 506 (1965).
60. M. Feldkimel-Gorodetzky and Y. Mazur, *Tetrahedron Letters*, **1963,** 369.
61. M. Gorodetzky and Y. Mazur, *J. Am. Chem. Soc.*, **86,** 5213 (1964).
62. A. Yogev, M. Gorodetzky, and Y. Mazur, *J. Am. Chem. Soc.*, **86,** 5208 (1964).
62a. A. Yogev, Y. Mazur, *J. Am. Chem. Soc.*, **87,** 3520 (1965).
63. J. C. Anderson and C. B. Reese, *Proc. Chem. Soc.*, **1960,** 217; R. A. Finnegan and J. J. Mattice, *Tetrahedron*, **21,** 1015 (1965).
64. H. Kobsa, *J. Org. Chem.*, **27,** 2293 (1962); See also R. A. Finnegan and D. Knutson, *Chem. Ind. (London)*, 1837 (1965).
65. D. P. Kelly and J. T. Pinhey, *Tetrahedron Letters*, **1964,** 3427.
66. C. Pac and S. Tsutsumi, *Bull. Chem. Soc. Japan*, **37,** 1392 (1964).
67. D. Elad, *Tetrahedron Letters*, **1963,** 873.

68. M. S. Kharasch, G. Stampa, and W. Nudenberg, *Science*, 116, 309 (1952).
69. G. W. Griffin and E. J. O'Connell, *J. Am. Chem. Soc.*, 84, 4148 (1962).
70. H. E. Zimmerman, H. G. C. Dürr, R. G. Lewis, and S. Bram, *J. Am. Chem. Soc.*, 84, 4149 (1962).
71. H. Schmid, M. Hochweber, and H. von Halban, *Helv. Chim. Acta*, 30, 1135 (1947).
72. D. W. Boykin, Jr. and R. E. Lutz, *J. Am. Chem. Soc.*, 86, 5046 (1964).
73. J. C. Sheehan and R. M. Wilson, *J. Am. Chem. Soc.*, 86, 5277 (1964).
74. M. J. Kamlet and L. A. Kaplan, *J. Org. Chem.*, 22, 576 (1957); R. Bonnett, V. M. Clark, and A. Todd, *J. Chem. Soc.*, 1959, 2102.
75. F. Kröhnke, *Ann.*, 604, 203 (1957); L. Kaminsky and M. Lamchen, *Chem. Commun.*, 1965, 130.
76. J. K. Landquist, *J. Chem. Soc.*, 1953, 2830.
76a. O. Buchardt, J. Becher, and C. Lohse, *Acta Chem. Scand.*, 19, 1120 (1965).
77. L. Chardonnens and P. Heinrich, *Helv. Chim. Acta*, 32, 656 (1949).
78. C. J. Pedersen, *J. Am. Chem. Soc.*, 79, 5014 (1957).
79. G. M. Badger and R. G. Buttery, *J. Chem. Soc.*, 1954, 2243.
80. J. H. Amin and P. de Mayo, *Tetrahedron Letters*, 1963, 1585.
81. H. Hart and A. J. Waring, *Tetrahedron Letters*, 1965, 325; H. Hart, *Abstract of Papers*, Am. Chem. Soc., *Detroit*, April, 1965, 51 P.
82. H. E. Zimmerman, *Pure Appl. Chem.*, 9, 493 (1964).
83. M. L. Scheinbaum, *J. Org. Chem.*, 29, 2200 (1964).
84. H. E. Zimmerman, R. C. Hahn, H. Morrison, and M. C. Wani, *J. Am. Chem. Soc.*, 87, 1138 (1965).
85. A. Padwa, *J. Am. Chem. Soc.*, 87, 4205 (1965).
86. K. Tsuda and R. Hayatsu, *J. Am. Chem. Soc.*, 77, 3089 (1955).
87. H. Thiefenthaler, W. Dörscheln, H. Göth, and H. Schmid, *Tetrahedron Letters*, 1964, 2999.
88. A. Mustafa, in "Advances in Photochemistry", vol. II, p. 112, W. A. Noyes, Jr., G. S. Hammond, J. N. Pitts, Jr. (eds.), Interscience, New York, 1964.
89. E. C. Taylor, B. Furth, and M. Pfau, *J. Am. Chem. Soc.*, 87, 1400 (1965).

Dimerization Reactions: Autoadditions

5-1 Types of Bimolecular Additions

The formation of dimers on irradiation of compounds that contain olefinic bonds is one of the oldest photochemical reactions known,[1] and a vast number of examples have been reported. Nevertheless, the mechanistic details of the dimerization step(s) are largely unknown, because although the gross structure of the dimeric products is often known, the elucidation of their stereochemistry has often raised such formidable problems that there are few cases for which this question has been clearly settled. The availability of physical tools such as nuclear magnetic resonance has greatly accelerated the progress made in this area in the last few years.

Three types of dimers are generally recognized. The first is a combination of two double bonds to form a cyclobutane derivative (I); the second is a Diels-Alder type of combination (II); the third is a 1,4–1,4 addition of dienes (III).

I

II

III

With reference to the stereochemistry one must notice that the dimer

obtained from an olefin of the type can in theory be one of some

twelve isomers (Fig. 5-1) depending on whether head-to-head or head-to-tail dimerization takes place with syn or anti and with cis or trans ring junctions. Several of the possible isomers may appear in each dimerization reaction. Contrary to earlier expectations, formation of a trans junction between a four- and a six-membered ring has been observed to be a rather general photochemical phenomenon,[7] especially in the combination of two dissimilar olefinic systems.[2]

Unfortunately, knowledge of the complete structure of the products from some of the dimerization reactions has thus far not been very helpful in allowing predictions to be made about others. The dimerization step is generally believed to involve the attack of one excited molecule on one in the ground state. Sometimes the products give the appearance that the process is a two-step sequence in which the two new bonds are formed in succession, while in other instances the process resembles a one-step, four-centered addition. In the excited state the distribution of charge over the two centers involved in bond formation may either be even, so that the species resembles IV, or dissimilar, so that it resembles

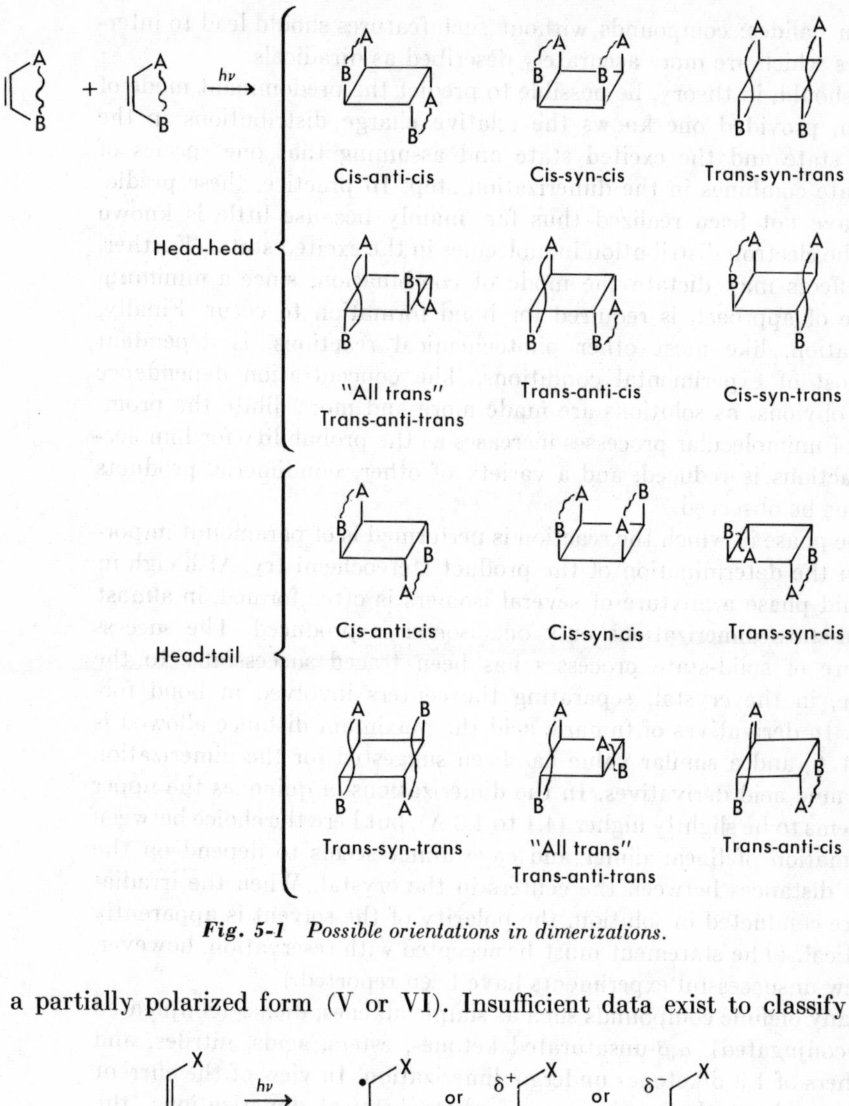

Fig. 5-1 Possible orientations in dimerizations.

a partially polarized form (V or VI). Insufficient data exist to classify

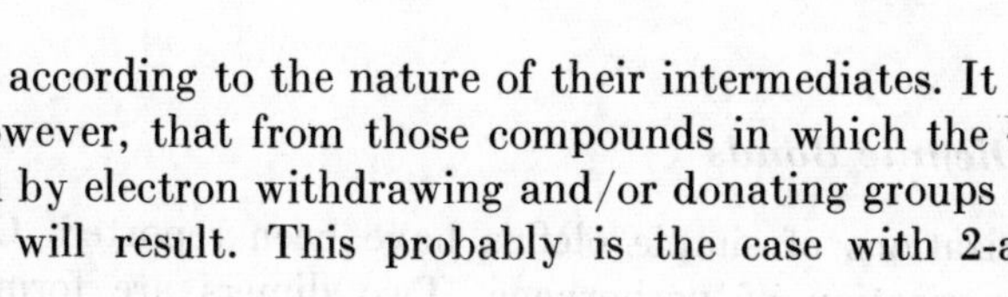

the reactions according to the nature of their intermediates. It is logical to expect, however, that from those compounds in which the π system is surrounded by electron withdrawing and/or donating groups a dipolar intermediate will result. This probably is the case with 2-aminopyridinium halides; compounds without such features should lead to intermediates which are more accurately described as diradicals.

It should, in theory, be possible to predict the predominant mode of addition, provided one knows the relative charge distributions in the ground state and the excited state and assuming that one species of each state combines in the dimerization step. In practice, these predictions have not been realized thus far, mainly because little is known about the electron distribution in molecules in the excited states. Further, steric effects may dictate the mode of combination, since a minimum distance of approach is required for bond formation to occur. Finally, dimerization, like most other photochemical reactions, is dependent on a host of experimental conditions. The concentration dependence will be obvious; as solutions are made more and more dilute the prominence of unimolecular processes increases as the probability for bimolecular reactions is reduced, and a variety of other, nondimeric, products may thus be observed.

The phase in which the reaction is performed is of paramount importance in the determination of the product stereochemistry. Although in the liquid phase a mixture of several isomers is often formed, in almost all solid-state dimerizations only one isomer is produced. The success or failure of solid-state processes has been traced successfully to the distance, in the crystal, separating the centers involved in bond formation. In derivatives of fumaric acid the maximum distance allowed is about 4 Å, and a similar value has been suggested for the dimerization of cinnamic acid derivatives. In the dimerizations of quinones the upper limit seems to be slightly higher (4.1 to 4.3 Å), but here the choice between the formation of linear dimer and cage dimer seems to depend on the relative distances between the centers in the crystal. When the irradiations are conducted in solution, the polarity of the solvent is apparently not critical. (The statement must be accepted with reservation, however, since few unsuccessful experiments have been reported.)

Many olefinic compounds such as simple alkenes, dienes (conjugated and unconjugated), α,β-unsaturated ketones, esters, acids, nitriles, and enol ethers of 1,3-diketones undergo dimerization. In view of the current knowledge about the mechanism of photochemical dimerizations, the discussion of specific examples presented below can be little more than a review of the types of chromophores studied.

5-2 *Isolated Olefinic Bonds*

Few dimerizations of simple olefins have been reported. One of them is the dimerization of norbornene. Two dimers are formed in acetone, but when benzophenone is present, addition to the carbonyl

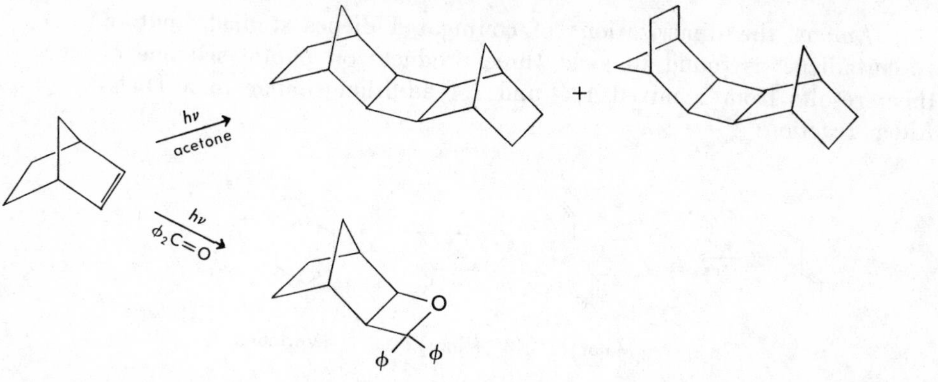

group occurs instead.[3] This oxetane formation is discussed in more detail in Chap. 6. The photolysis of cyclopentene in acetone leads to a variety of products, some of which are the result of hydrogen abstraction from and addition to the solvent.

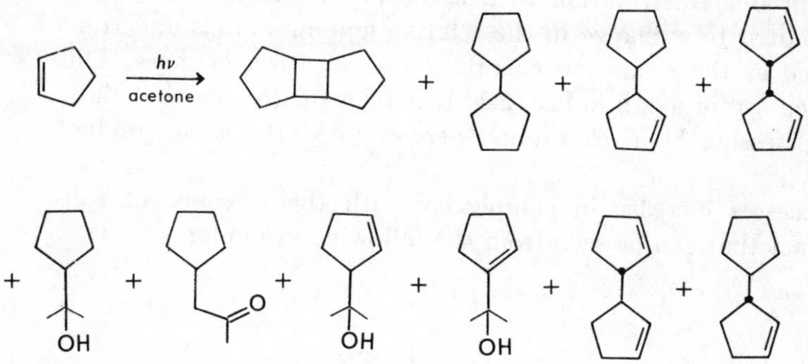

[4]

The dimer that is formed from 1,3,3-trimethylcyclopropene readily undergoes valence-bond tautomerization.

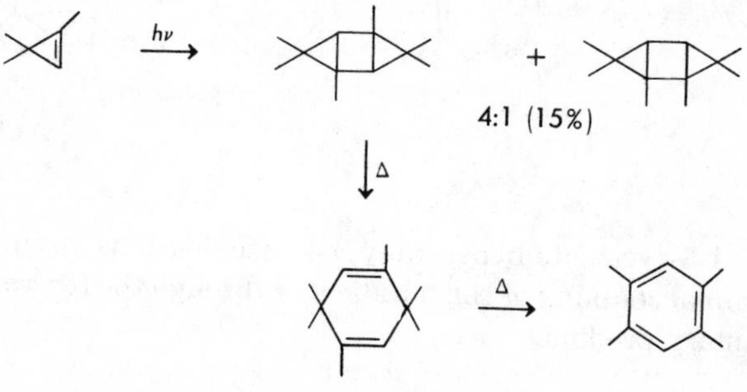

4:1 (15%)

[5]

5-3 Conjugated Dienes

Among the dimerizations of conjugated dienes studied, that of 1,3-butadiene[6] is found to yield three products on photolysis; one of them results from a mixed 1,2- and 1,4 addition similar to a Diels-Alder reaction:

(Major)   (Minor)   (Variable)

The relative amounts of the three dimers that form vary with the sensitizers used. Since the process as a whole is dependent on the presence of sensitizers, a triplet state is almost certain to be involved.[7] This variation in product distribution with the type of sensitizer employed may be attributed to a change in the relative amounts of cis and trans triplets formed as the excitation energy of the sensitizer changes. This subject is discussed in detail in Sec. 2-1. It is relevant to note that those sensitizers possessing high excitation energies yield the same product distribution.[7]

The processes increase in complexity with the presence of substituents, a fact that can be seen from the following example:

[9, 10]

The formation of 1,5-cyclooctadienes may be visualized as occurring either through terminal coupling of the biradical or through the rearrangement of other, primary products.

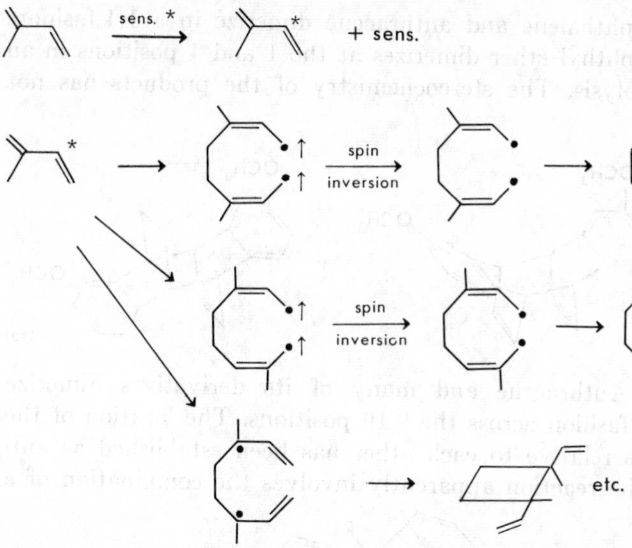

Mixtures of *cis-* and *trans*-piperylene lead to at least 15 dimers upon irradiation in the presence of a sensitizer. Three of them have been tentatively identified:

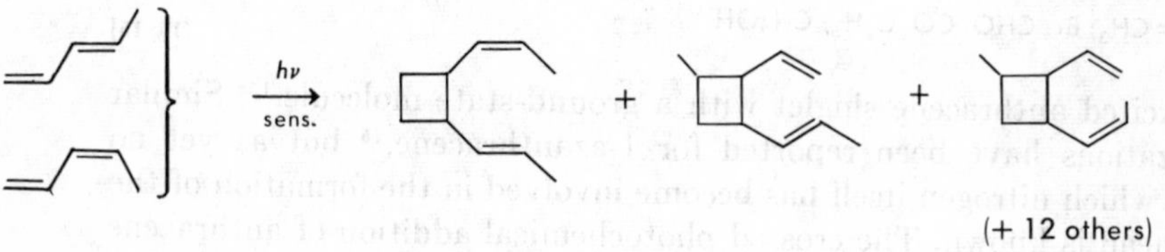

(+ 12 others)

[7]

Studies with similar compounds in the vapor phase, and in solution without sensitizers, showed that internal cycloaddition is the major process taking place. Cyclopentadiene yields three dimers,[7,11] two of which are the result of Diels-Alder type of additions. Similar results are obtained from the irradiation of cyclohexadiene.[8]

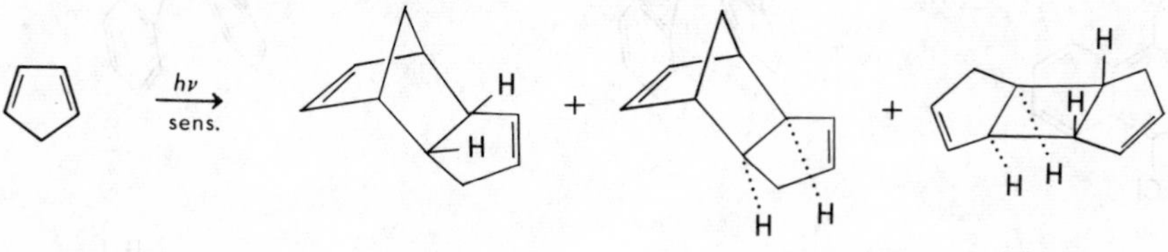

Derivatives of naphthalene and anthracene dimerize in a 1,4 fashion. Thus methyl-β-naphthyl ether dimerizes at the 1 and 4 positions in an unsensitized photolysis. The stereochemistry of the products has not

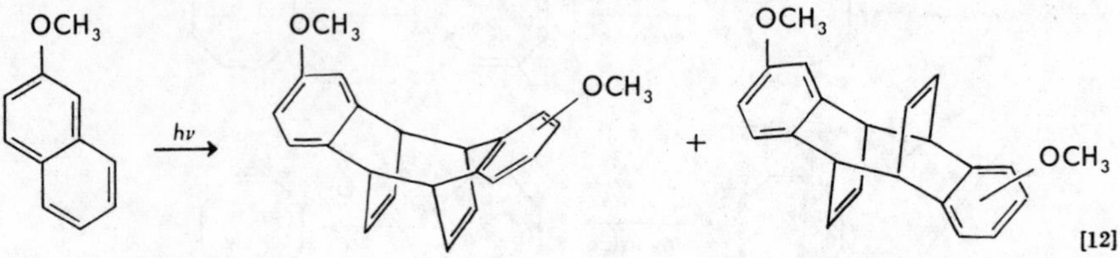

[12]

been elucidated. Anthracene and many of its derivatives dimerize similarly in a 1,4 fashion across the 9,10 positions. The location of the two 9-substituents relative to each other has been established as anti in many cases. The reaction apparently involves the combination of a

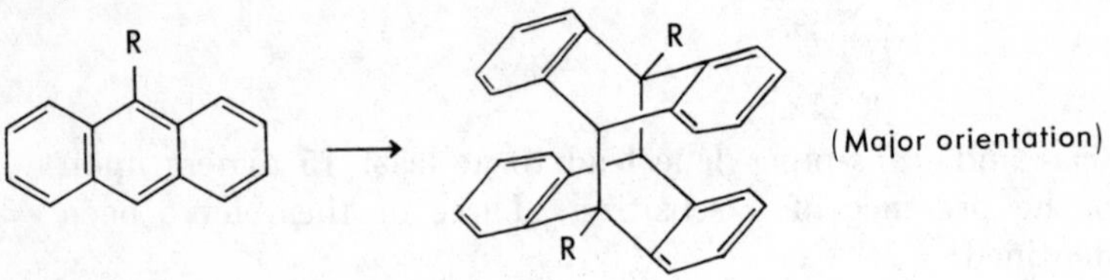

(Major orientation)

$R = CH_3$; Br; CHO; $CO_2C_2H_5$; CH_2OH [13–15]

π-π* excited anthracene singlet with a ground-state molecule.[15a] Similar dimerizations have been reported for 1-azanthracene,[16] but as yet no case in which nitrogen itself has become involved in the formation of the bridgehead is known. The crossed photochemical addition of anthracene and 9,10-dichloroanthracene may be mentioned here; the product is of interest because, on treatment with triphenylmethylsodium, a substituted Dewar anthracene is obtained.

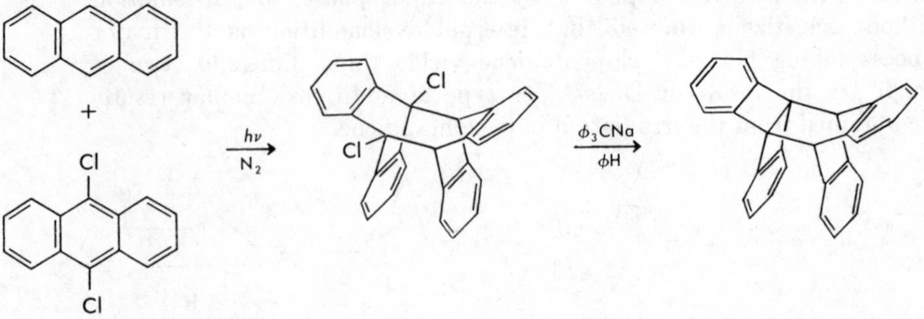

[17]

Some examples of conjugated olefins forming cyclobutane derivatives on irradiation are shown below:

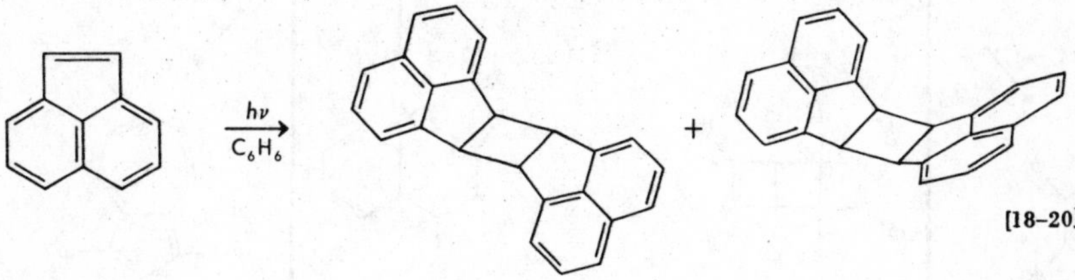

[18–20]

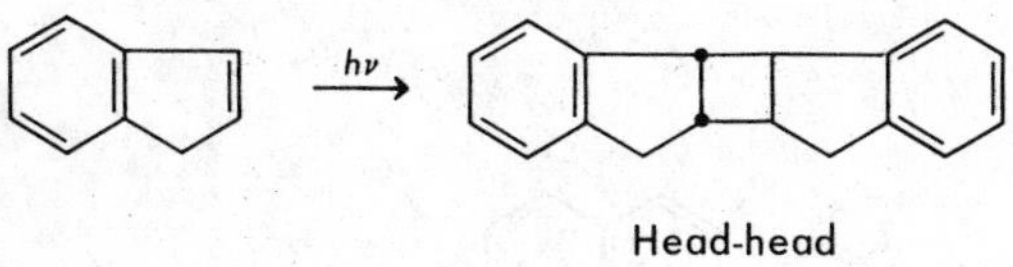

Head-head

[21]

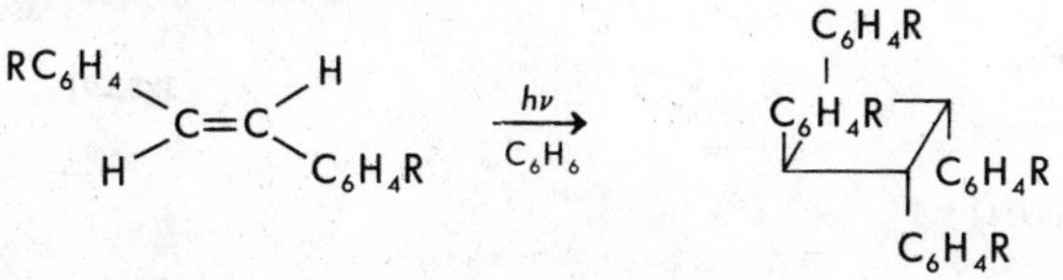

[22–25]

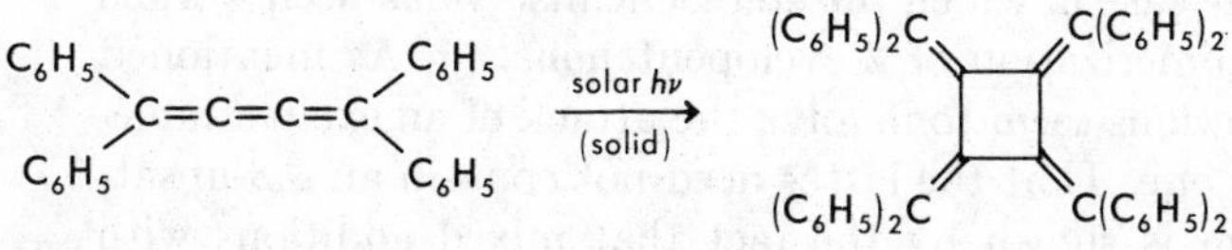

[26]

In the reaction of diphenylacetylene there is participation of the phenyl groups. Tetraphenylcyclobutadiene might be a transient intermediate in the formation of some of the products. It was thought at first that the cyclobutadiene dimerized to form octaphenylcubane, but subsequent x-ray crystallographic studies have shown that the product is octaphenylcyclooctatetraene:[27]

[28,29]

5-4 α,β-Unsaturated Ketones

Simple α,β-unsaturated ketones dimerize quite readily. Many instances have been reported, but only a few representative examples will be cited here. One case in which the stereochemistry has been worked out in detail is the dimerization of 2-cyclopentenone.[30,31] As mentioned previously, these reactions seem to involve the attack of an excited molecule on an unexcited one. That the latter need not contain an α,β-unsaturated ketone system is shown by the fact that mixed additions with simple olefins may compete favorably with dimerization.

(67%)   [30,31]

The process, involving n-π^* excitation, is thought to take place through singlet-triplet crossover in the excited state. From the very slight selectivity of the excited cyclopentenone molecule in head-head versus head-tail addition one may infer that whatever natural polarization of the double bond exists in the ground state has been reduced in the excited state to the point where the electron densities at the α and β carbons are about the same.

The dimerization of cyclohexenone occurs in a similar manner.[33] Examples of the dimerization of other cyclohexenone derivatives are given below:

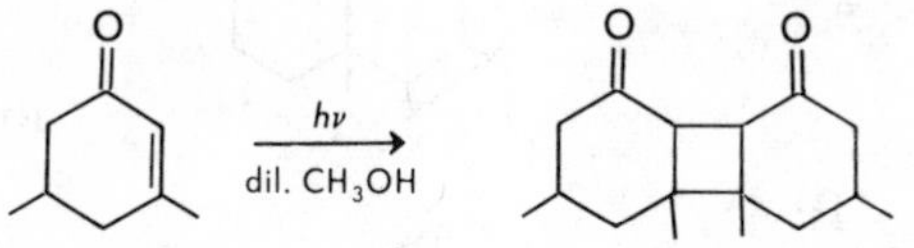

[34]

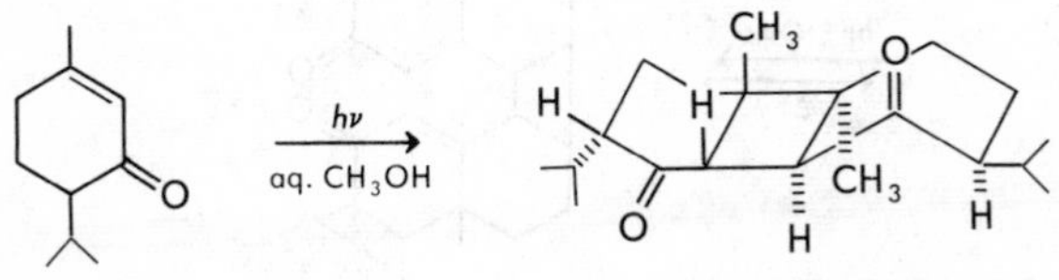

One of three dimers; all head-head, one of which has a trans ring junction

[35,36]

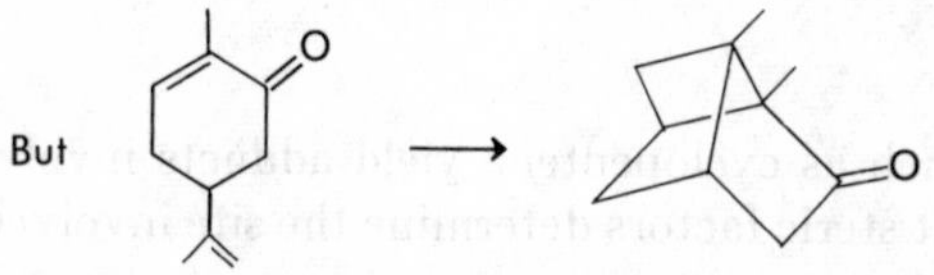

But

[37]

The dimerization of 2-cyclooctenone has already been referred to in connection with the cis-trans isomerization that precedes it. The structures of the two dimers that are isolated have not yet been elaborated.†

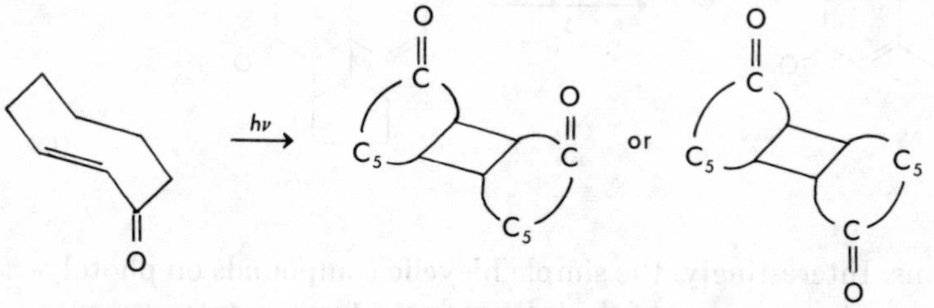

[38]

† The dimerizations of *trans*-2-cyclooctenone and of *trans*-2-cycloheptenone are thermal processes. The dimers have trans ring junctions (see Chap. 6, ref. 11; footnote 5).

Δ^4-3-Ketosteroids are also reported to dimerize, but the stereochemistry of the products is not known.[39] From the corresponding dienones a dimer may be formed between the α,β bond of one molecule and the γ,δ bond of a second; in other instances the dimer has been observed to form by the combination of two γ,δ bonds:[40-42]

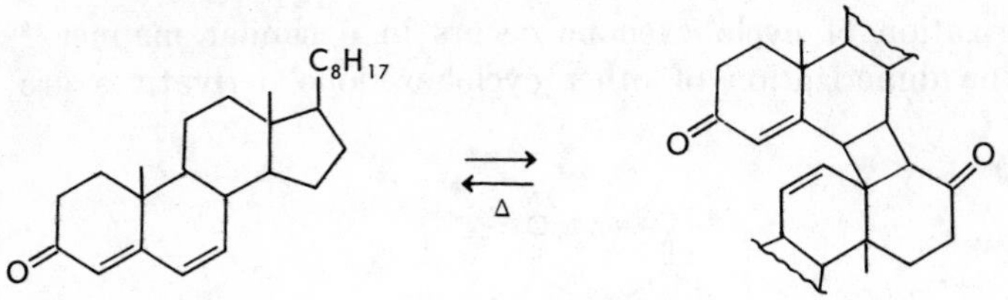

[41]

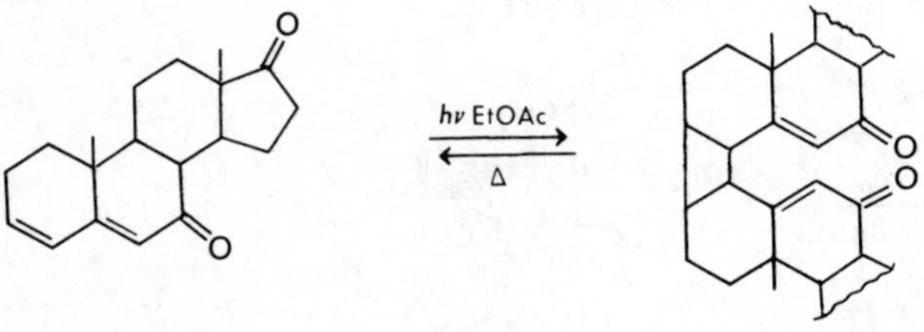

(or head-tail isomer)

[42]

Mixed additions with olefins such as cyclopentene yield adducts involving the α,β bond. It is likely that steric factors determine the site involved

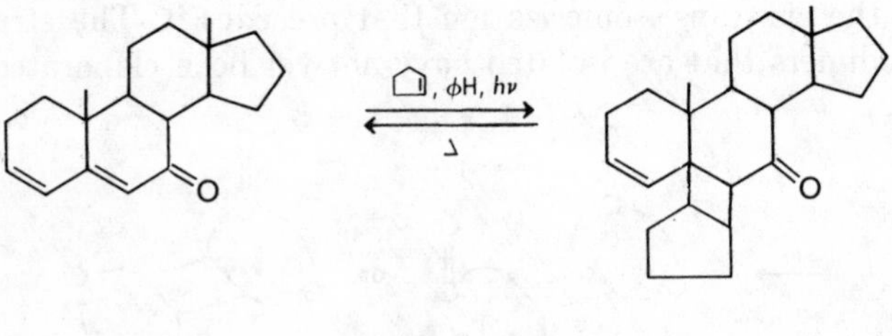

[42]

in the additions. Interestingly, the simple bicyclic compounds on photolysis often form polymeric material and products from rearrangements.

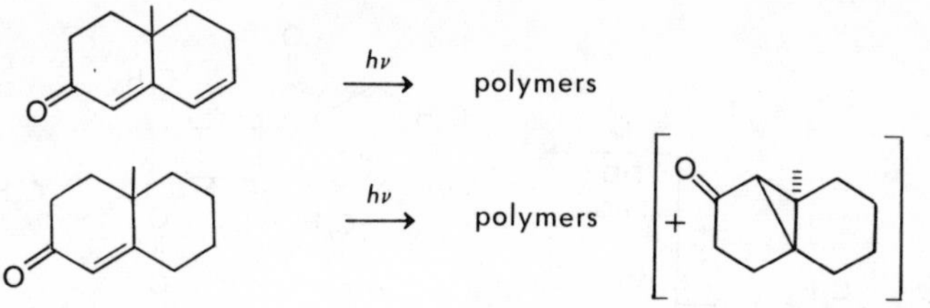

[42]

The dimerization of benzalacetone is representative of processes observed from α,β-unsaturated ketones that are conjugated with aromatic rings.

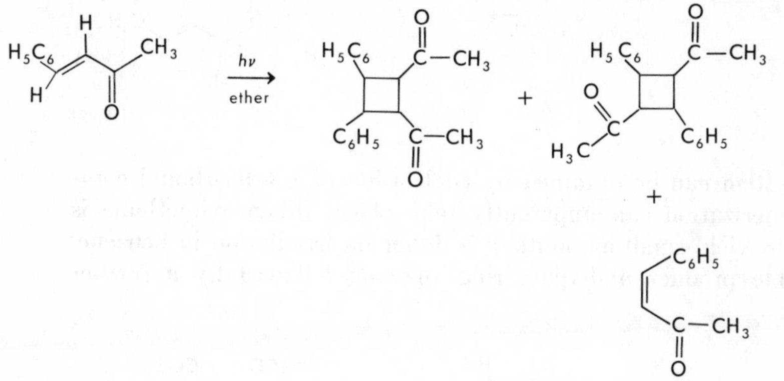

[43,44]

Derivatives of the compound vary in reactivity; the meta-nitro-substituted compound dimerizes, whereas the para isomer does so only poorly.[45] Irradiation of benzalacetophenone produces a similar dimer the structure of which depends on the reaction phase employed.

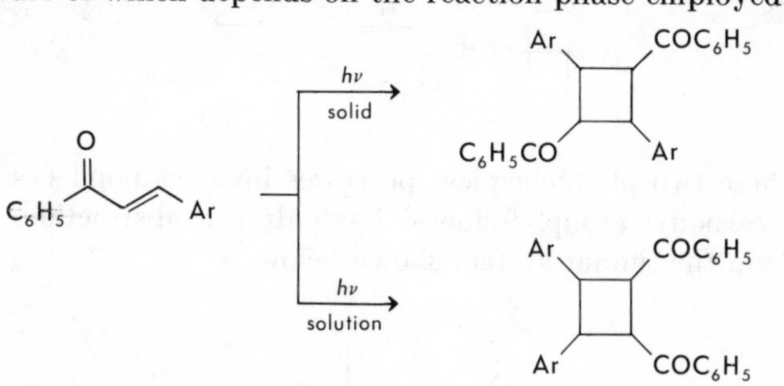

$Ar = C_6H_5;\ pCH_3O-C_6H_4$

[46,47]

The products from dibenzalacetone are similar, but here their structure is dependent on the solvent in the photolysis. When the α,β-unsaturated

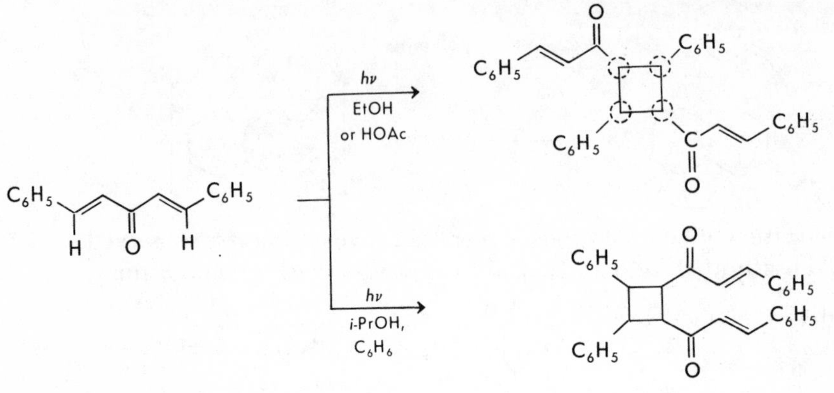

[48,49]

carbonyl system can be obtained by enolization of 1,3-dicarbonyl compounds, dimerization can apparently take place; dibenzoylmethane is reported[50] to yield small amounts of a dimer on irradiation in benzene. The unstable product undergoes ring opening followed by a further conversion:

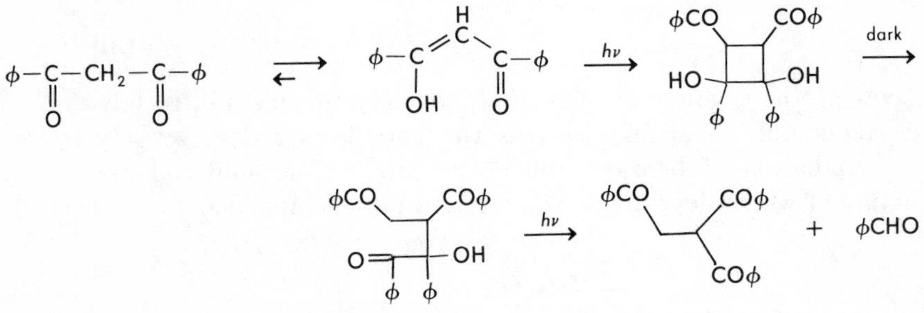

The second of these two photochemical processes involves bond fission adjacent to the carbonyl group, followed by hydrogen abstraction. It is observed also[50] in the similar system shown below.

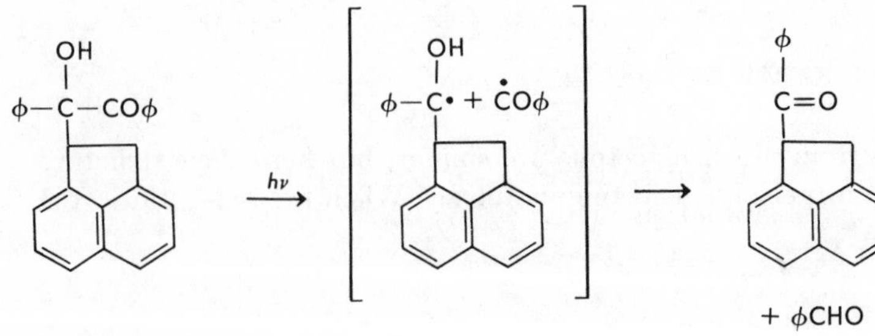

An interesting example of a "double-barrel" dimerization is the following:

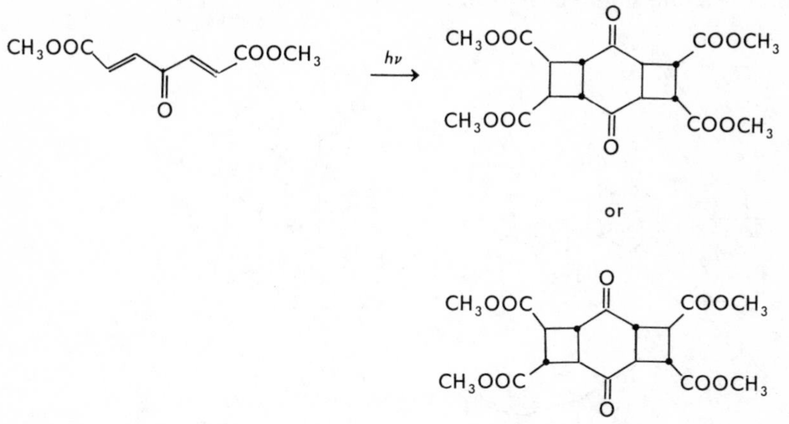

[51–54]

The derivatives of indenone are among the other aromatic compounds that undergo dimerization.

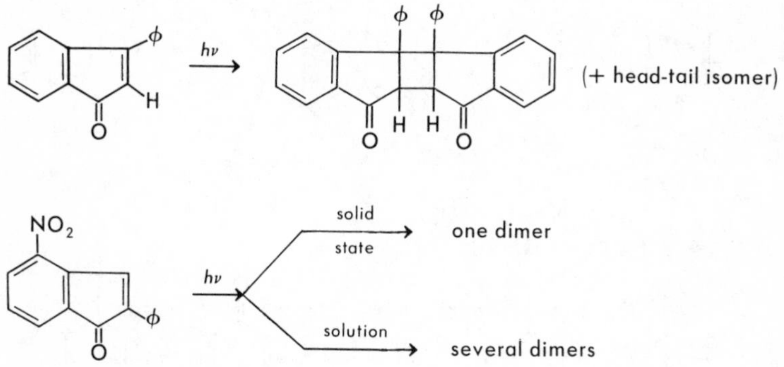

[55]

5-5 *Quinone Derivatives*

The photochemical behavior of *p*-quinones is quite varied. *p*-Quinone and its dimethyl derivatives form cage dimers in fairly low yields, mostly upon irradiation in the solid state with the use of suitable filters and light sources. In addition, time-limited irradiations of the disubstituted quinones yield a second type of dimer; these convert to the cage structure on further irradiation, and they have been shown to contain cyclobutane rings in which the two six-membered rings are attached on the same side (cis-syn-cis).[56,57]

The location of the substituents in the cage dimers has not been firmly settled. In the case of 2,3-dimethylquinone the structure of the intermediate dimer, established by nuclear magnetic resonance spectroscopy,[56] seems to leave no doubt about the cage structure derived from it. However, from the report[57] that 2,5-dimethylquinone is found among the products of pyrolysis of this cage dimer it would seem that the four methyl groups cannot be located on the same side of the molecule. It is quite likely that different crystalline modifications leading to different dimers have been employed by the two groups of investigators. The structures of the other cage dimers have been inferred from the fact that the dimers yield only the original quinones on pyrolysis. A third type of addition involves the attachment of the olefinic bond of one quinone to the carbonyl group of the next. Two of these have been identified.[58] These dimers

are, of course, not further convertible to cage dimers. *p*-Quinone itself undergoes dimerization only with great difficulty. Its cage dimer has been obtained by photolysis in liquid maleic anhydride.[60]

(Pentacyclo [6.4.0.0^{2,7}.0^{4,11}.0^{5,10}] dodeca-3,6,9,12-tetraone)!

A similar structure is obtained quite easily from 2,6-dimethyl-4-pyrone, while 1,4-naphthoquinone can, of course, form only the cyclobutane derivative.

[61–63]

[59]

The variation in the type of dimer obtained in solid-state dimerizations of the *p*-quinones has been interpreted in terms of the distances between the double bonds in the crystalline state.[64] Thus in one type of molecular packing in the crystal a distance of 4.03 Å exists between adjacent molecules, and cyclobutane derivatives are favored to form. Double dimerizations to form a cage have stricter spatial requirements and occur rarely when the contact distance is greater than 4.01 Å.[65] The low yield of cage dimers observed may to some extent be due to steric effects exerted by the methyl groups. In pyrone, however, the contact distance in the box between two pairs of double bonds is only 3.48 Å, whereas that between adjacent molecules in the same plane is 4.33 to 4.11 Å, and the cage structure forms preferentially.

5-6 *Fumaric and Maleic Acid Derivatives*

A considerable number of photochemical dimerizations of the derivatives of maleic and fumaric acid has been reported. The compounds undergo sensitized dimerizations with relative ease, and the stereochemistry of the dimers has been elucidated in many cases. The dimerization of the maleic anhydrides and maleimides may serve as examples.

[21,66]

$R = R' = H$; $R = H$, $R' = CH_3$; $R = R' = CH_3$

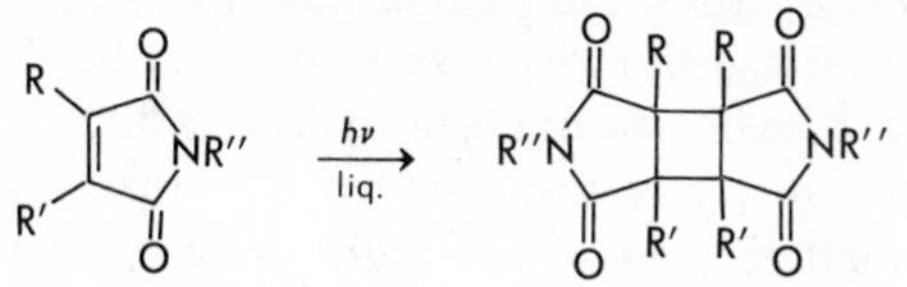

$$R = R' = CH_3, \; R'' = H; \; R = R' = H, \; R'' = C_6H_{11}, \; C_6H_5$$ [21]

Maleic anhydride itself yields two dimers on irradiation in solution, while only one of them is obtained on irradiation of the solid.

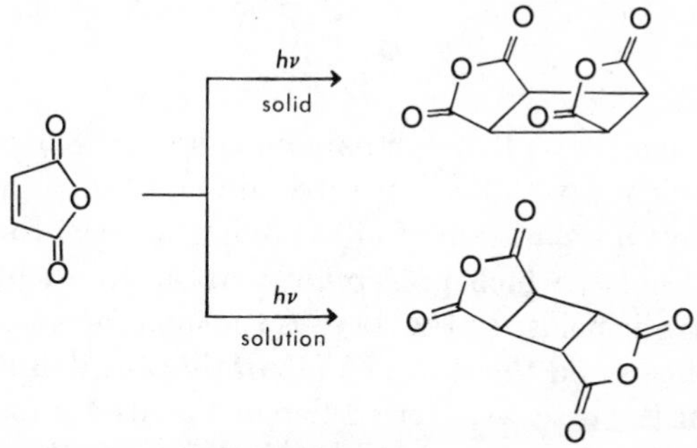

[21,66]

As mentioned previously, solid-state irradiations in general yield only one isomer, in contrast to the mixtures of isomers often obtained from solution photochemistry. The stereochemistry of the products obtained from the solid-state dimerizations of fumaric acid derivatives is apparently dependent on the molecular packing in the crystal.[51]

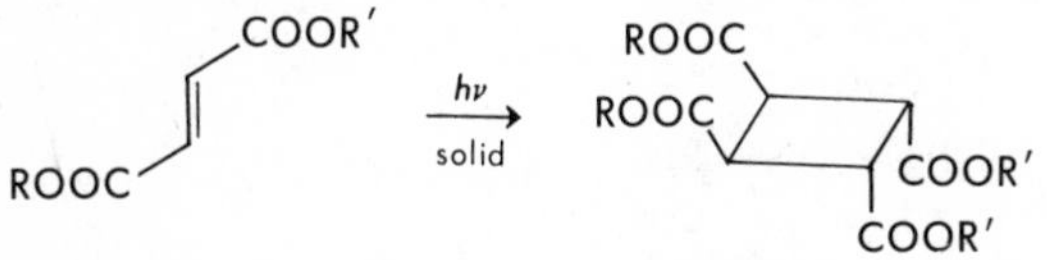

$$R = R' = CH_3$$
$$R = CH_3; \; R' = H$$

[67]

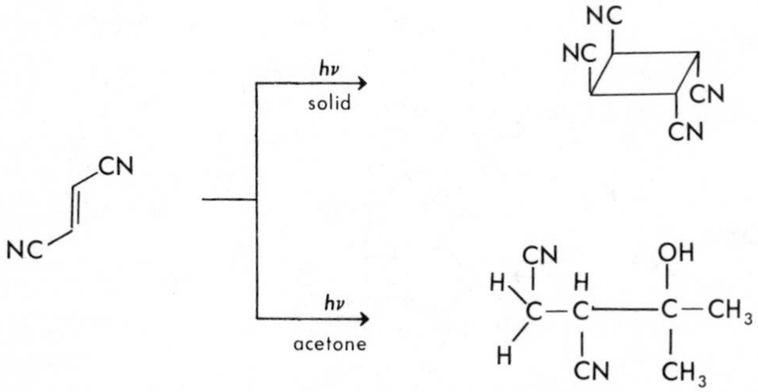

[66,68,69]

It has been mentioned before that the distance between two adjacent double bonds in the crystal is ordinarily less than 4 Å; in the case of dimethylmaleate it is 3.92 Å, while in fumaronitrile it is 3.89 Å.[70] Direct bond formation between the nearest molecules can take place until the upper limit for this distance, set at 4.0 ± 0.1 Å, has been reached.

The solid-state photochemistry of the cinnamic acids is rather complex. The *trans*-cinnamic acids crystallize in three different modifications. Of these the α types have a separation of about 3.6 Å between the double bonds of adjacent molecules, which presumably are arranged head-tail. They give rise to α-truxillic acids. In the β types the molecules lie parallel and presumably head-head and the distance separating the double bonds is about the same as in the α series. Here β-truxinic acids are formed on photolysis. The γ modifications are photochemically inert; the distance between the nearest double bonds is 4.7 to 5.1 Å, apparently too large for bond formation. The examples are an illustration of "topochemical control"; the relative geometries of the nearest neighbors in the lattice determine the molecular structure of the products and whether products form at all. At higher temperatures the β modification may convert to the α form, and α-truxillic acid will then be observed from the irradiation of the β form also.[65] Many substituted cinnamic acids and esters react;

α-Truxillic acid

β-Truxinic acid

[71,72]

the products obtained have all been related to the corresponding truxinic and truxillic acids.[73]

The fact that the cis isomer of an olefin can rearrange to the trans isomer in the solid state is unusual.[74] Presumably the rearrangement occurs via some metastable complex resembling a dimer. Such a trans-cis isomerization in the solid state has also been observed with dibenzoylethylene. Since isotope studies have demonstrated that dimerization-dissociation is not involved, the isomerization is likely to involve an excited state different from that leading to dimerization. It is thought that isomerization involves the longer-lived triplet state and that dimers form from the excited singlet state.[75] Other dimerizations, similar in nature, have been observed with β-nitrostyrene and with the quaternary salt of 2-styrylpyridine.[76,77]

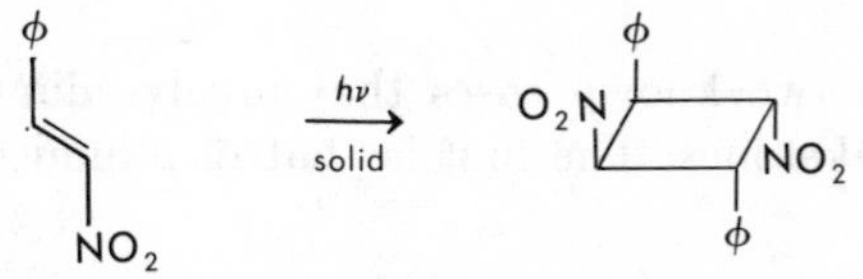

The dimer of the malonic acid derivative shown below has been related to α-truxillic acid.[78] However, the corresponding monocarboxylic acid leads to quite a different product.[79] It is clear from these examples that no predictions about the course of such solid-state reactions can be made without information concerning the crystal lattice geometry.

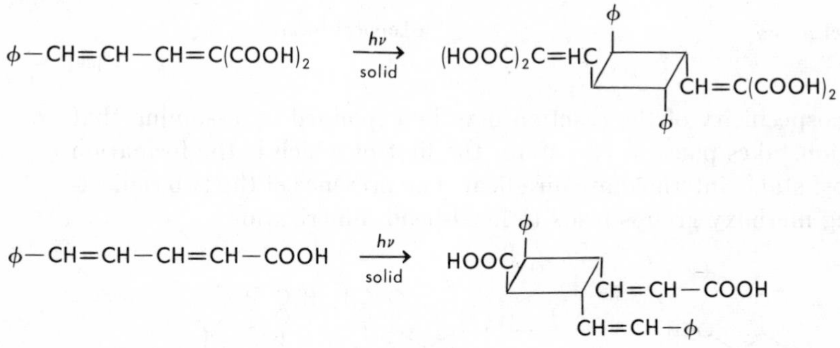

Several isomers are obtained from the irradiation of benzene solutions of *trans,trans*-methylsorbate:[100]

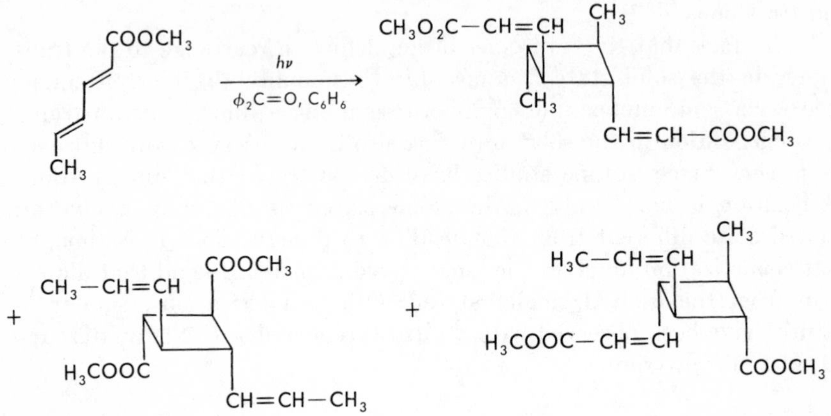

5-7 Enol Ethers

There are at least two known cases that involve dimerization of the enol ethers of 1,2-diketones. The first is that of β-lumicolchicine to form α-lumicolchicine.

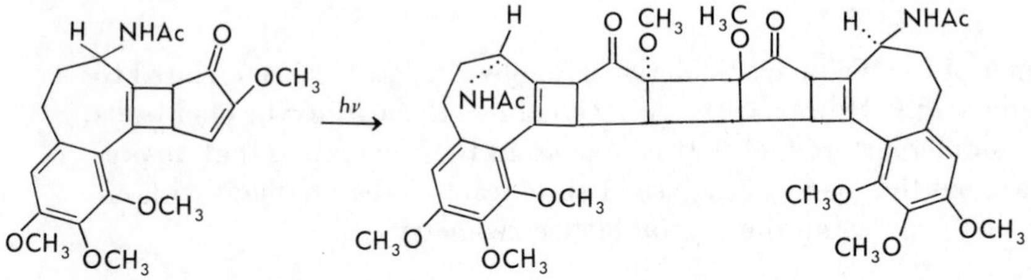

β-Lumicolchicine

α-Lumicolchicine

[80]

The stereospecificity of the reaction may be explained by assuming that the reaction takes place in two steps, the first of which is the formation of the most stable intermediate diradical. The presence of the two radical-stabilizing methoxy groups leads to head-head dimerization.

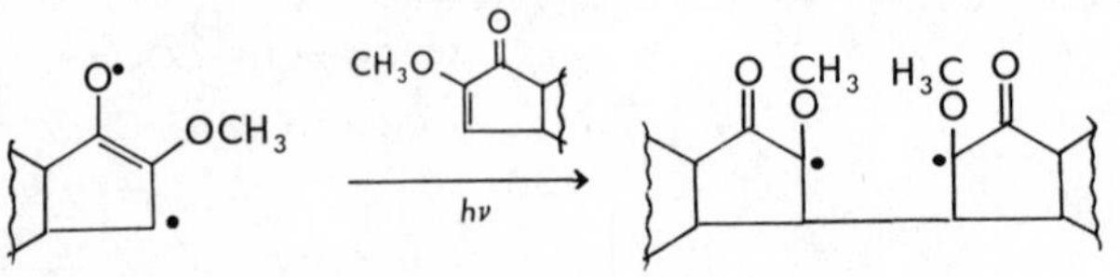

A second case of an enol ether dimerization involves the formation of rather unusual products:[81]

The first of these may be visualized to form as follows:[81]

The second product can form either by a separate photochemical process or by rearrangement of the first.

5-8   *Heterocyclic Compounds*

Among the sensitized dimerizations of heterocyclic compounds that of α-coumarin is of special interest; singlet excitation is transferred from the coumarin to the sensitizer, converted to triplet energy, and then once more transferred to the coumarin![82] Thus it is found that even when most of the light is absorbed by the coumarin, benzophenone still controls the reaction. This sensitizer also quenches the fluorescence of coumarin in benzene. The transfer of singlet excitation can occur because there is considerable overlap between the absorption spectrum of benzophenone and the emission spectrum of coumarin. That no triplet excitation transfer takes place to benzophenone is inferred from the fact that the triplet excitation energy of the latter is more than 6 kcal/mole higher than that of coumarin. Triplet coumarin combines with unexcited coumarin to form VIII and IX; VII is formed from the excited singlet.

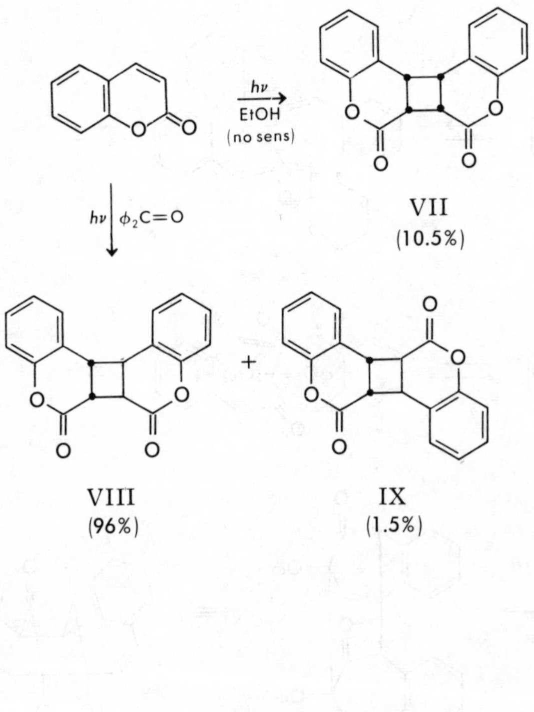

VII
(10.5%)

VIII
(96%)

+

IX
(1.5%)

[82,83]

The unsensitized dimerization of N-methyl-2-quinolone yields only the trans-head-head dimer. However, since the compound is irradiated in suspension, one might really be dealing with a solid-state irradiation.

[84]

The monocyclic analogs behave quite differently. Steric barriers to 1,4 dimerization are apparently small. 2,4-Dimethyl coumarin forms a 1,4 dimer as well as a 1,2 dimer; the latter converts on heating to a new 1,4 dimer.[85] The effect of substituents on the photochemical behavior of α-pyrones is remarkable. The compounds can undergo dimerization in two ways and can also rearrange (page 99).

The anti-trans 1,4 dimers are the only products obtained on photolysis of a larger number of 2-pyridones and 2-aminopyridines:

$R = CH_3$; C_2H_5; $n\text{-}C_3H_7$; $CH_2 = CH - CH_2$; $i\text{-}C_3H_7$; $HO - CH_2CH_2$; $(C_2H_5)_2N$; $p\text{-}CH_3OC_6H_4$
CH_3 at C_3, C_4, C_5, or C_6 [86–90]

CH_3 at C_3, C_4, C_5, or C_6 and NHR ($R = H$, CH_3, and $CH_2C_6H_5$)   [86]

The reaction of the latter group occurs only in an acidic medium. It is evident that protonation has taken place first, which, occurring at the ring nitrogen, imparts a partial diene character to the 2-aminopyridines.

The stereochemistry of these dimers has been established firmly by x-ray crystallographic studies.[90,91] This work has shown[91] that the possibility of introducing two substituents other than hydrogen at adjacent bridge-heads is rather remote. Thus, 3,6-disubstituted-2-pyridones or 2-amino-pyridines will probably have a good chance of being converted to the Dewar benzene analog of the pyridines. The synthesis of the starting materials is a formidable obstacle against verification.

In conclusion, some miscellaneous dimerizations that involve other heterocyclic compounds may be mentioned. Thiophosgene is believed to lead to the 1,3-dithiacyclobutane.

[92]

Benzothiophene forms adducts with concomitant elimination of hydrogen and hydrogen sulfide,[93,94] while benzothiophene-1-dioxide[95,96] dimerizes "normally":

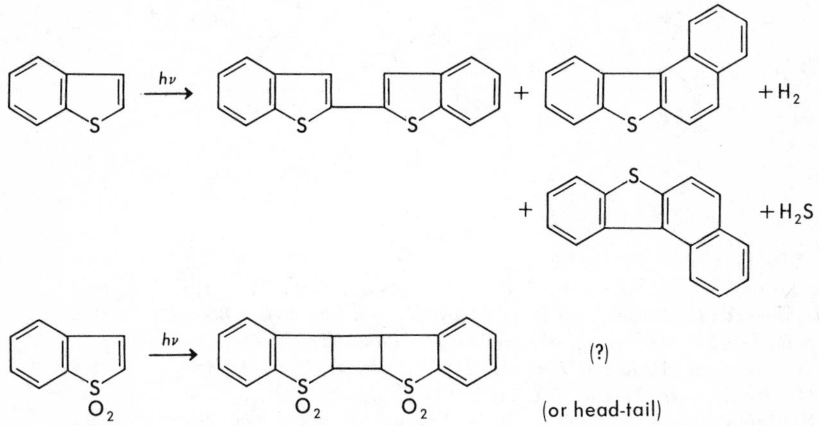

Another case of interest is the dimerization of *o*-nitrosobenzaldehyde:

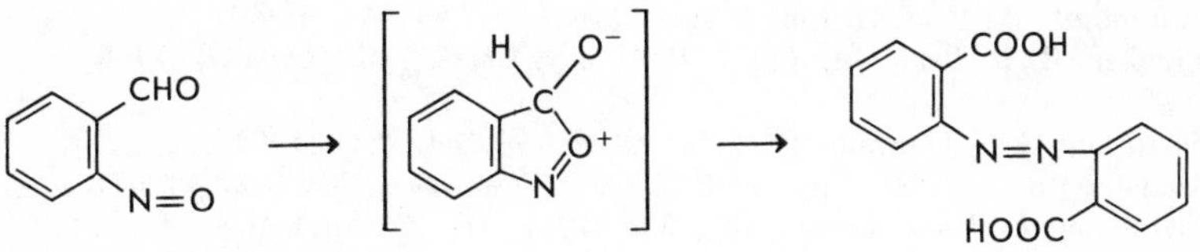

3-Benzilidene phthalide has been reported to give, upon solid-state irradiation, a dimer for which the structure shown below has been proposed.

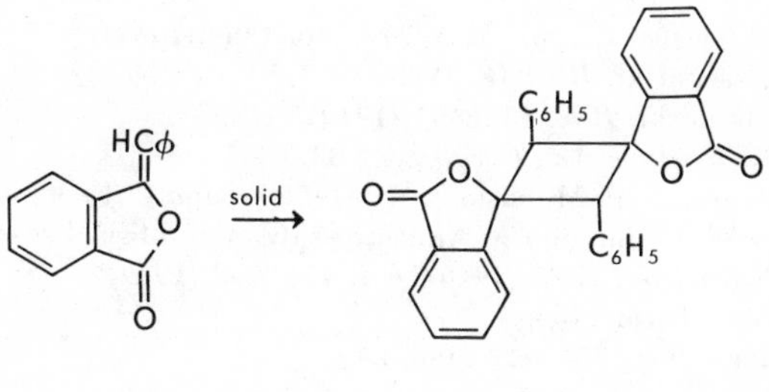

[98]

The reported dimerization of a pseudoxazolone takes a similar course:

[99]

References

1. A. Mustafa, *Chem. Rev.*, **51**, 1 (1951).
2. P. de Mayo, R. W. Yip, and S. T. Reid, *Proc. Chem. Soc.*, **1963**, 54; E. J. Corey, J. D. Bass, R. LeMahieu, and R. B. Mitra, *J. Am. Chem. Soc.*, **86**, 5570 (1964).
3. D. Scharf and F. Korte, *Tetrahedron Letters*, **1963**, 821.
4. H. D. Scharf and F. Korte, *Ber.*, **97**, 2425 (1964).
5. H. H. Stechl, *Angew. Chem.*, **75**, 1176 (1963).
6. G. S. Hammond, N. J. Turro, and A. Fischer, *J. Am. Chem. Soc.*, **83**, 4674 (1961).
7. G. S. Hammond, N. J. Turro, and R. S. H. Liu, *J. Org. Chem.*, **28**, 3297 (1963); R. S. H. Liu, N. J. Turro, and G. S. Hammond, *J. Am. Chem. Soc.*, **87**, 3406 (1965).
8. D. Valentine, N. J. Turro, Jr., and G. S. Hammond, *J. Am. Chem. Soc.*, **86**, 5202 (1964).
9. G. S. Hammond and R. S. H. Liu, *J. Am. Chem. Soc.*, **85**, 477 (1963).
10. D. J. Trecker, R. L. Brandon, and J. P. Henry, *Chem. Ind. (London)*, **1963**, 652.
11. N. J. Turro and G. S. Hammond, *J. Am. Chem. Soc.*, **84**, 2841 (1962).
12. J. S. Bradshaw and G. S. Hammond, *J. Am. Chem. Soc.*, **85**, 3953 (1963).
13. C. J. Fritzsche, *J. Prakt. Chem.*, **101**, 333 (1867); D. E. Applequist, E. C. Friedrich, and M. T. Rogers, *J. Am. Chem. Soc.*, **81**, 457 (1959); R. Calas, R. Lalonde, J. G. Faugere, and F. Moulines, *Bull. Soc. Chim. France*, **1965**, 119, 121.
14. A. Fischer and H. Ziegler, *J. Prakt. Chem.*, [2], **86**, 289 (1912).
15. F. D. Greene, S. L. Misrock, and J. R. Wolfe, Jr., *J. Am. Chem. Soc.*, **77**, 3853 (1955).
15a. Chap. 3, ref 1a.
16. R. Huisgen, *Ann.*, **564**, 16 (1949).
17. D. E. Applequist and R. Searle, *J. Am. Chem. Soc.*, **86**, 1389 (1964).
18. K. Dziewónski and C. Paschalski, *Ber.*, **46**, 1986 (1913).
19. K. Dziewónski and G. Rapalski, *Ber.*, **45**, 2491 (1912).
20. G. W. Griffin and D. F. Veber, *J. Am. Chem. Soc.*, **82**, 6417 (1960).
21. G. O. Schenck, W. Hartmann, S. P. Mannsfeld, W. Metzner, and C. H. Krauch, *Ber.*, **95**, 1642 (1962); G. W. Griffin and A. Annastrassiov, unpublished results.
22. J. D. Fulton, *Brit. J. Pharmacol.*, **3**, 75 (1948), *CA*, **43**, 2982 (1949).
23. A. J. Henry, *J. Chem. Soc.*, **1946**, 1156.
24. G. Ciamician and P. Silber, *Ber.*, **35**, 4128 (1902).

25. J. D. Fulton and J. D. Dunitz, *Nature*, **160**, 161 (1947); H. Stobbe, *Ber.*, **47**, 2701 (1914).
26. H. Shechter and R. O. Uhler, *Dissertation Abstr.*, **21**, 765 (1960); R. O. Uhler, H. Shechter, and G. V. D. Tiers, *J. Am. Chem. Soc.*, **84**, 3397 (1962).
27. H. P. Throndsen, P. J. Wheatley, and H. Zeiss, *Proc. Chem. Soc.*, **1964**, 357.
28. G. Büchi, C. W. Perry, and E. W. Robb, *J. Org. Chem.*, **27**, 4106 (1962).
29. D. Bryce-Smith and J. E. Lodge, *J. Chem. Soc.*, **1963**, 695.
30. P. E. Eaton, *J. Am. Chem. Soc.*, **84**, 2344 (1962).
31. P. E. Eaton, *J. Am. Chem. Soc.*, **84**, 2454 (1962).
32. O. L. Chapman and S. L. Smith, *J. Org. Chem.*, **27**, 2291 (1962).
33. P. E. Eaton, unpublished results.
34. W. Treibs, *J. Prakt. Chem.*, **138**, 299 (1933).
35. W. Treibs, *Ber.*, **63**, 2738 (1930).
36. H. Ziffer, N. E. Sharpless, and R. O. Kan, in press.
37. G. Büchi and I. M. Goldman, *J. Am. Chem. Soc.*, **79**, 4741 (1957).
38. P. E. Eaton and K. Lin, *J. Am. Chem. Soc.*, **86**, 2087 (1964).
39. A. Butenandt and L. Poschmann, *Ber.*, **73**, 893 (1940).
40. M. B. Rubin, G. E. Hipps, and D. Glover, *J. Org. Chem.*, **29**, 68 (1964).
41. H. P. Throndsen, G. Cainelli, D. Arigoni, and O. Jeger, *Helv. Chim. Acta*, **45**, 2342 (1962).
42. M. B. Rubin, D. Glover, and R. G. Parker, *Tetrahedron Letters*, **1964**, 1075.
43. A. Butenandt, L. Karlson-Poschmann, G. Failer, U. Schiedt, and E. Biekert, *Ann.*, **575**, 123 (1952).
44. H. O. House, *J. Org. Chem.*, **23**, 1374 (1959).
45. I. Tanasescu and F. Hodosan, *CA*, **50**, 14628 (1956).
46. H. Stobbe and K. Bremer, *J. Prakt. Chem.*, **123**, 1 (1929).
47. H. Stobbe and A. Hensel, *Ber.*, **59**, 2254 (1926).
48. G. Ciamician and P. Silber, *Ber.*, **42**, 1386 (1909); P. Praetorius and F. Korn, *Ber.*, **43**, 2744 (1910).
49. G. W. Recktenwald, J. N. Pitts, Jr., and R. L. Letsinger, *J. Am. Chem. Soc.*, **75**, 3028 (1953).
50. G. Kornis and P. de Mayo, *Can. J. Chem.*, **42**, 2822 (1964); P. de Mayo and A. Stoessl, *Can. J. Chem.*, **40**, 57 (1962).
51. M. D. Cohen and G. M. J. Schmidt, *J. Chem. Soc.*, **1964**, 1996.
52. J. Corse, B. J. Finkle, and R. E. Lundin, *Tetrahedron Letters*, **1**, 1 (1960).
53. H. Stobbe and E. Färber, *Ber.*, **58**, 1548 (1925).
54. F. Straus, *Ber.*, **37**, 3293 (1904).
55. M. Bakunim and E. Lanis, *Gazz. Chim. Ital.*, **41**, II, 155 (1911).
56. R. C. Cookson and J. Hudec, *Proc. Chem. Soc.*, **1959**, 11; R. C. Cookson, D. A. Cox, and J. Hudec, *J. Chem. Soc.*, **1962**, 1717.
57. W. Flaig, J. C. Salfeld, and A. Llanos, *Angew. Chem.*, **72**, 110 (1960).
58. R. C. Cookson, J. J. Frankel, and J. Hudec, *Chem. Commun.*, **1965**, 16.
59. A. Schönberg, A. Mustafa, M. Z. Barakat, N. Latif, R. Moubasher, and Mrs. A. Mustafa, *J. Chem. Soc.*, **1948**, 2126.
60. D. Bryce-Smith and A. Gilbert, *J. Chem. Soc.*, **1964**, 2428.
61. E. Paterno, *Gazz. Chim. Ital.*, **44**, 151 (1914).
62. M. Giua and M. Civera, *Gazz. Chim. Ital.*, **81**, 875 (1951).
63. P. Yates and M. J. Jorgenson, *J. Am. Chem. Soc.*, **80**, 6150 (1958).
64. D. Rabinovich and G. M. J. Schmidt, *J. Chem. Soc.*, **1964**, 2030.
65. M. D. Cohen, G. M. J. Schmidt, and F. I. Sonntag, *J. Chem. Soc.*, **1964**, 2000.
66. G. W. Griffin, J. E. Basinski, and A. F. Vellturo, *Tetrahedron Letters* **3**, 13 (1960).

67. G. W. Griffin, A. F. Vellturo, and K. Furukama, *J. Am. Chem. Soc.*, **83**, 2725 (1961).
68. G. W. Griffin, R. B. Hager, and D. F. Veber, *J. Am. Chem. Soc.*, **84**, 1008 (1962).
69. G. W. Griffin, J. E. Basinski, and L. I. Peterson, *J. Am. Chem. Soc.*, **84**, 1012 (1962).
70. T. Sadeh and G. M. J. Schmidt, *J. Am. Chem. Soc.*, **84**, 3970 (1962).
71. G. M. J. Schmidt, *Acta Cryst.*, **10**, 793 (1957).
72. H. I. Bernstein and W. C. Quimby, *J. Am. Chem. Soc.*, **65**, 1845 (1943).
73. G. M. J. Schmidt, *J. Chem. Soc.*, **1964**, 2014.
74. J. Bregman, K. Osaki, G. M. J. Schmidt, and F. I. Sonntag, *J. Chem. Soc.*, **1964**, 2021.
75. G. W. Griffin, E. J. O'Connell, and J. M. Kelliher, *Proc. Chem. Soc.*, **1964**, 337.
76. D. B. Miller and H. Shechter, *Abstract of Papers*, Am. Chem. Soc., April, 1958, 79N.
77. J. L. R. Williams, S. K. Webster, and J. A. Van Allan, *J. Org. Chem.*, **26**, 4893 (1961).
78. C. N. Rüber, *Ber.*, **35**, 2411 (1902).
79. C. N. Rüber, *Ber.*, **46**, 335 (1913).
80. O. L. Chapman, H. G. Smith, and R. W. King, *J. Am. Chem. Soc.*, **85**, 806 (1963).
81. O. L. Chapman, H. G. Smith, R. W. King, D. J. Pasto, and M. R. Stone, *J. Am. Chem. Soc.*, **85**, 2031 (1963).
82. G. S. Hammond, C. A. Stout, and A. A. Lamola, *J. Am. Chem. Soc.*, **86**, 3103 (1964).
83. G. O. Schenck, I. V. Wilucki, and C. H. Krauch, *Ber.*, **95**, 1409 (1962).
84. E. C. Taylor and W. W. Paudler, *Tetrahedron Letters*, No. **25**, 1 (1960); O. Buchardt, *Acta Chem. Scand.*, **18**. 1389 (1964).
85. P. de Mayo and R. W. Yip, *Proc. Chem. Soc.*, **1964**, 84.
86. E. C. Taylor and R. O. Kan, *J. Am. Chem. Soc.*, **85**, 776 (1963).
87. W. A. Ayer, P. Hayatsu, P. de Mayo, S. T. Reid, and J. B. Stothers, *Tetrahedron Letters*, **1961**, 648.
88. G. Slomp, F. A. MacKellar, and L. A. Paquette, *J. Am. Chem. Soc.*, **83**, 4472 (1961).
89. L. A. Paquette and G. Slomp, *J. Am. Chem. Soc.*, **85**, 765 (1963).
90. M. Laing, *Proc. Chem. Soc.*, **1964**, 343.
91. R. A. Jacobson and B. Gorres, private communication.
92. J. I. Jones, W. Kynaston, and J. L. Hales, *J. Chem. Soc.*, 614 (1957).
93. W. E. Haines, G. L. Cook, and J. S. Ball, *J. Am. Chem. Soc.*, **78**, 5213 (1956).
94. W. E. Haines, R. V. Helm, G. L. Cook, and J. S. Ball, Jr., *J. Phys. Chem.*, **60**, 549 (1956).
95. W. Davies and F. C. James, *J. Chem. Soc.*, **1955**, 314.
96. A. Mustafa, *Nature*, **175**, 992 (1955).
97. W. Ried and M. Wilk, *Ann.*, **590**, 91 (1954).
98. M. J. Jorgenson, *J. Org. Chem.*, **28**, 2929 (1963).
99. R. Filler and E. J. Piasek, *J. Org. Chem.*, **28**, 221 (1963).
100. H. P. Kaufmann and A. K. S. Gupta, *Ann.*, **681**, 39 (1965).

6

Mixed Additions

6-1 The Formation of Cyclobutane Rings

From the abundance of photochemical dimerizations presented in Chap. 5 one may expect that mixed bimolecular additions of an almost endless variety should be possible. Such is indeed the case; combinations are known of olefins, α,β-unsaturated ketones, saturated ketones, quinones, and aromatic compounds. It would seem that each photochemical combination would lead to a vast array of products, considering the possibilities for autoadditions of each of the substrates and the variety of structural and stereoisomerism that can be displayed by each adduct. However, the two components in the addition reactions usually have widely different reactivities both toward excitation and toward attack on or by excited states; the high degree of orientation and stereospecificity displayed during the addition step often precludes the formation of more than one or two isomers.

α,β-Unsaturated ketones and their derivatives add to a variety of olefins and acetylenes in reactions that closely resemble the dimerizations discussed in Chap. 5 involving the conjugated carbonyl system.[1] Thus, cyclopentenone, upon irradiation in the presence of dimethylacetylene, yields the expected bicyclic system, which itself can undergo subsequent rearrangement (page 45).

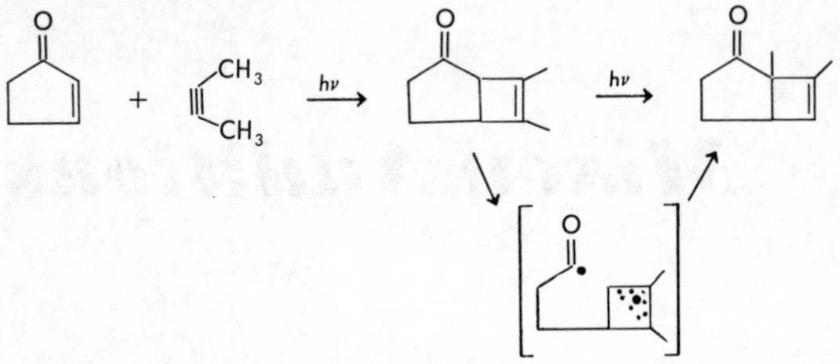

[2,3]

Three other examples, giving an indication of the wide choice of addends available, are shown below:†

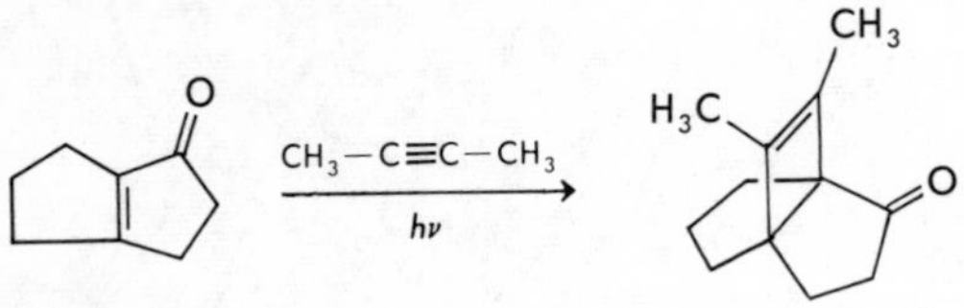

[4]

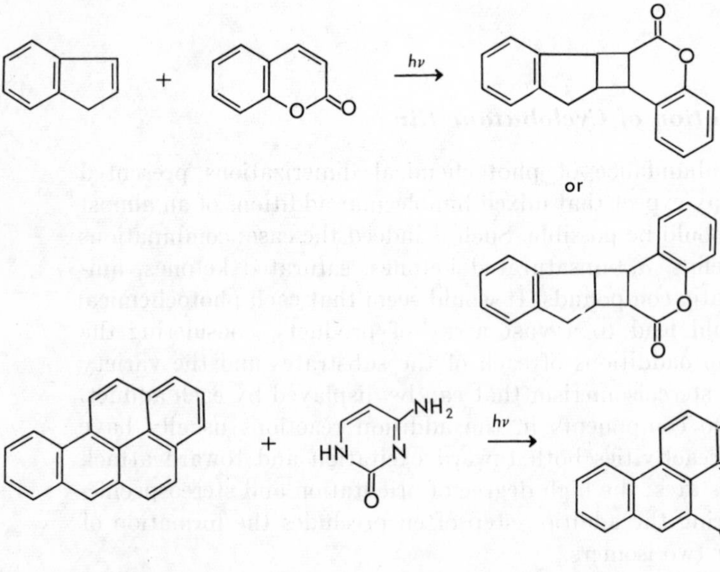

or

[5]

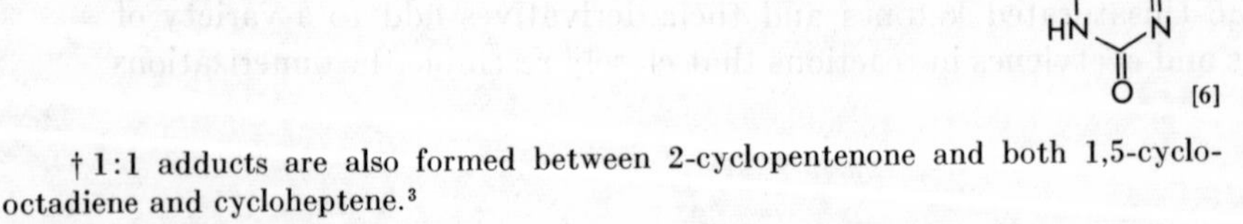

[6]

† 1:1 adducts are also formed between 2-cyclopentenone and both 1,5-cyclo-octadiene and cycloheptene.[3]

The addition of olefins to 1,3-diketones, or their enol esters, is frequently followed by a reverse aldol condensation. Thus, cyclohexene adds to acetylacetone, with subsequent adduct rearrangement in the following manner:

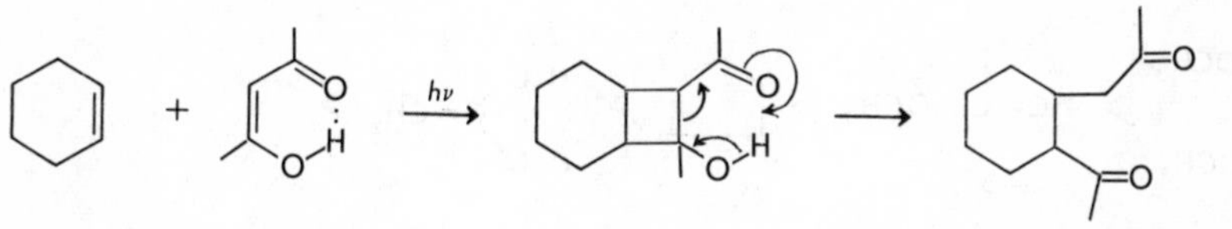

[7]

This type of addition has the potential of being of considerable synthetic utility; it may serve as a general method of ring syntheses. Other examples may be found in refs. 8 and 9.

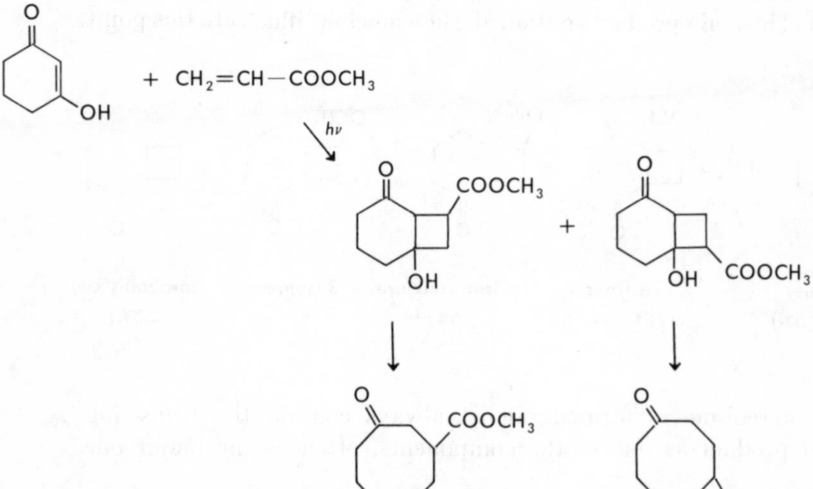

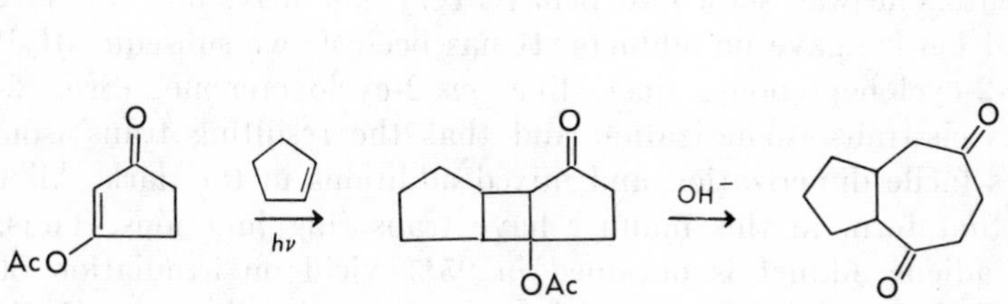

[9]

The first systematic study of the addition of olefins to enones has been made by Corey and coworkers.[10] Using 2-cyclohexenone, they studied the orientation of olefin additions, the stereochemistry of the adducts, and the relative reactivities of a series of olefins. The following three trends became apparent:

1.   The reactivity of olefins is in the following order:

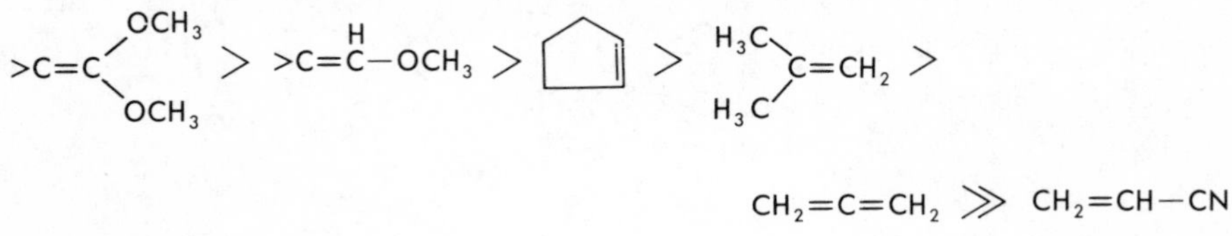

$$CH_2=C=CH_2 \gg CH_2=CH-CN$$

(It may be seen that the presence of electron-donating groups at the double bond facilitates addition.)

2.   The orientation is always such that the α-carbon of 2-cyclohexenone becomes attached to the most nucleophilic carbon of the double bond. The main products obtained, shown below, illustrate this point.

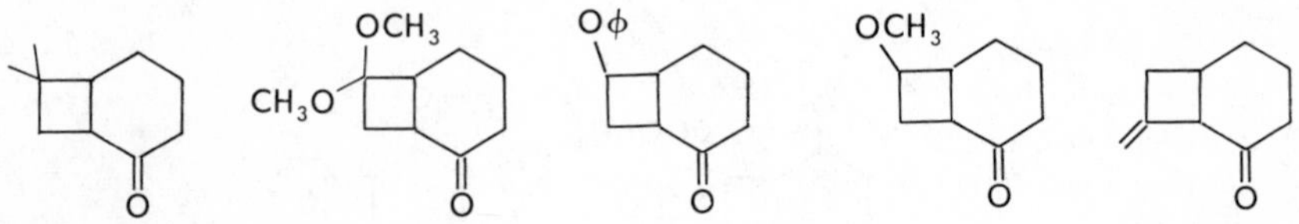

cis:trans	cis:trans	cis-trans mixture	3 isomers	(probably cis)
(6.5% : 26.5%)	(21% : 49%)	(65%)		(55%)

3.   The stereoisomers formed almost always contain the trans-ring-fused product as one of the components, often as the major one.

The effect of the ring size of the cyclic ketones was also studied; 2-cyclopentenone was shown to behave very similarly, but the seven-membered ketone gave no adducts. It has been shown subsequently[11,12] that *cis*-2-cycloheptenone, just like *cis*-2-cyclooctenone (Sec. 2-1) undergoes cis-trans isomerization and that the resulting trans isomer undergoes facile dimerization and mixed additions in the dark. All the adducts that form in this manner have trans ring junctions. Thus, a cyclopentadiene adduct is obtained in 95% yield on irradiation of a mixture of *cis*-2-cycloheptenone with an excess of the diene at $-50°C$;[12] the two furan adducts, to which the stereochemistry shown below has been assigned,[11] form in a similar fashion:

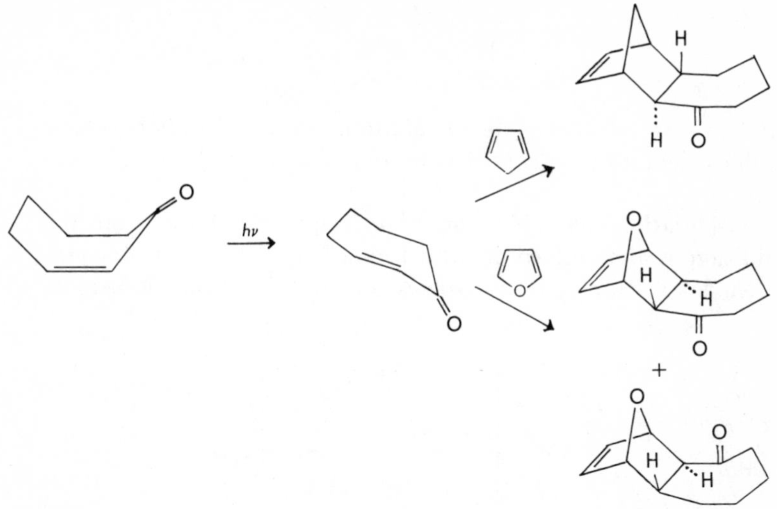

The same product mixture is obtained from 2-cyclohexenone with either *cis*- or *trans*-2-butene,[10] which indicates that no one-step addition of the enone to the unactivated olefin occurs. Finally, in determining the effect of substituents on the enone double bond, it was found (qualitatively) that 3-methyl-2-cyclohexenone reacts at about the same rate as the unsubstituted ketone but that the product orientation and identity

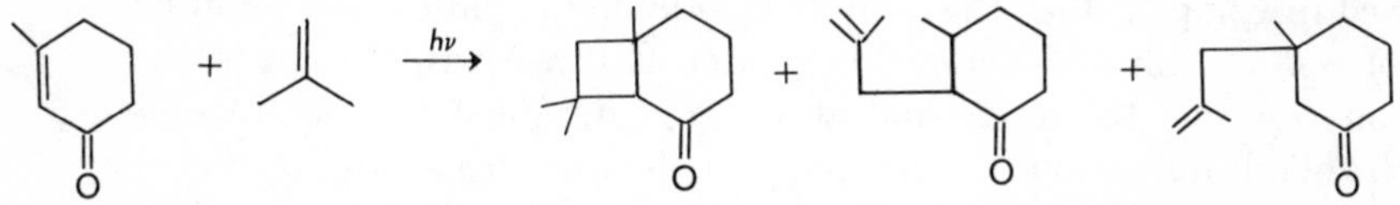

differ. 2-Methyl-2-cyclohexenone is much less reactive, yielding complex mixtures on photolysis with olefins. From the results presented above, one cannot conclusively establish the mechanism of the additions but one can exclude certain possibilities. Thus, the stereochemistry of the products is incompatible with four-centered additions or specific cis additions; that the cis and trans fused adducts do not arise from different excited forms of the enone seems apparent from the consistency of the cis/trans ratios obtained, even in the presence of other olefins. Insofar as the facts might point to a two-step addition, with the intermediacy of diradicals of the type shown here, it is seen that their relative stabilities do not control the mode of addition; in the 2-cyclohexenone adducts, the orientation is contrary to the relative stability of such diradicals.

These considerations have led Corey[10] to suggest that the geometry in the addition is determined by the formation of a donor (olefin)–acceptor (enone) π complex that involves the *excited state* of the ketone.

(Spectroscopic data provide no evidence for the existence of donor-acceptor complexes in the ground state.) Then, making use of the fact, discussed in Chap. 4, that the relative charge density in the $n-\pi^*$ excited state of α,β-unsaturated ketones is greater at the β-carbon than at the α-carbon (relative to the ground state), the diradical formed by subsequent bond formation in the complex follows from the predicted geometry of the complex. (It is admitted that the identity of the excited state has by no means been established with certainty to be of the $n-\pi^*$ type.)

It is doubtful that such a mechanism can explain or predict the orientation observed in dimerizations, because even though the excited complexes or excimers may have a preferred geometry, like addends have much less tendency to form such charge-transfer complexes. Neither does it allow a distinction between oxetane and cyclobutane formation.

The addition of β-nitrostyrene to olefins[13] such as cyclohexene, 1,1-diphenylethylene, and styrene is stereospecific in that the phenyl and the nitro group derived from β-nitrostyrene (which apparently adds only as the trans isomer) are situated trans to each other in all cases examined.

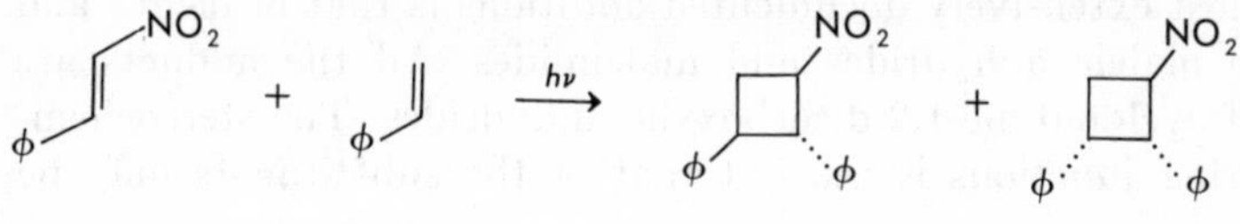

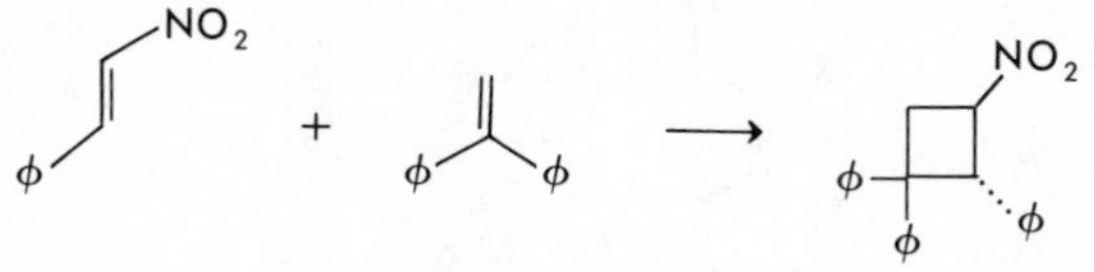

(only one isomer formed)

The phenyl group of the nitrostyrene and the phenyl groups of styrene or 1,1-diphenylethylene become located at adjacent positions in the adduct. Such a preferential orientation may possibly find its origin in the following mechanism:

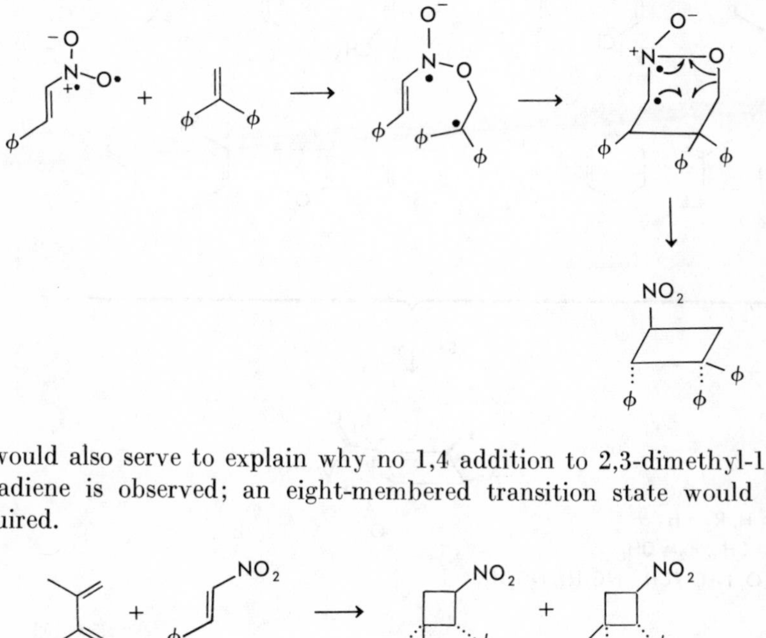

It would also serve to explain why no 1,4 addition to 2,3-dimethyl-1,3-butadiene is observed; an eight-membered transition state would be required.

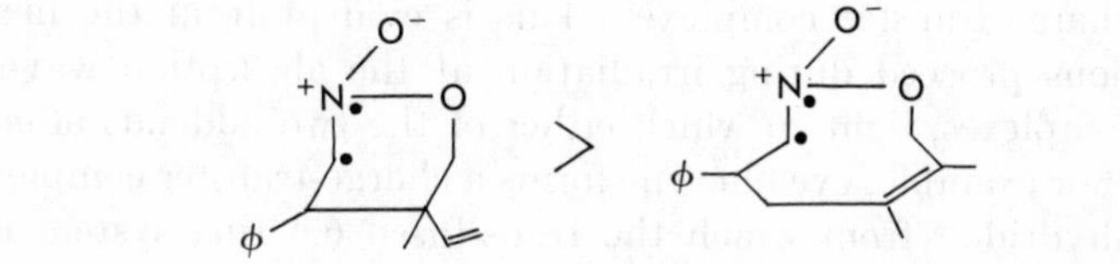

One of the most extensively documented additions is that of olefins and acetylenes to maleic anhydrides and maleimides. All the adducts are derivatives of cyclobutane-1,2-dicarboxylic anhydrides. The stereochemistry of the ring junctions is cis, but that of the substituents may be trans:

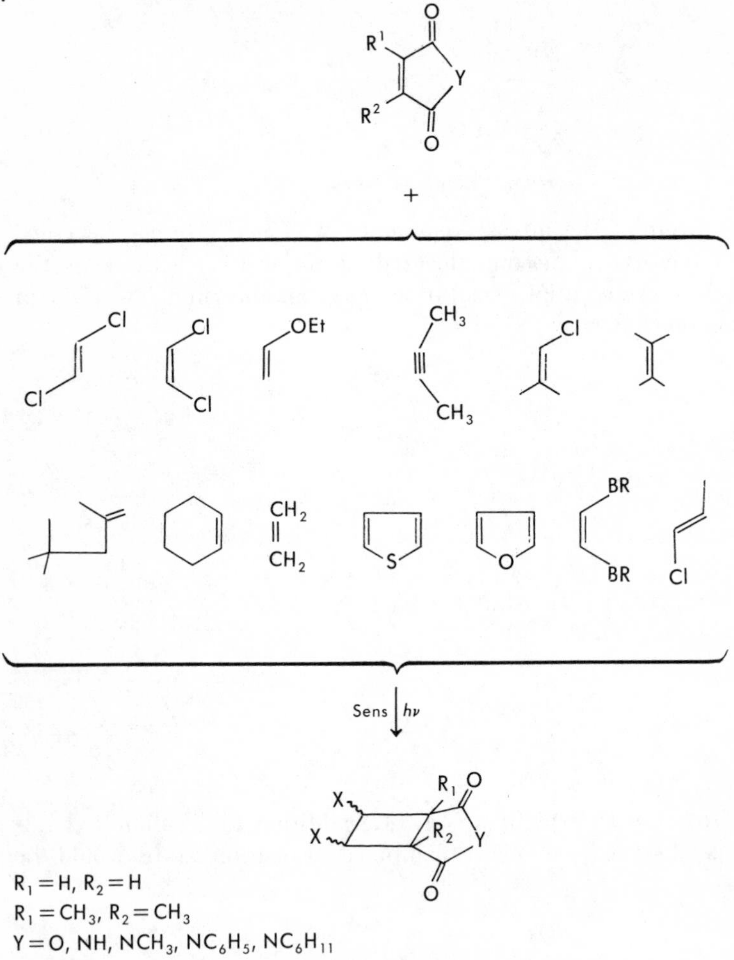
R¹
R²
O
Y
O
+
Cl
Cl
Cl
Cl
OEt
CH3
CH3
Cl
BR
BR
Cl
CH2
CH2
S
O
Sens
hν
X
X
R1
R2
O
Y
O
R1 = H, R2 = H
R1 = CH3, R2 = CH3
Y = O, NH, NCH3, NC6H5, NC6H11

[5,14,15]

Many of these additions apparently take place through intermediate, ground-state, charge-transfer complexes. This is evident from the fact that the additions proceed during irradiation at the absorption wavelength of the complexes, light to which either of the two addends alone is transparent. For example, cyclohexene forms a charge-transfer complex with maleic anhydride[16] from which the trans-fused 6,4 ring system is one of the several products found.

[17]

Similar complexes are involved in the additions to maleo- and fumaro-nitriles,[16,17] but dimethyl maleate forms no such complexes, as deduced from spectral information and the constancy of the quantum yield over

a wide spectral range (254 to 290 mμ).[8] Its additions are due to activation of the dimethyl maleate alone. While the adducts formed through the intermediacy of π complexes display a certain degree of stereospecificity in that only a few of the possible stereoisomers are formed, most of the possible adducts are obtained from dimethyl maleate:

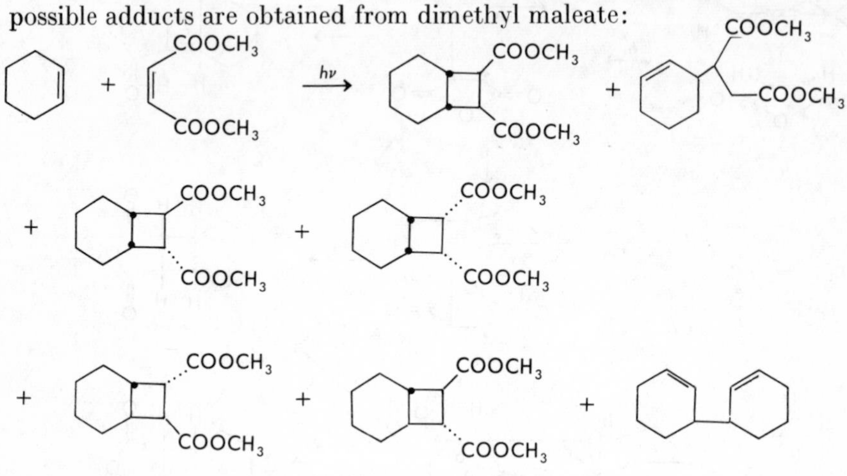

+ polymer   [16,18,8]

Substituted quinones add to a variety of olefins to yield related derivatives.[19] A dual addition to dienes, whereby cage structures are formed, may occur.[20] A few of the products from such reactions are shown below:

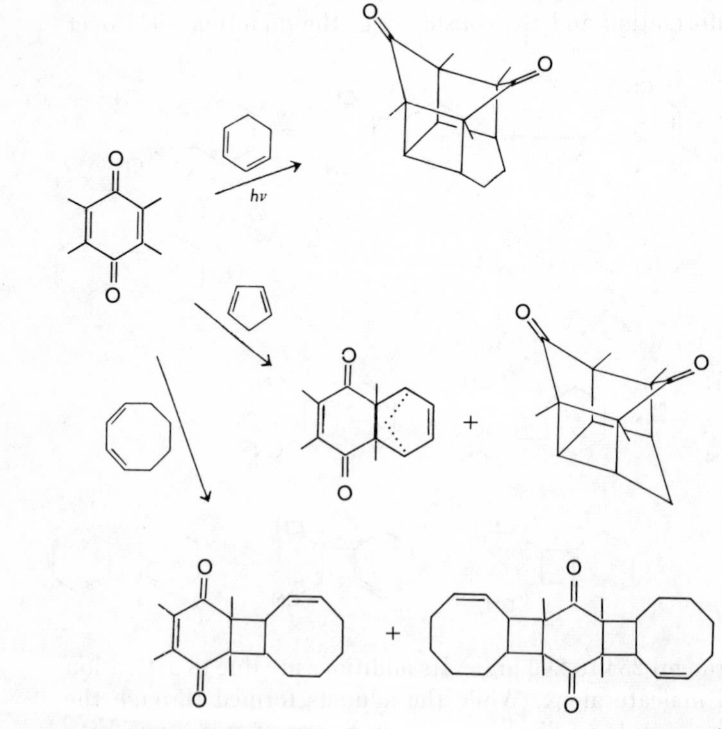

Alternate modes of addition include the formation of oxetanes (Sec. 6-3).

6-2 Additions to Aromatic Systems

The photochemistry of benzene has received only scant attention during the last two decades, mainly because earlier investigators thought that the compound was photochemically inactive. Later it was found that, on irradiation of benzene under an atmosphere of nitrogen at 50°, some fulvene is formed.[21]

Subsequently the formation of an adduct with maleic anhydride was discovered. This adduct contains one molecule of benzene for every two molecules of the anhydride.[22–25] It is formed both in the presence and absence of sensitizers,[24,26] although the unsensitized process is much less efficient. The sensitized reaction is inhibited by oxygen, and it has been demonstrated[28] that the triplet state of the sensitizer is involved. Oxygen inhibition is not observed in unsensitized additions of maleic anhydride, which has led to the conclusion that this addition is one involving the singlet state.[26] Both reactions probably proceed through a charge-transfer complex of benzene and maleic anhydride. It is not known with certainty whether the second maleic anhydride addition is photochemical or takes place by a dark reaction; there is evidence that the addition of the first molecule of maleic anhydride is rate-determining.[27] Although the structure of the adduct is now taken

to be as shown, there has been a considerable amount of discussion on the subject.[22,23,30] Maleic anhydride forms similar 2:1 adducts with some substituted benzenes (toluene, *t*-butylbenzene, chlorobenzene, *o*-and *p*-xylene, etc.), but their rate of formation is less than that with benzene itself because of a combination of steric and electronic factors. Highly substituted benzenes, such as durene, and those which form no charge-transfer complexes (such as benzonitrile), undergo no addition at all.[27]

Condensed aromatic compounds form only 1:1 adducts with maleic anhydride; when the site of addition has appreciable olefinic character, cyclobutane derivatives are formed. Thus phenanthrene yields a 1:2 adduct,[31] while naphthalene forms a Diels-Alder adduct on photolysis with the anhydride:[32]

The last reaction shown leads to a variety of isomers the detailed structure of which is not definitely known. The significance in the study of such processes lies in the possibility of providing clues for the mechanism of the Diels-Alder reaction itself. There is a lively debate about whether the reaction proceeds via a diradical mechanism or through a dipolar process. Simons[33] has related the two types of mechanisms to the multiplicity of the excited state in the photochemical additions, arguing that the triplet state in polyatomic molecules such as anthracene is a true diradical, whereas the singlet state should have a dipolar character, undergoing addition by dipole-dipole interaction. The Diels-Alder reaction of anthracene and maleic anhydride is enhanced by light. Since maleic anhydride rapidly quenches the fluorescence of anthracene, there

should be no time for intersystem crossing before addition occurs, and a singlet state must be involved, suggesting that the "photochemical Diels-Alder addition," in this case, is of a dipolar nature.

Benzene also combines photochemically with derivatives of acetylene. The products, unstable valence-bond tautomers of cyclooctatetraenes, can rearrange to the latter and do not undergo a second, Diels-Alder type of addition.[29,34] (Mechanistic details for the second of these

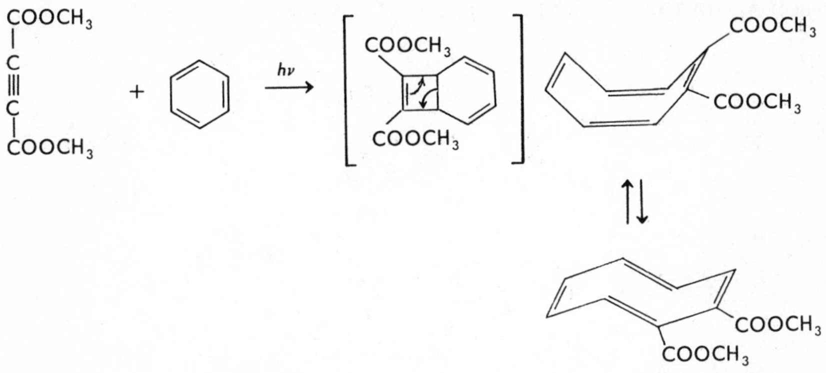

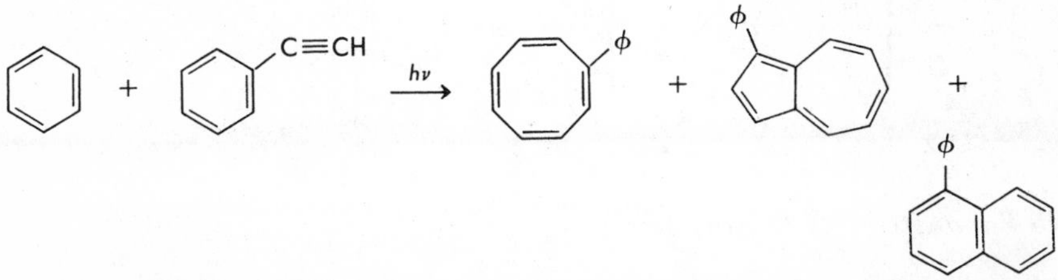

examples are similar to those given in Sec. 5-3 for the polymerization of tolane.) These reactions are reversible, as demonstrated by the irradiation of 1,2,4,7-tetraphenylcyclooctatetraene, as well as cyclooctatetraene itself.

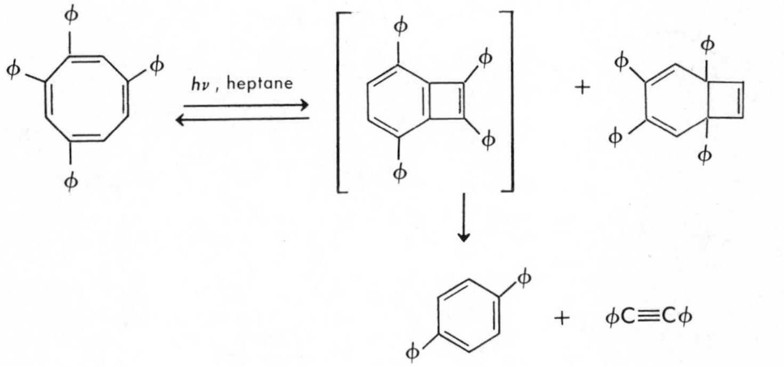

[35]

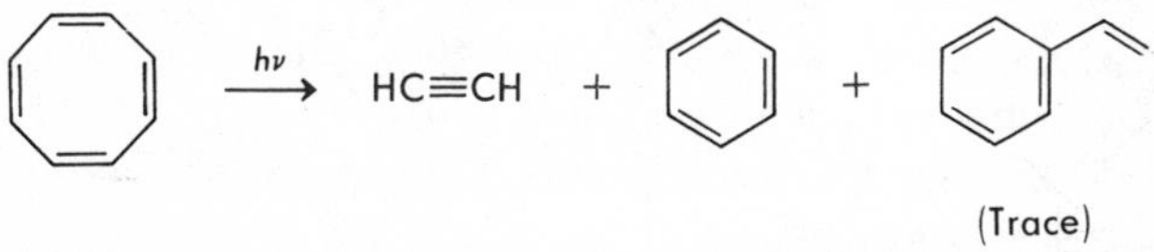

[36,37]

Benzonitrile is photochemically a very reactive substituted benzene. The nitrile group activates the ring in a variety of photochemical addition reactions but is itself inert, a somewhat surprising result considering the great reactivity of the carbonyl group in aryl ketones.

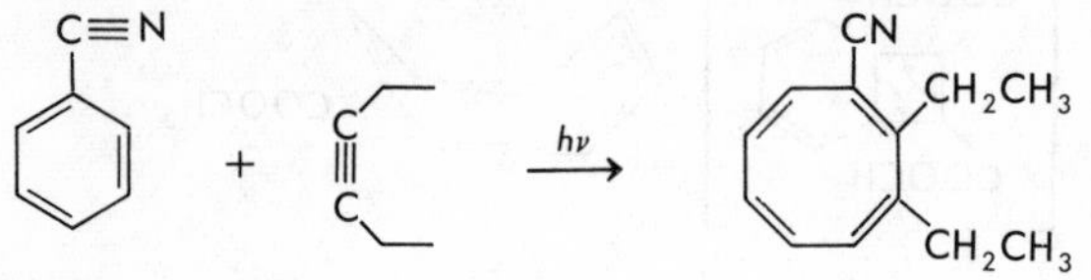

[38]

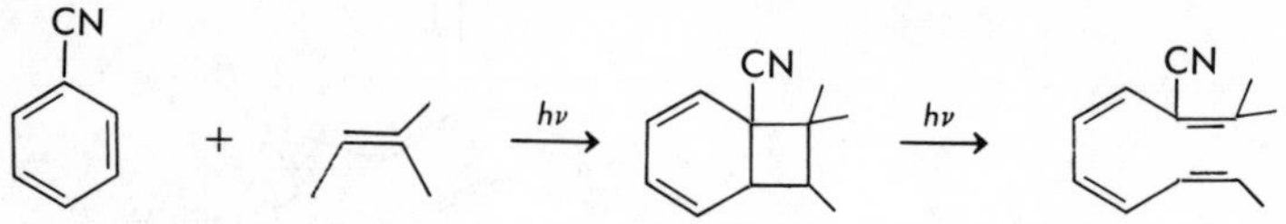

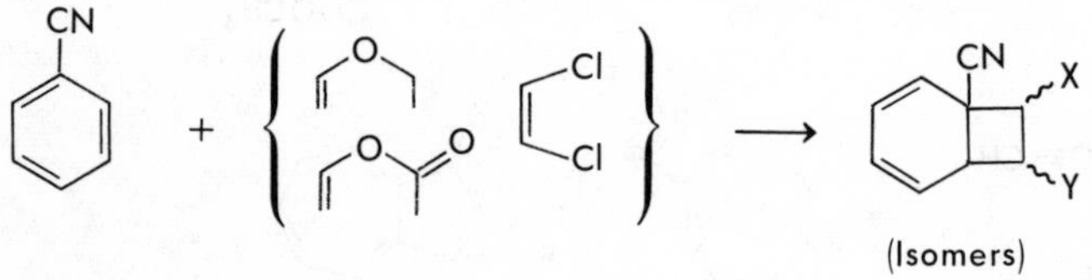

(Isomers)

[38,39]

6-3   The Formation of Oxetanes

Carbonyl compounds may form oxetanes on irradiation in the presence of olefins; the addition is often referred to as the Paterno-Büchi reaction.[40] Aromatic and aliphatic ketones and aldehydes undergo the reaction readily.[41]

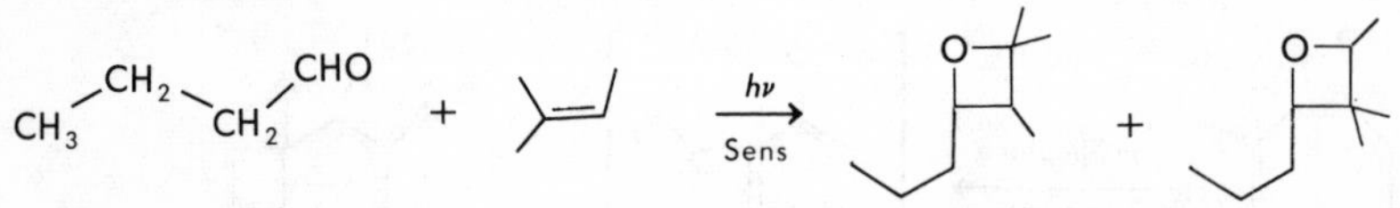

[42]

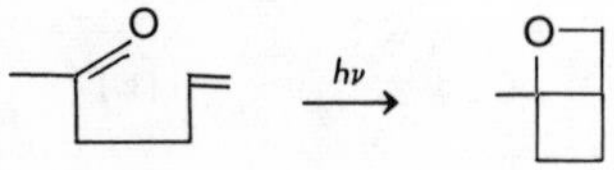

[43]

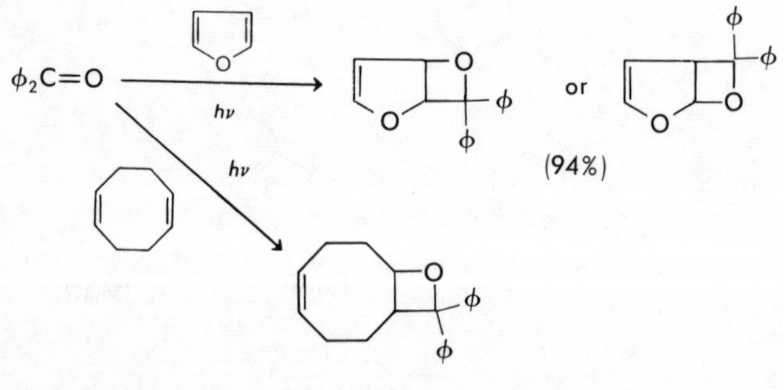

(94%)

[14,44]

However, there is wide variation in the quantum yields,[44] the chemical yields of oxetanes, and the stereospecificity observed in going from benzophenone or benzaldehyde to 1- and 2-naphthaldehyde and to 1- and 2-acetonaphthone; the latter pair is unreactive.[40] Although part of these differences have been ascribed to a change in the nature of the lowest excited triplet (from n-π^* to π-π^*), there is no straightforward correlation, and other factors must be operating as well. (From the retarding effect exerted by paramagnetic salts, Yang and coworkers[40] have concluded that the triplet state is involved in the additions.) From the distribution and stereospecificity of the products obtained in the addition of benzaldehyde to 2-methyl-2-butene it can be inferred that the addition bears some characteristics of a diradical process. This is indicated in the following sequence:[40,42]

4 isomers (64%)

Similar considerations can explain the product selectivity in the additions to haloolefins;[46] but it is to be noted that true free radicals are probably absent in the reaction, since α,β-unsaturated aldehydes yield only four-membered rings:[40]

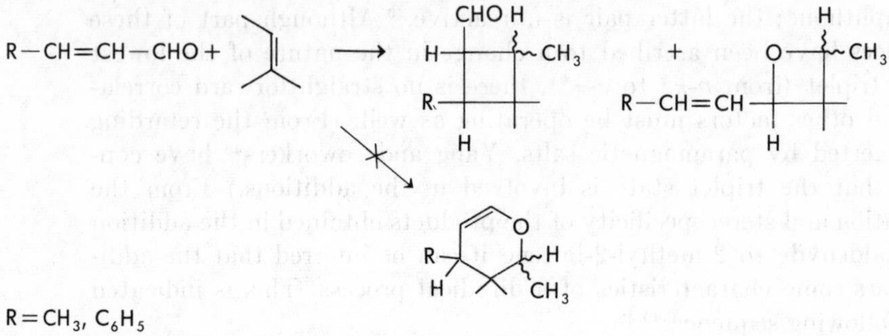

$$R-CH=CH-CHO + \begin{array}{c}\diagup\\\diagdown\end{array} \longrightarrow$$

$$R = CH_3, C_6H_5$$

Two significant alternate reactions may be observed during oxetane formation. The presence of protic solvents such as isopropanol leads to hydrogen abstraction by the carbonyl group with the formation of pinacols and carbinols (Sec. 7-2). There is indication that the excited state in both processes is the same, as seen from the fact that the inability of the carbonyl compounds to undergo one of the processes is coupled with a similar inertness toward the second.[41] A second alternate reaction is the result of energy transfer from carbonyl component to olefins, and dimerization of the olefin takes place. For the latter to occur, the carbonyl excitation energy should be sufficient for triplet-triplet transfer to the olefin. D. R. Arnold[45] has shown that a difference in triplet excitation energy of only about 0.5 kcal is determining in the photolysis of norbornene. Thus, with 4-chloroacetophenone as sensitizer (its triplet energy is about 72.1 kcal, measured in hydrocarbon solvents) irradiation of norbornene leads almost exclusively to the two dimers (Sec. 5-2), while the use of 3-trifluoromethylacetophenone (which has a triplet excitation energy of about 71.6 kcal in hydrocarbon solvents) yields an oxetane:dimer ratio of 46:4!

The oxetane formation process has been applied to numerous systems. Thus, acetone and fumaronitrile produce mixtures of *cis* and *trans*-oxetanedinitriles[47] on irradiation, while iminooxetanes are formed in the example illustrated below.[48]

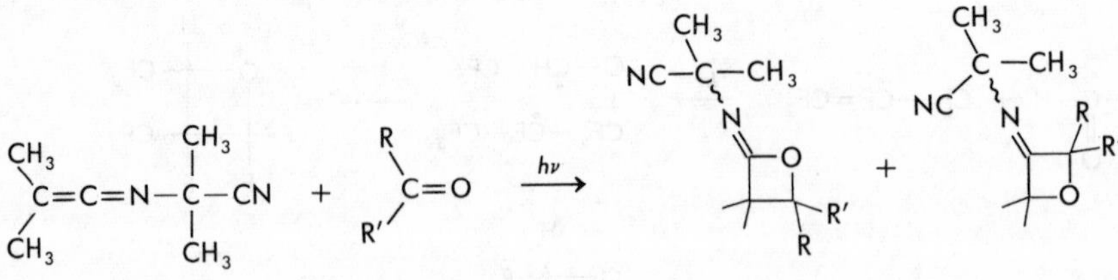

Additions to quinones can occur in several ways; that by cyclooctene leads first to an oxetane, which subsequently undergoes a 1,3 shift or a dienone-phenol rearrangement (see page 112). An oxetane forms with an *excess* of chloranil, but the use of equivalent amounts of chloranil and olefin results in an addition to the quinone double bond.[49]

Another variation is the 1,4 addition of conjugated dienes to the carbonyl group of a quinone by which dihydropyran derivatives are formed; the addition of acetylenes yields products that probably arise via an unstable oxetene:

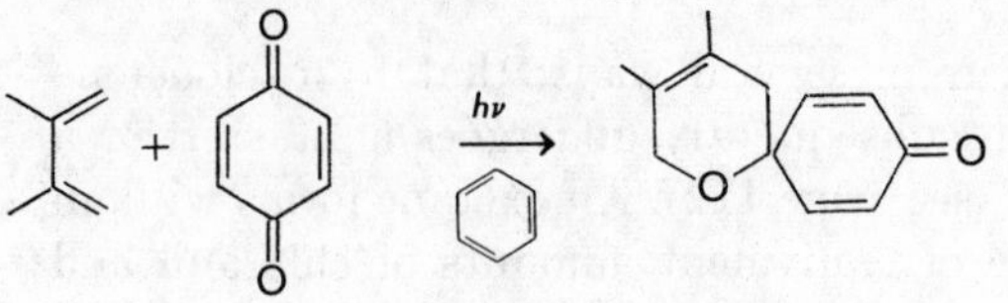

[50]

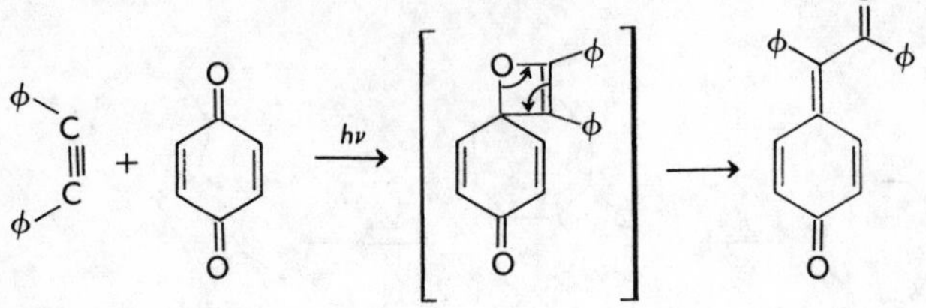

[51]

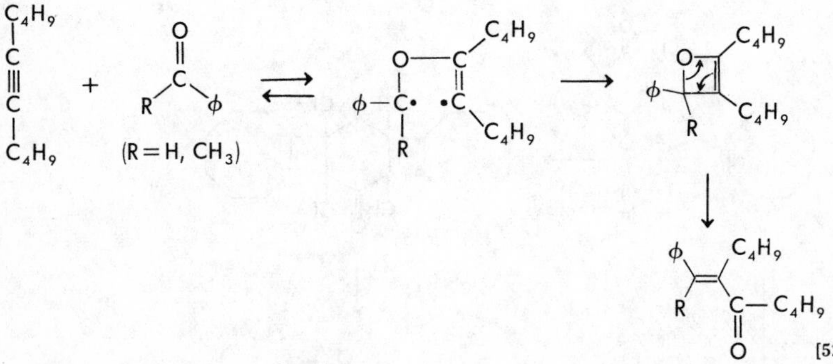

[52]

The substitution of thioketones for ketones leads to the formation of new olefins[53] and, presumably, thioaldehydes, which arise by formation and subseqeunt dissociation of cyclic adducts:

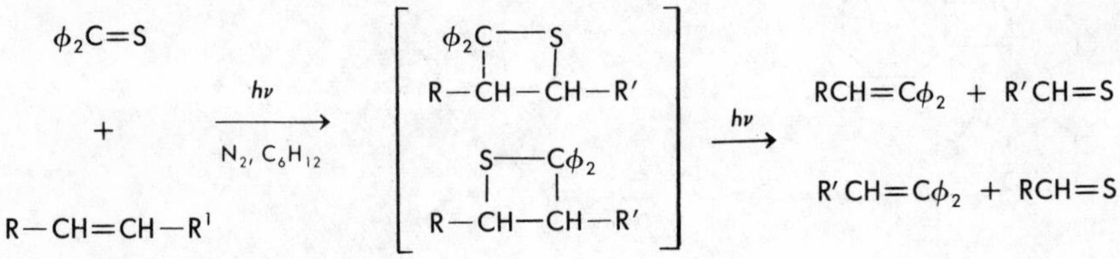

A similar course of events is probably responsible for the formation of a thioborinate and the tetraphenylethylene formed on photolysis of 4,4-bisdimethylaminobenzothiophenone and tributylborane[54] illustrated below.

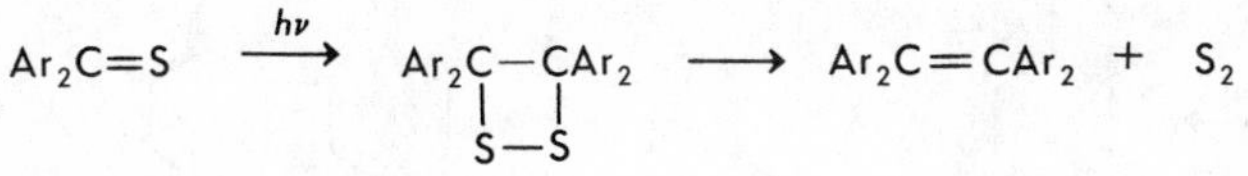

$$Ar_2C{=}S \xrightarrow{h\nu} Ar_2\underset{\underset{S-S}{|}}{C}{-}\underset{|}{C}Ar_2 \longrightarrow Ar_2C{=}CAr_2 + S_2$$

$$S_2 + 2R_3B \longrightarrow 2R_2BSR$$

$$\left(\begin{array}{l} Ar = p\text{-}(CH_3)_2N{-}C_6H_4 \\ R = n\text{-}C_4H_9 \end{array} \right)$$

6-4 *Other Coupling Reactions*

Additions of olefins to carbonyl compounds, ethers, and alcohols often take place with a transfer of hydrogen. Although these reactions might be appropriately considered as oxidations and reductions, we shall consider them here, because the most prominent feature of the processes is still the bimolecular addition step (see also Sec. 7-3).

Alcohols may result from allylic or benzylic hydrogen abstraction by carbonyl groups, although in one known example hydrogen is abstracted from a saturated hydrocarbon. The three types are shown below.

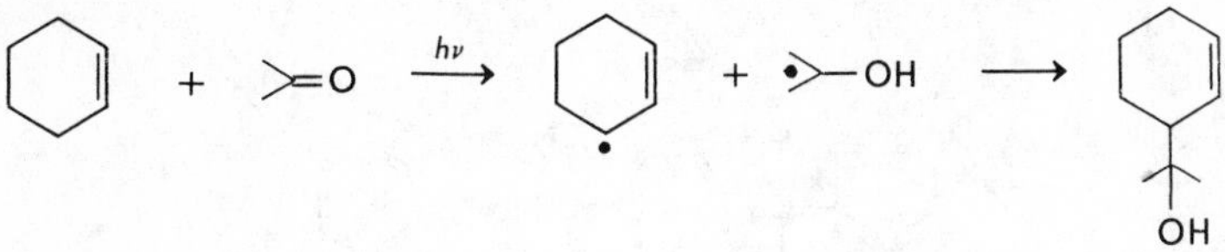

[55]

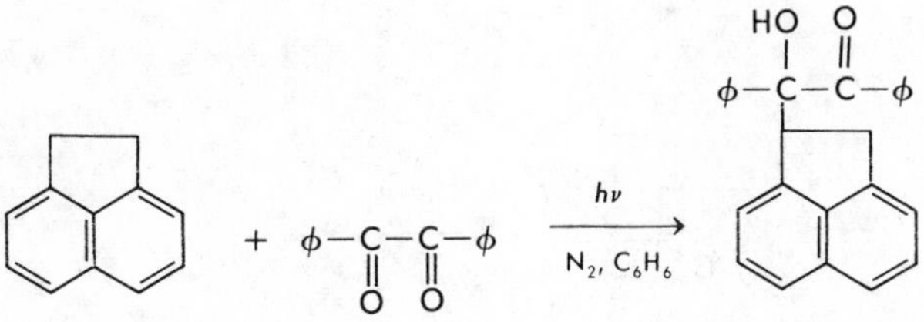

[56]

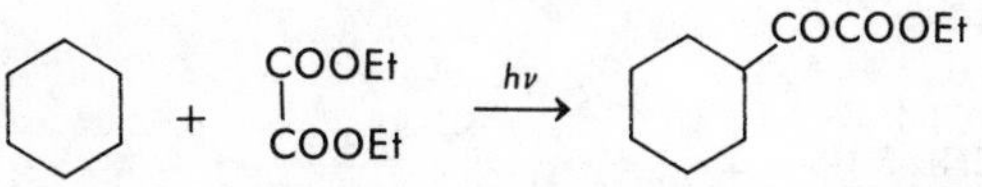

[57]

With cyclohexanone a similar type of addition occurs in cyclohexene by abstraction of hydrogen from the ketone itself:

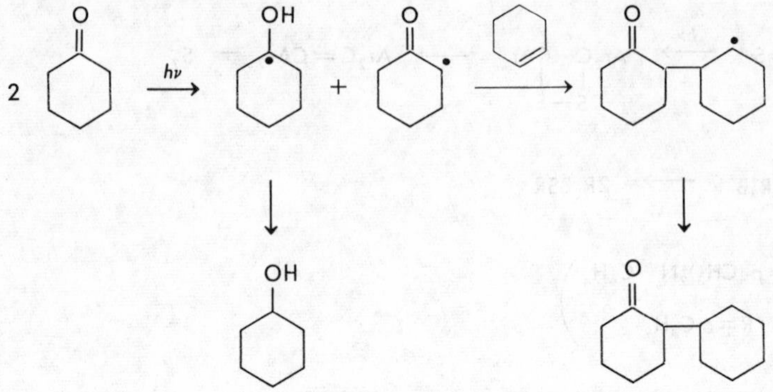

[55,58]

When a quinone is the hydrogen acceptor, the resulting semiquinone combines with the hydrocarbon radical. Such additions are illustrated for chloranil and a quinodimethane. Addition to tetracyanoethylene occurs twice; the second time only the cyano group is involved. The examples shown below are true free-radical reactions; they may be carried out in the dark with the use of di-*tert*-butyl peroxide.

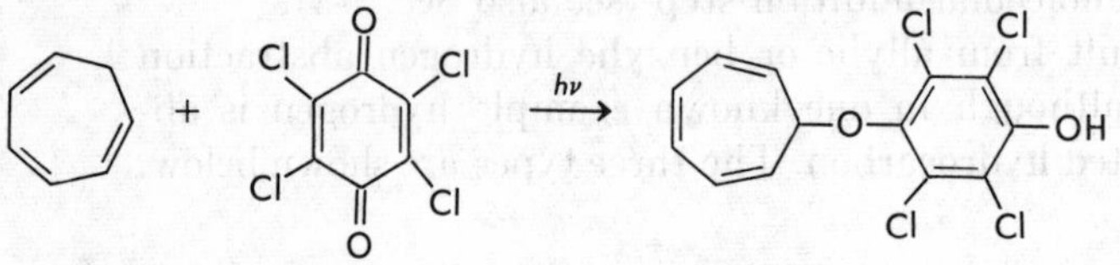

[59]

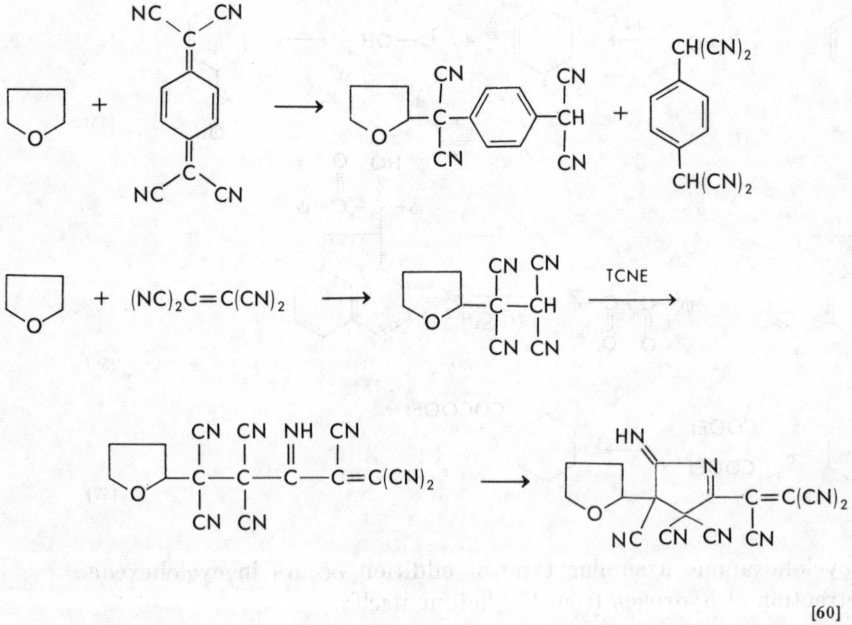

[60]

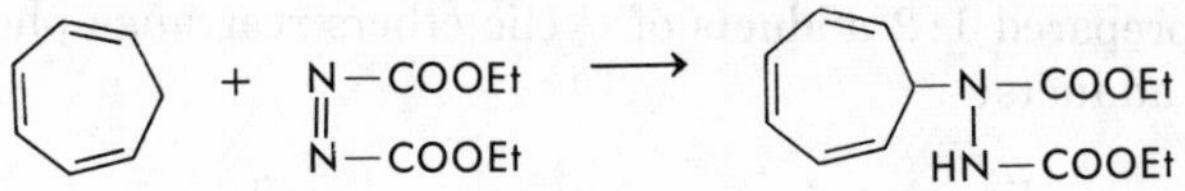

[59]

Cyclic ethers may add to olefins either in a normal 1,2 fashion, or in a 1,4 addition as in the case of phenanthraquinone:

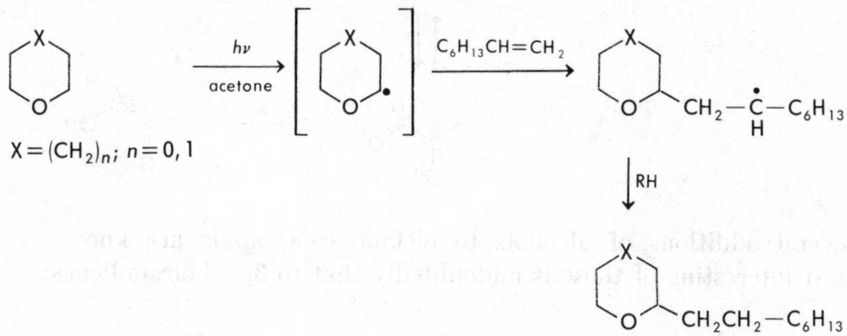

$X = (CH_2)_n; n = 0, 1$

[61]

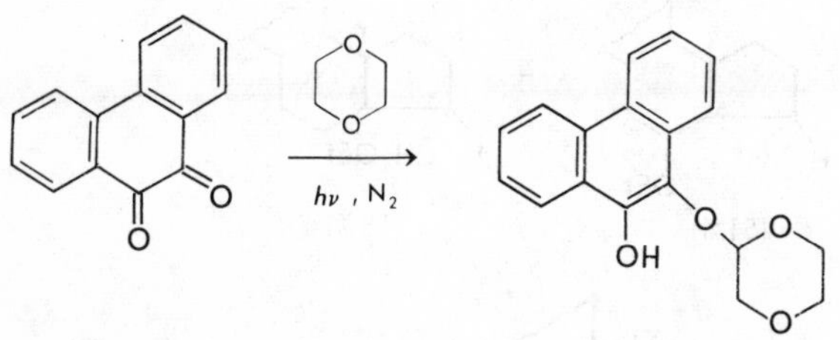

[62]

The latter reaction is not unexpected in view of the wide variety of substituted toluenes which undergo 1,2 addition to 9,10-phenanthrene quinones, apparently through the same type of radical-chain mechanism.

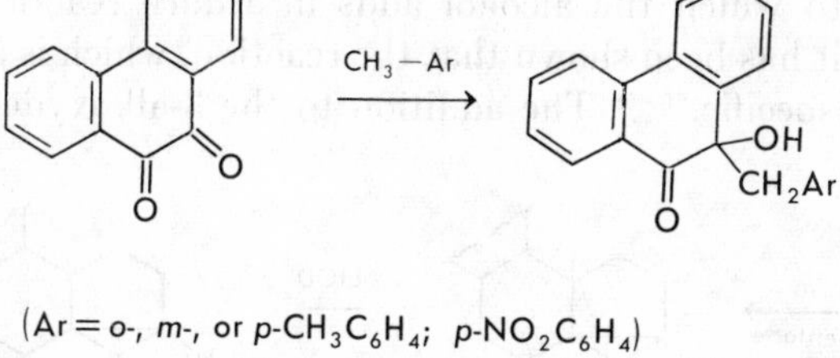

$(Ar = o\text{-}, m\text{-}, \text{ or } p\text{-}CH_3C_6H_4; p\text{-}NO_2C_6H_4)$

[63]

This type of addition has been traced to the establishment of an equilibrium which allows radical combination in either of two ways. Evidence in support of such an equilibrium has been obtained[63] by showing that the synthetically prepared 1:2 adducts of cyclic ethers rearrange photo-chemically to 1:4 adducts:

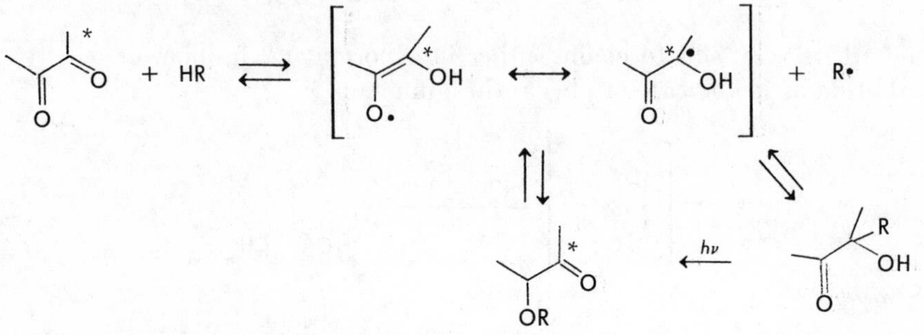

Several additions of alcohols to olefinic compounds are known. The most interesting of these is undoubtedly that to 3,5-cholestadienes:

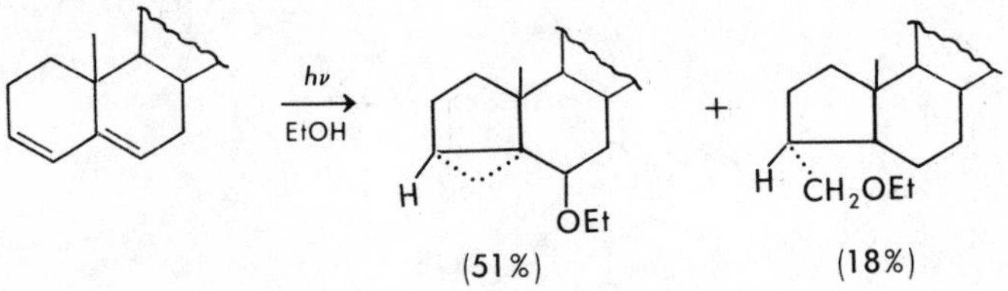

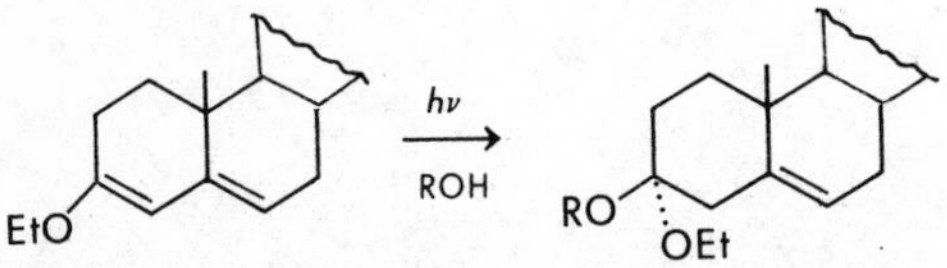

(51%)   (18%)

[64–66]

Although superficially similar, the two additions shown here apparently follow different pathways. It was found[64–66] that irradiation of the diene itself in pentane leads to an unstable derivative of bicyclo[1.1.0] butane (page 36), to which the alcohol adds in a dark reaction. With the aid of C_2H_5OD it has been shown that the reaction, which is sensitive to oxygen, is stereospecific.[66–68] The addition to the 3-alkoxyderivative,

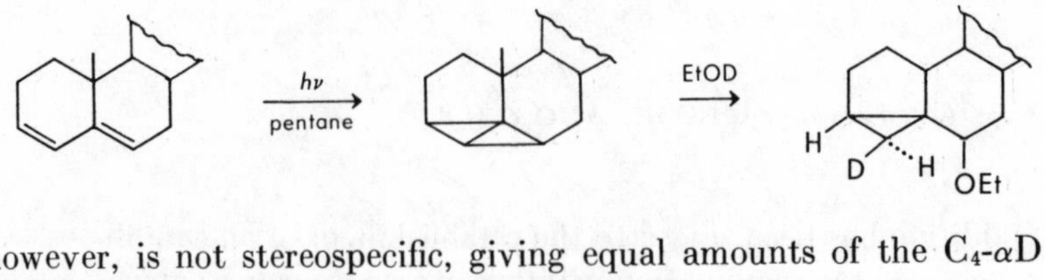

however, is not stereospecific, giving equal amounts of the C_4-αD and C_4-βD isomers. Moreover, the reaction is insensitive to oxygen, and all attempts to isolate a bicyclobutane derivative in pentane have failed.

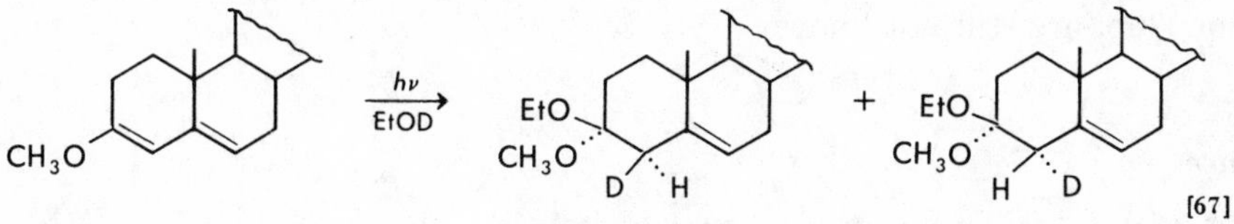

[67]

Addition of the 3-methyl substituted diene is similar to that of cholesta-
diene.[67] It has been suggested[64] that other intermediates aside from the
bicyclo[1.1.0]butane are involved in the reaction. What they are is
not certain.

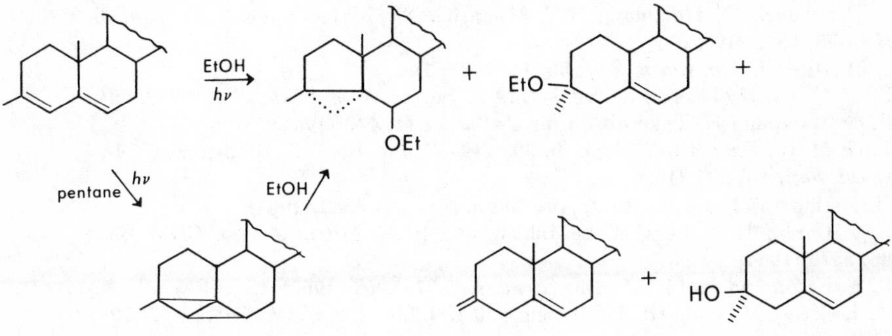

Finally, addition of methanol to the C=N bond has been observed to
follow any of three paths.

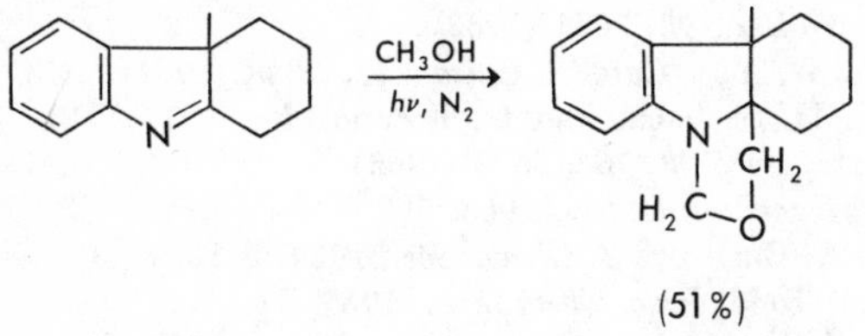

[69]

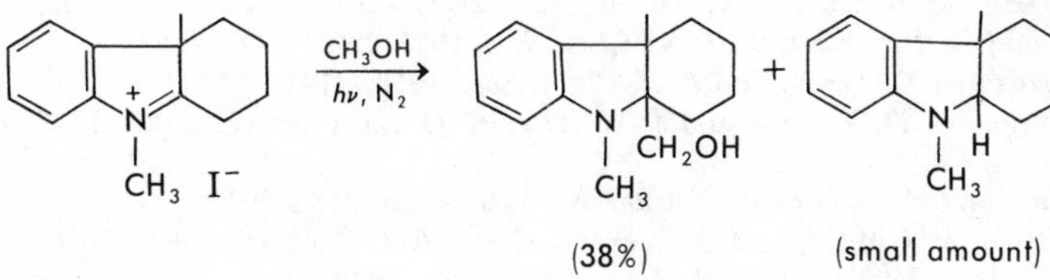

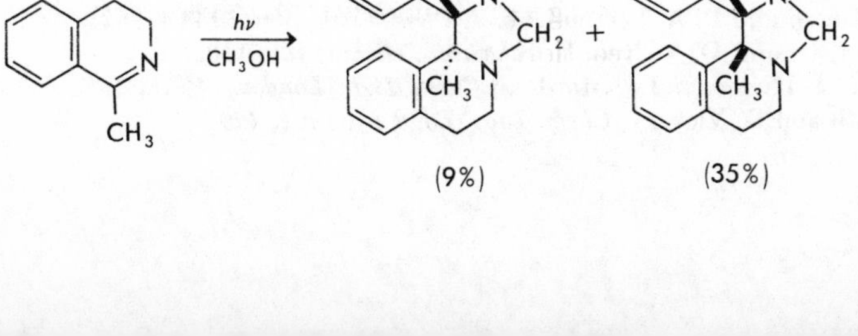

(51%)

(38%)   (small amount)

(9%)   (35%)

[70]

The mechanisms involved in these additions, which must involve an oxidation step, are still not known.

References

1. P. E. Eaton, *J. Am. Chem. Soc.*, **84**, 2454 (1962).
2. P. E. Eaton, *Tetrahedron Letters*, **1964**, 3695.
3. R. Criegee and H. Furrer, *Ber.*, **97**, 2949 (1964); G. W. Griffin, R. Mateer, unpublished results.
4. R. L. Cargill, J. Dorn, and A. E. Siebert, *Abstract of Papers, Am. Chem. Soc., Chicago*, August, 1964, 25S.
5. G. O. Schenck, W. Hartmann, S. P. Mannsfeld, W. Metzner, and C. H. Krauch, *Ber.*, **95**, 1642 (1962).
6. J. M. Rice, *J. Am. Chem. Soc.*, **86**, 1444 (1964).
7. P. de Mayo, H. Takeshita, and A.B.M.A. Sattar, *Proc. Chem. Soc.*, **1962**, 119; P. de Mayo and H. Takeshita, *Can. J. Chem.*, **41**, 440 (1963).
8. P. de Mayo, *Pure Appl. Chem.*, **9**, 597 (1964); see also J. S. Bradshaw, *J. Am. Chem. Soc.*, **88**, 237 (1966).
9. H. Hikino and P. de Mayo, *J. Am. Chem. Soc.*, **86**, 3582 (1964).
10. E. J. Corey, J. D. Bass, R. LeMahieu, and R. B. Mitra, *J. Am. Chem. Soc.*, **86**, 5570 (1964).
11. P. E. Eaton and K. Lin, *J. Am. Chem. Soc.*, **87**, 2052 (1965).
12. E. J. Corey, M. Tada, R. LeMahieu, and L. Libit, *J. Am. Chem. Soc.*, **87**, 2051 (1965).
13. O. L. Chapman, A. A. Griswold, E. Hoganson, G. Lenz, and J. Reasoner, *Pure Appl. Chem.*, **9**, 585 (1964); O. L. Chapman, private communication.
14. G. O. Schenck, W. Hartmann, and R. Steinmetz, *Ber.*, **96**, 498 (1963); G. O. Schenck, R. Steinmetz, *Bull. Soc. Chim. Belges*, **71**, 781 (1962); R. Steinmetz, W. Hartmann, and G. O. Schenck, *Ber.*, **98**, 3854 (1965).
15. P. de Mayo, S. T. Reid, and R. W. Yip, *Can. J. Chem.*, **42**, 2828 (1964); R. Criegee, U. Zirngibl, H. Furrer, D. Seebach, and G. Freund, *Ber.*, **97**, 2942 (1964); H. D. Scharf and F. Korte, *Ber.*, **98**, 764, 3672 (1965).
16. J. A. Barltrop and P. Robson, *Tetrahedron Letters*, **1963**, 597.
17. P. Robson, P. W. Grubb, and J. A. Barltrop, *J. Chem. Soc.*, **1964**, 2153.
18. P. de Mayo, R. W. Yip, and S. T. Reid, *Proc. Chem. Soc.*, **1963**, 54.
19. G. O. Schenck, I. Hartmann, and W. Metzner, *Tetrahedron Letters*, **1965**, 347.
20. G. Koltzenburg, K. Kraft, and G. O. Schenck, *Tetrahedron Letters*, **1965**, 353.
21. J. M. Blair and D. Bryce-Smith, *Proc. Chem. Soc.* **1957**, 287.
22. H. J. F. Angus and D. Bryce-Smith, *J. Chem. Soc.*, **1960**, 4791.
23. E. Grovenstein, Jr., D. V. Rao, and J. W. Taylor, *J. Am. Chem. Soc.*, **83**, 1705 (1961).
24. G. O. Schenck and R. Steinmetz, *Tetrahedron Letters*, no. 21, 1 (1960).
25. D. Bryce-Smith, A. Gilbert, and B. Vickery, *Chem. Ind. (London)*, **1962**, 2060; H. J. F. Angus and D. Bryce-Smith, *Proc. Chem. Soc.*, **1959**, 326.
26. D. Bryce-Smith and J. E. Lodge, *J. Chem. Soc.*, **1962**, 2675.
27. D. Bryce-Smith and A. Gilbert, *J. Chem. Soc.*, **1965**, 918.
28. G. S. Hammond and W. M. Hardham, *Proc. Chem. Soc.*, **1963**, 63; G. S. Hammond, N. J. Turro, and P. A. Leermakers, *J. Phys. Chem.*, **66**, 1144 (1962).
29. E. Grovenstein, Jr. and D. V. Rao, *Tetrahedron Letters*, **1961**, 148.
30. R. C. Cookson, J. Hudec, and J. Mardsen, *Chem. Ind. (London)*, **1961**, 23.
31. D. Bryce-Smith and B. Vickery, *Chem. Ind. (London)*, **1961**, 429.

32. G. O. Schenck, J. Kuhls, S. P. Mannsfeld, and C. H. Krauch, *Ber.*, **96,** 813 (1963).
33. J. P. Simons, *Trans. Faraday Soc.*, **56,** 391 (1960).
34. D. Bryce-Smith and J. E. Lodge, *Proc. Chem. Soc.*, **1961,** 333, *J. Chem. Soc.*, **1963,** 695.
35. E. H. White and R. L. Stern, *Tetrahedron Letters*, **1964,** 193; See also W. H. F. Sasse, P. J. Collin, and G. Sugowdz, *Tetrahedron Letters* **1965,** 3373.
36. H. Yamazaki and S. Shida, *J. Chem. Phys.*, **24,** 1278 (1956).
37. I. Tanaka and M. Okuda, *J. Chem. Phys.*, **22,** 1780 (1954).
38. J. G. Atkinson, D. E. Ayer, G. Büchi, and E. W. Robb, *J. Am. Chem. Soc.*, **85,** 2257 (1963).
39. D. E. Ayer and G. H. Büchi, U.S. Patent 2,805,242 (1957), *CA*, **52,** 2904a (1958).
40. N. C. Yang, M. Nussim, M. J. Jorgenson, and S. Murov, *Tetrahedron Letters*, **1964,** 3657; N. C. Yang, *Pure Appl. Chem.*, **9,** 591 (1964).
41. D. R. Arnold, R. L. Hinman, and A. H. Glick, *Tetrahedron Letters*, **1964,** 1425.
42. G. Büchi, C. G. Inman, and E. S. Lipinsky, *J. Am. Chem. Soc.*, **76,** 4327 (1954).
43. R. Srinivasan, *J. Am. Chem. Soc.*, **82,** 775 (1960).
44. G. S. Hammond and N. J. Turro, unpublished results.
45. D. R. Arnold, *Abstract of Papers*, *Am. Chem. Soc.*, *Detroit*, 1965, 50 P; unpublished results.
46. J. F. Harris, Jr. and D. D. Coffman, *J. Am. Chem. Soc.*, **84,** 1553 (1962).
47. J. J. Beereboom and M. S. V. Wittenau, *J. Org. Chem.*, **30,** 1231 (1965).
48. L. A. Singer and P. D. Bartlett, *Tetrahedron Letters*, **1964,** 1887.
49. D. Bryce-Smith and A. Gilbert, *Proc. Chem. Soc.*, **1964,** 87, *Tetrahedron Letters*, **1964,** 3471.
50. J. A. Barltrop and B. Hesp, *Proc. Chem. Soc.*, **1964,** 195; *J. Chem. Soc.*, 5182 (1965).
51. D. Bryce-Smith, G. I. Fray, and A. Gilbert, *Tetrahedron Letters*, **1964,** 2137; H. E. Zimmerman, and L. Craft, *Tetrahedron Letters*, **1964,** 2131.
52. G. Büchi, J. T. Kofron, E. Koller, and D. Rosenthal, *J. Am. Chem. Soc.*, **78,** 876 (1956); H. E. Zimmerman and R. D. Simkin, *Tetrahedron Letters*, **1964,** 1847.
53. E. T. Kaiser and T. F. Wulfers, *J. Am. Chem. Soc.*, **86,** 1897 (1964).
54. M. Inatome and L. P. Kuhn, *Tetrahedron Letters*, **1965,** 73.
55. P. de Mayo, J. B. Stothers, and W. Templeton, *Can. J. Chem.*, **39,** 488 (1961).
56. P. de Mayo and A. Stoessl, *Can. J. Chem.*, **40,** 57 (1962).
57. Y. Odaira, T. Tominaga, T. Sugihara, and S. Tsutsumi, *Tetrahedron Letters*, **1964,** 2527.
58. P. de Mayo, in "Advances in Organic Chemistry," vol. 2, p. 378, R. A. Raphael, E. C. Taylor, H. Wijnberg (eds.), Interscience, New York, 1960.
59. G. O. Schenck, E. Koerner von Gustorf, B. Kim, G. von Bünau, and G. Pfundt, *Angew. Chem.*, **74,** 510 (1962).
60. J. Diekmann and C. J. Pedersen, *J. Org. Chem.*, **28,** 2879 (1963).
61. D. Elad and R. D. Youssefyeh, *J. Org. Chem.*, **29,** 2031 (1964).
62. M. B. Rubin, *J. Org. Chem.*, **28,** 1949 (1963).
63. M. B. Rubin and P. Zwitkowits, *J. Org. Chem.*, **29,** 2362 (1964).
64. W. G. Dauben and F. G. Willey, *Tetrahedron Letters* **1962,** 893; W. G. Dauben and W. T. Wipke, *Pure Appl. Chem.*, **9,** 539 (1964).
65. G. Just and V. DiTullio, *Can. J. Chem.*, **42,** 2153 (1964).
66. G. Just and C. C. Leznoff, *Can. J. Chem.*, **42,** 79 (1964).
67. C. C. Leznoff and G. Just, *Can. J. Chem.*, **42,** 2801 (1964); See also C. H. Robinson, O. Gnoj, and F. E. Carlson, *Tetrahedron*, **21,** 2509 (1965).
68. G. Just, G. Bauslaugh, and V. DiTullio, unpublished results.
69. P. Cerutti and H. Schmid, *Helv. Chim. Acta*, **45,** 1992 (1962).
70. P. Cerutti and H. Schmid, *Helv. Chim. Acta*, **47,** 203 (1964).

7

Oxidations and Reductions

7-1 Photochemical Oxidations

The exclusion of oxygen from photochemical reactions is no idle precaution; oxygen may act as quencher, form peroxides and hydroperoxides, cause oxidation of functional groups, and effect oxidative coupling.[1]

There are two mechanisms by which oxygen is incorporated in photochemical oxidation reactions.[2] The first is the Bäckstrom mechanism, or photosensitized oxidation mechanism. Its main feature is abstraction of hydrogen by the sensitizer (in its excited triplet state) followed by (indiscriminate) addition of oxygen to the newly created radical.

$$\text{Sens} \quad \xrightarrow{h\nu} \quad \cdot\text{Sens}\cdot$$

$$\cdot\text{Sens}\cdot + \text{AH} \quad \longrightarrow \quad \cdot\text{Sens-H} + \text{A}\cdot$$

$$\text{A}\cdot + \text{O}_2 \quad \longrightarrow \quad \text{AOO}\cdot$$

$$\text{AOO}\cdot + \text{AH} \quad \longrightarrow \quad \text{AOOH} + \text{A}\cdot$$

$$\text{AOO}\cdot + \cdot\text{Sens-H} \quad \longrightarrow \quad \text{AOOH} + \cdot\text{Sens}\cdot$$

Examples of photosensitized reactions that take place by this mechanism are found among the oxidations of secondary alcohols to hydroxy-hydroperoxides, which in aqueous media decompose to form ketones and hydrogen peroxide:[3]

$$R-\underset{\underset{OH}{|}}{\overset{\overset{H}{|}}{C}}-R' \xrightarrow[\phi_2C=O]{h\nu,\ O_2} R-\underset{\underset{OOH}{|}}{\overset{\overset{OH}{|}}{C}}-R' \xrightarrow{H_2O} R-\underset{}{\overset{\overset{O}{\parallel}}{C}}-R' + H_2O_2$$

$R = R' = CH_3$ (25%)

$R = R' = C_2H_5$ (16%)

$R = CH_3;\ R' = C_2H_5$ (23%)

$R = CH_3;\ R' = C_3H_7$ (18%)

Mechanism

$$\phi-\overset{\overset{O}{\parallel}}{C}-\phi \xrightarrow{h\nu} \phi-\underset{\bullet}{\overset{\overset{O\bullet}{|}}{C}}-\phi \xrightarrow{R-\underset{\underset{H}{|}}{\overset{\overset{OH}{|}}{C}}-R'} \phi-\underset{\bullet}{\overset{\overset{OH}{|}}{C}}-\phi + R-\underset{\bullet}{\overset{\overset{OH}{|}}{C}}-R'$$

$$R-\underset{\bullet}{\overset{\overset{OH}{|}}{C}}-R' \xrightarrow{O_2} R-\underset{\underset{OO\bullet}{|}}{\overset{\overset{OH}{|}}{C}}-R' \xrightarrow{R-\underset{\underset{H}{|}}{\overset{\overset{OH}{|}}{C}}-R'} R-\underset{\underset{OOH}{|}}{\overset{\overset{OH}{|}}{C}}-R' + R-\underset{\bullet}{\overset{\overset{OH}{|}}{C}}-R'$$

$$\phi-\underset{\bullet}{\overset{\overset{OH}{|}}{C}}-\phi \xrightarrow{O_2} \phi-\underset{\underset{OO\bullet}{|}}{\overset{\overset{OH}{|}}{C}}-\phi$$

$$\phi-\underset{\underset{OO\bullet}{|}}{\overset{\overset{OH}{|}}{C}}-\phi + R-\underset{\underset{OO\bullet}{|}}{\overset{\overset{OH}{|}}{C}}-R' \longrightarrow \phi-\overset{\overset{O}{\parallel}}{C}-\phi + O_2 + R-\underset{\underset{OOH}{|}}{\overset{\overset{OH}{|}}{C}}-R'$$

(It will be seen that the reaction is closely related to that involving the formation of pinacols from ketones and aldehydes discussed in Sec. 7-2.†) The second mechanism, that of "photosensitized oxygen transfer,"

† The photochemical behavior of amines is rather similar; hydrogen may be lost from nitrogen, from the adjacent carbon atom, or both, and the radicals that form couple to give the expected products. For example, diethylamine yields *N,N′*-diethyl-butane-2,3-diamine, 1,3-diethyl-2,4,5-trimethylimidazolidine, tetraethyl hydrazine, and *N*-but-2-enylidene-ethylamine.[3a]

involves the direct combination of the substrate with oxygen. There are two proposals regarding the state of the oxygen involved. Schenck[2] favors an oxygen-transfer step in which the (triplet) sensitizer forms an adduct with (triplet) oxygen, while Foote[4,5] favors the idea of singlet oxygen being the sole agent in the transfer step:

Schenck:

$$\text{sens.} \xrightarrow{h\nu} \text{•sens.• (triplet)}$$

$$\text{•sens.•} + O_2 \longrightarrow \text{•sens.-O-O•}$$

$$A + \text{•sens.-O-O•} \longrightarrow AO_2 + \text{sens.}$$

Foote:

$$\text{sens.} \xrightarrow{h\nu} \text{sens.*(triplet)}$$

$$O_2(\text{triplet}) + \text{sens.*(triplet)} \longrightarrow O_2(\text{singlet}) + \text{sens.}$$

$$A + O_2(\text{singlet}) \longrightarrow AO_2$$

Before elaborating on this point it is useful to discuss the characteristic features of these oxidations. Photochemical reactions of this type, in which the sensitizer is a dye such as bengal red, fluorescein, or halo-fluorescein, include the oxidation of dienes, furans, and substituted olefins:[6]

(88%)   [6]

(21%)   [7]

$$2\,(CH_3CH_2)_2S \rightarrow O \xrightarrow[\text{sens.}]{h\nu,\,O_2} 2\,(CH_3CH_2)_2SO_2 \qquad [8]$$

The formation of hydroperoxides in photosensitized oxygen-transfer reactions that follow the Schenck type of mechanism occurs only when hydrogen is present in the allylic position of the olefin. The reaction has, moreover, some definite steric and electronic requirements. Oxygen always becomes attached to one carbon of the double bond, which then shifts into the allylic position:

$$\underset{H}{\overset{1\quad2\quad3}{C=C-C}} \quad\xrightarrow[\text{sens.}]{h\nu,\,O_2}\quad \underset{OOH}{\overset{1\quad2\quad3}{C-C=C}}$$

This mode of insertion has been demonstrated elegantly in the photo-sensitized oxidation of (+)-limonene.[2,9] The products, isolated as the corresponding alcohols, are, among others, (−)-*cis*- and (−)-*trans*-carveol, but no (+)-carveols, which would have formed from attack at the allylic position.

In the analogous steroidal systems Nickon and Bagli[10] have demonstrated that only the allylic hydrogen cis to oxygen attack is removed. Thus, cholesterol-7α-*d* yields 3β-hydroxy-5α-hydroperoxy-Δ⁶-cholestene with only 8.5% of the original deuterium present after photosensitized oxidation, while cholesterol-7β-*d* gives the same material with 95% of the original deuterium present:

$$R=H,\,R'=D \quad\longrightarrow\quad 8.5\%\ D\ \text{left}$$

$$R=D,\,R'=H \quad\longrightarrow\quad 95\%\ D\ \text{left}$$

The abstraction of axial or quasi-axial allylic hydrogen takes place preferentially. The total product distribution from the (+)-limonene oxidation proves this to be true.[2]

Influence of steric bulk may be seen in the ready oxidation of $(+)$-Δ^3-carene when existing in the conformation which removes the interaction between the three-membered ring and the axial hydrogens to be abstracted and in the inertness of the alternate conformer toward oxidation:[2]

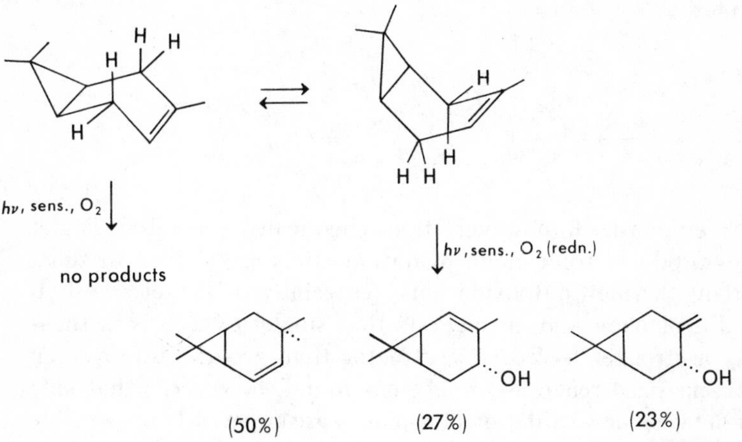

hν, sens., O₂ — no products

hν, sens., O₂ (redn.)

(50%)　　　(27%)　　　(23%)

The electron density at the unsaturated center influences the reaction rate; the quantum yields of olefin oxidations follow the order:

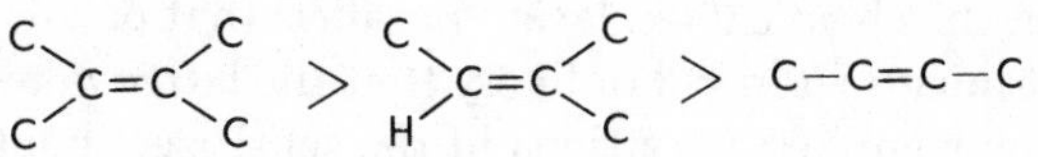

[2]

The stereoselectivity discussed above can best be accommodated by a concerted cyclic mechanism[2,10] for the hydrogen-abstraction–oxygen-addition step:

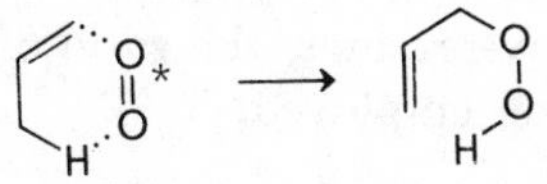

The nature of the oxygen-transferring species is not known with certainty. Foote[11] and Corey[12] have studied peroxidations with singlet oxygen[13] generated by the reaction of sodium hypochlorite and hydrogen peroxide and by the electrodeless discharge of triplet oxygen, respectively. Applying the hypochlorite-peroxide method to a number of systems, Foote obtained yields and observed a stereoselectivity identical with those reported by Schenck, and he concluded that singlet oxygen is, in fact, the intermediate in the photosensitized oxidations. The sensitizer-oxygen complex, or "moloxide," idea was especially criticized in the transannular oxidation of anthracene;[5] kinetic studies having shown that one molecule of anthracene acts as sensitizer and a second as substrate, it would be difficult to see why the sensitizer, when existing in an oxygen complex, should not act as substrate and form peroxide by collapse of such a complex:

Schenck has emphasized, however, that chemically generated singlet oxygen gives products from olefin oxidations that are similar to those obtained from thermal autooxidations (especially with tetramethylethylene and α-pinene), and he suggests that singlet oxygen is in those cases merely a stronger hydrogen abstractor than ground-state oxygen of the photosensitized reactions. Foote has found, however,[9a] that side reactions in the very slow oxidation of α-pinene are apparently responsible for the anomalous product distribution obtained. Indeed, in the presence of free radical inhibitors (such as 2,6-di-*tert*-butylphenol) the product distribution of the NaOCl/H_2O_2 oxidation approaches that of the photo-oxidation. It has further been noted that since the remarkable stereo-selectivity displayed in the chemical oxidation parallels that of the photo-sensitized oxidation, it must be termed unlikely that the latter takes place with a sensitizer-oxygen complex; variations in the sensitizer should lead to changes in the product distribution contrary to what is observed.[9a]

The stereospecificity of the oxidation reaction is rapidly increasing its use as a synthetic tool. For example, collapse of the hydroperoxides formed from the hematoporphyrin-sensitized photooxygenation of Δ^4-cholesten-3-ols in pyridine leads to good yields of the epoxylactones.[10] Some enone also is formed as by-product, the ratio of epoxide to enone being dependent on the sensitizer employed.

Among the other photochemical oxidation reactions of interest is the oxidative Diels-Alder reaction shown below. It occurs on irradiation in the presence of oxygen and methylene blue:

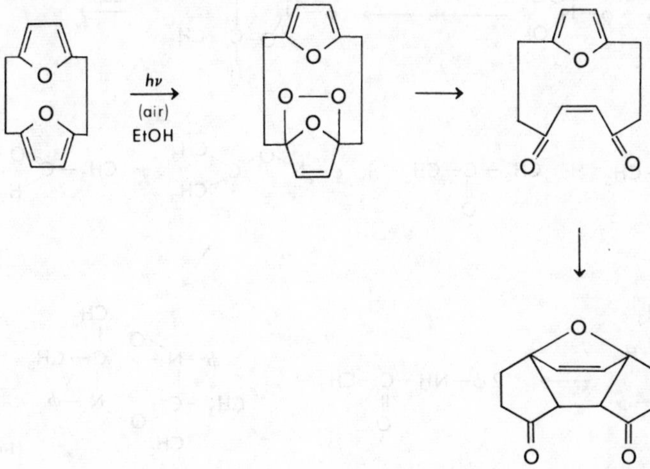

[14]

Oxidative coupling reactions have been observed on photolysis of several phenols in the presence of oxygen:

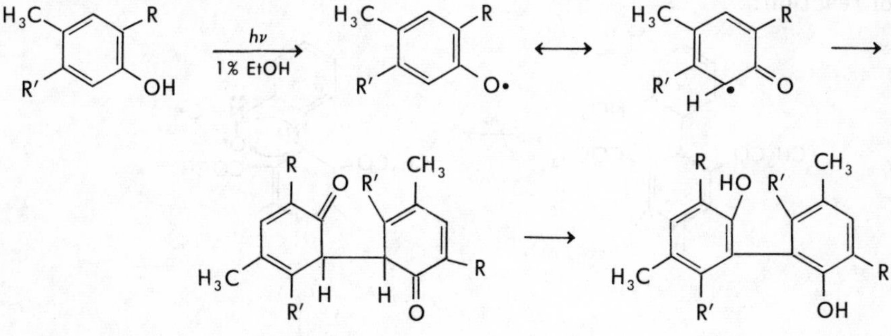

(R = (CH₃)₂CH, R' = CH₃; R = CH₃, R' = H)

[8,15]

A reaction of particular interest is the oxidation of olefins, on irradiation in the presence of nitrobenzene, to yield products that are similar to those derived from ozonolysis reactions. The process occurs through addition of the nitro groups in the primary reaction:

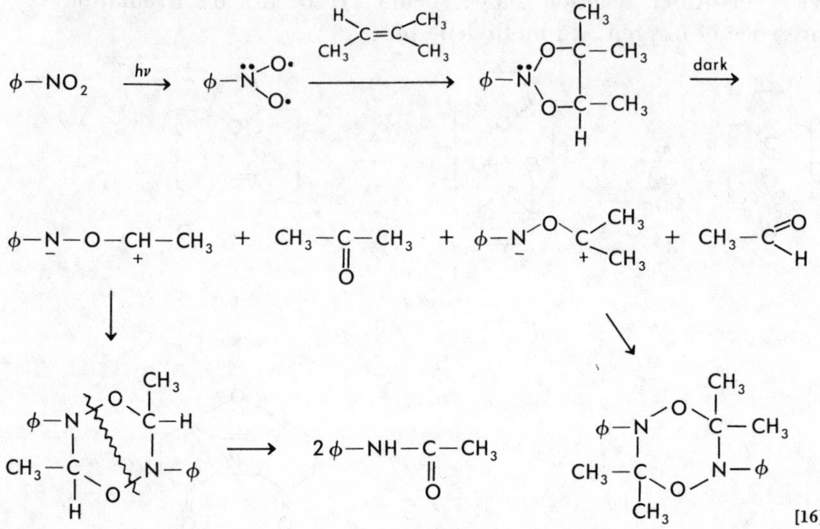

$$[16]$$

The nitro group manifests its photochemical reactivity in a number of other ways. The rearrangement of 9-nitroanthracene, discussed in Chap. 8, is one involving the formation of nitrite esters, while the intramolecular oxidation-reduction reactions shown below are examples of yet another mode of reaction:

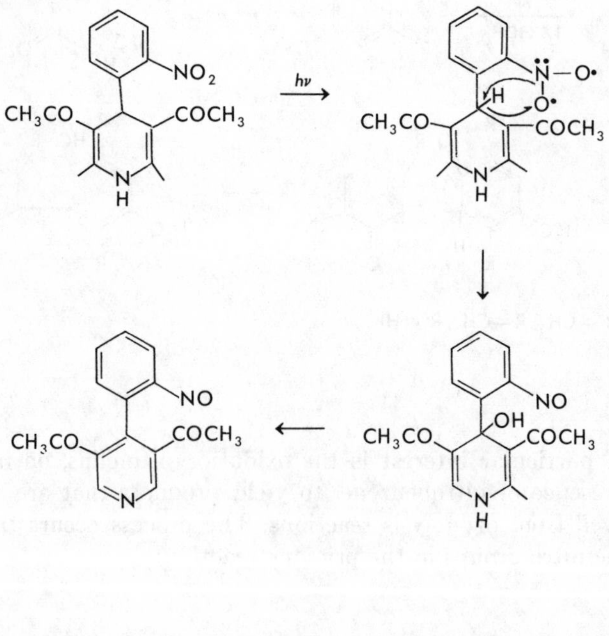

$$[17]$$

[18]

The oxidative cyclization of conjugated trienes to form aromatic systems is one of the more extensively studied photochemical oxidations. The conversion of *cis*-stilbene to phenanthrene is a prime example of such a ring closure:[9,10]

The reaction takes place in the vapor phase as well as in solution,[21] although in the latter case the presence of some oxidant (O_2, $FeCl_3$, or I_2) is required.[22] The yields of the reaction are quite good (60 to 85%), and the reaction has been applied successfully to stilbenes bearing a variety of substituents (F, Cl, Br, CH_3O, CH_3, CF_3, C_6H_5, COOH),[19,20,22] although those with a nitro, acetyl, or dimethylamino group have been found to be inert.[19]

Iodine as substituent is usually lost: *para*-iodostilbene gives phenanthrene; diphenylacetylene is obtained in an elimination from α,α'-diiodostilbene. The replacement of iodine by hydrogen is a relatively facile photochemical reaction because of the ready dissociation of the C—I bond. It has been effected with a variety of substituted iodobenzenes on their photolysis in methanol.[23] Coupling is the main side reaction, leading to biphenyls, *p*-terphenyls, and quadriphenyls.[24]†

† An extremely specific aryl coupling reaction is achieved in the photolysis of lithium aryls. Thus, 2,2′-binaphthyl is the only product obtained from the photochemical decomposition of 2-naphthyllithium. The reaction may very well involve aryl radical anions, since no deuterium is incorporated in the workup with D_2O.[24a]

In the conversion of stilbene to phenanthrene, the formation of a dihydrophenanthrene intermediate is likely. Such an intermediate can return to starting material in a reversible reaction or be converted irreversibly to products by the action of an oxidant. There are two facts supporting the correctness of this assumption: (1) there is spectroscopic evidence for the transient existence of such an intermediate,[25] and (2) 9,10-dihydrophenanthrenes have been isolated from the photolysis of *trans*-α,β-dicyanostilbene and of diphenylmaleimide. In both cases, the dihydrophenanthrene probably arises by rearrangement of the labile intermediate dihydroderivative, that forms reversibly on photolysis:[26]

It has further been shown that *trans*-stilbene must first isomerize to *cis*-stilbene before ring closure can occur[25] and that cyclization takes place from the excited singlet state.[19]

The intermediate dihydroderivative is thought to have trans hydrogens, from analogy with other systems and from the reluctance toward
hydrogen elimination in the absence of oxidants, a process that should
occur with considerable facility in the cis isomer.[19,27] Hydrogen abstraction must in this case be a two-step process.

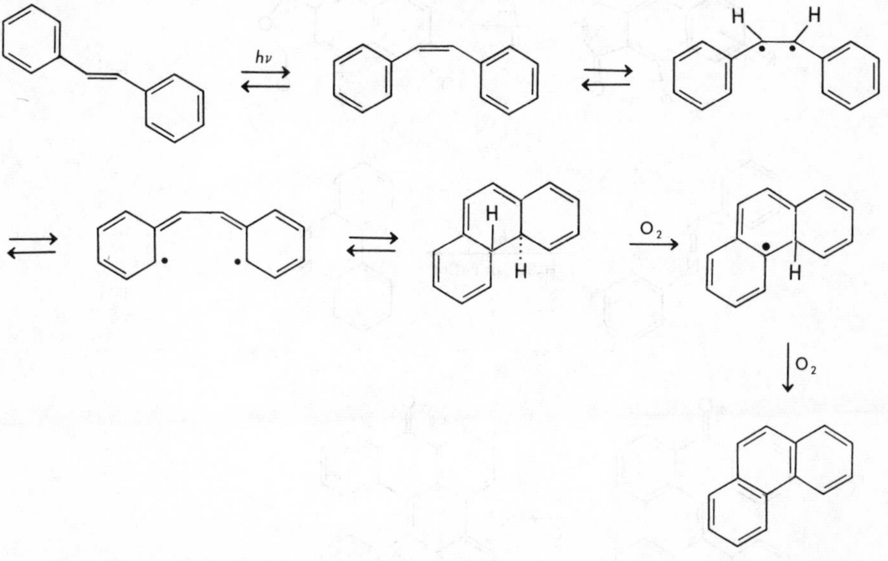

Some studies have been made of the effect of substituents on the
rate of the reaction.[27] Of the two intermediates formed in the hydrogen-
abstraction process shown below, the second one provides for the most
logical sequence, since it would be stabilized by the phenyl group; in
support, correlations with the Hammett σ_m constants have been observed,
but the interpretation is rather tentative.

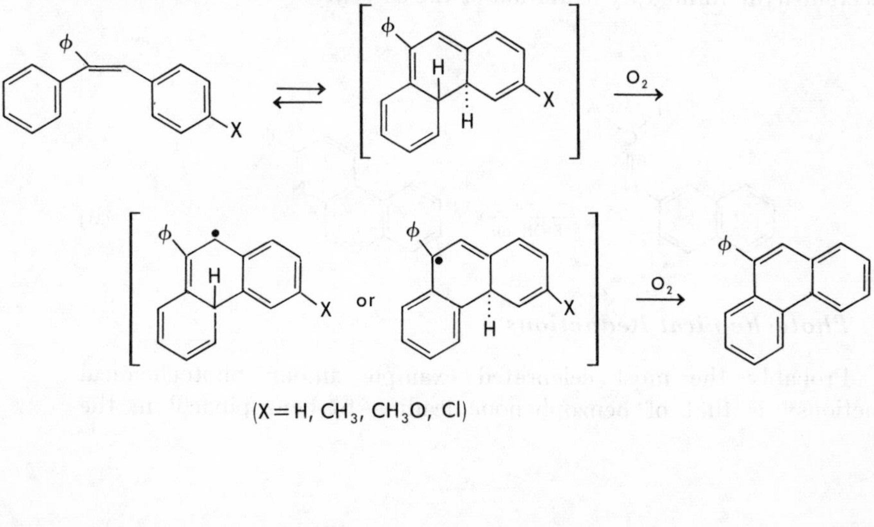

$(X = H, CH_3, CH_3O, Cl)$

The following few examples show that the reaction may be applied to a wide variety of systems:

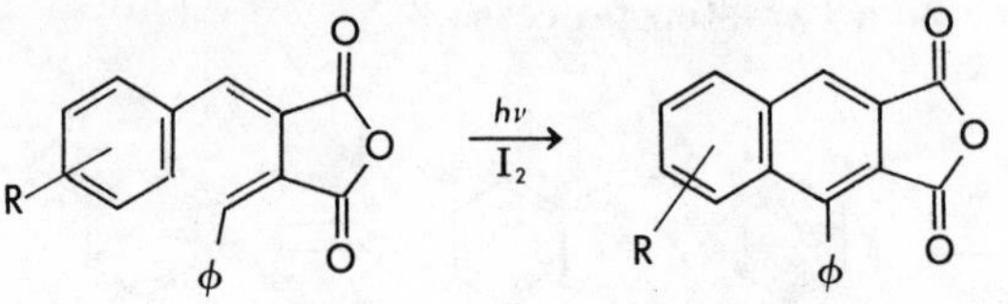

[28]

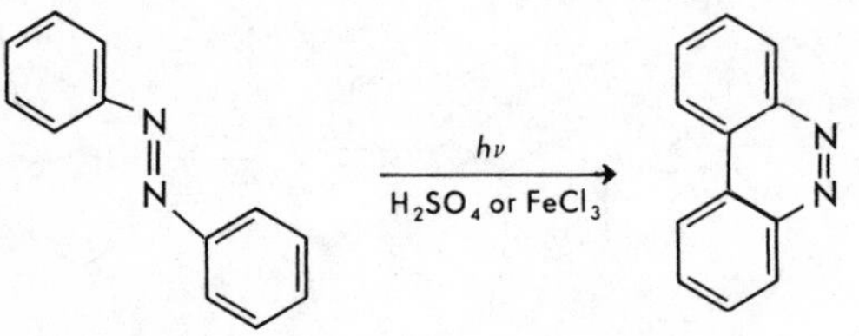

[29]

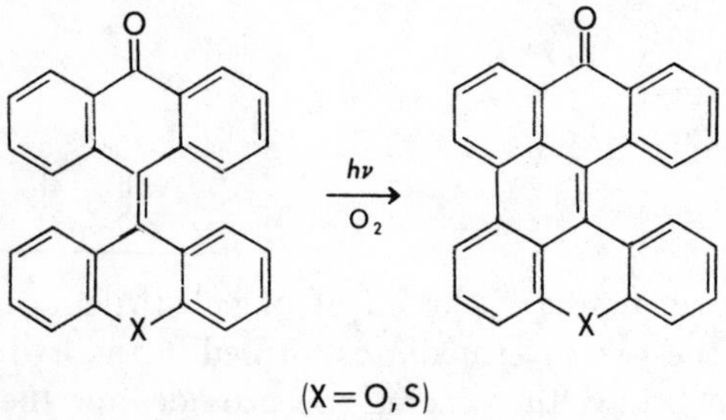

(X = O, S)

[30]

A most remarkable ring closure, in which a two-carbon fragment is supplied, is shown below. The fragment supplied originates probably as acetaldehyde formed by oxidation of the solvent:

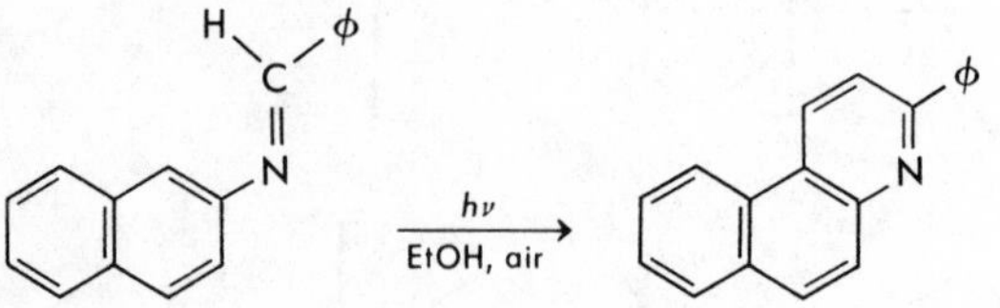

[31]

7-2 *Photochemical Reductions*

Probably the most celebrated example among photochemical reductions[32] is that of benzophenone leading to benzopinacol in the presence of a hydrogen donor. The reaction, which has received much attention, may be visualized as follows:

$$\phi_2C=O \xrightarrow{h\nu} \phi_2\overset{*}{C}=O \text{ (singlet)} \longrightarrow \phi_2\overset{*}{C}=O \text{ (triplet)}$$

$$\phi_2\overset{*}{C}=O \text{ (triplet)} \xrightarrow{RH} \phi_2\underset{\cdot}{C}-OH + R\cdot$$

$$2\,\phi_2\underset{\cdot}{C}-OH \longrightarrow \begin{array}{c} \phi_2C-C\phi_2 \\ | \quad | \\ OH\ OH \end{array}$$

$$\phi_2\overset{\cdot}{C}-OH + R\cdot \longrightarrow \begin{array}{c} \phi_2-C-R \\ | \\ OH \end{array}$$

$$\phi_2\overset{\cdot}{C}-OH + RH \longrightarrow \phi_2CHOH + R\cdot$$

$$2R\cdot \longrightarrow R-R \qquad\qquad\qquad [33,34]$$

Studies in both the liquid[33] and the solid state (in a KBr disk)[35] have shown the reduction to proceed via the triplet state.[36] The reaction is extremely general,[37] and it can be observed with aliphatic and aromatic ketones and aldehydes alike:

$$(CH_3)_2C=O + (CH_3)_2CHOH \xrightarrow{h\nu} \begin{array}{c} (CH_3)_2C-C(CH_3)_2 \\ | \quad | \\ OH\ OH \end{array} \qquad [38]$$

Among the solvents that may be employed as hydrogen donors, alcohols and alkyl benzenes such as toluene and cumene figure prominently.[39,40] When one uses the alcohol derived from the ketone to be reduced, only one product is obtained. Mixed additions rarely occur and can be completely avoided by the use of solvents which, on hydrogen abstraction, form radicals that are too short-lived to combine with others before they are deactivated by other processes such as further hydrogen expulsion.

When the radicals are fairly long-lived, the pinacol derived from the alcohol present will be the main product. Therefore isopropanol is the solvent of choice in the pinacol formation from α-tetralone, and reduction of acetone by benzhydrol yields only the pinacol derived from the latter:

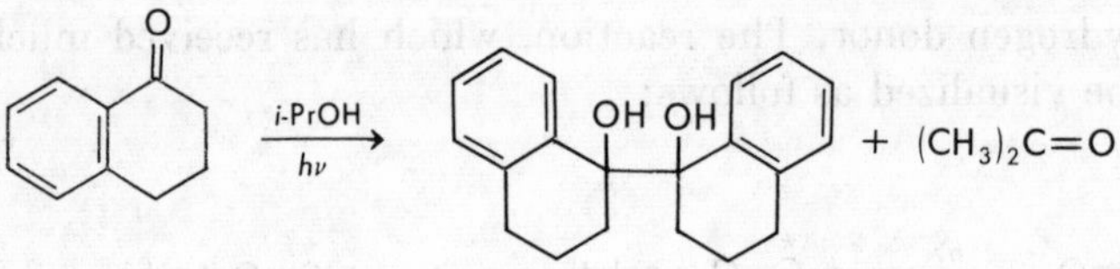

[41]

$$\phi_2CHOH \;+\; CH_3-\underset{\underset{O}{\|}}{C}-CH_3 \;\xrightarrow{h\nu}\; \phi_2-\underset{\underset{OH}{|}}{C}-\underset{\underset{OH}{|}}{C}-\phi_2 \;+\; (CH_3)_2CHOH$$

[37]

Two of the more unusual examples of pinacol formation follow below:

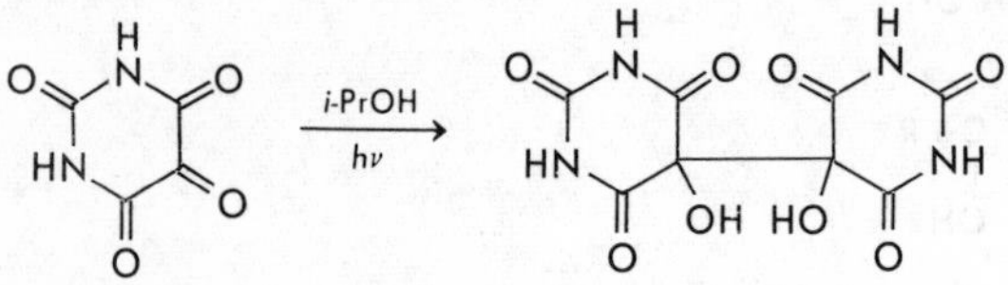

[42]

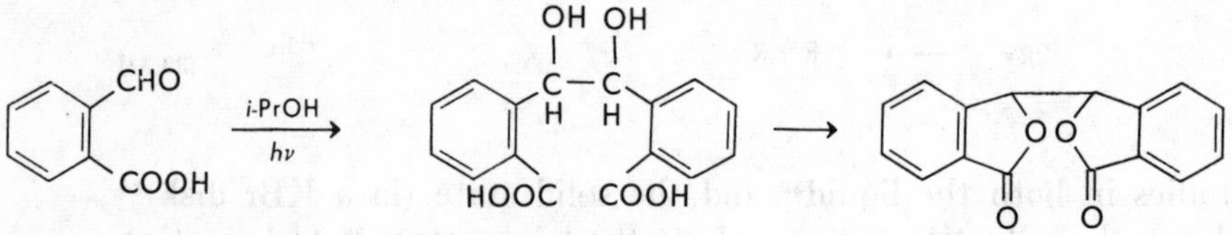

[43]

Since the reaction is essentially an oxidation-reduction one, the reverse process, formation of a carbonyl compound from a pinacol, may be observed also, especially when steric factors make the existence of the pinacol less favorable or when a particularly effective hydrogen acceptor, such as *p*-quinone, is employed:

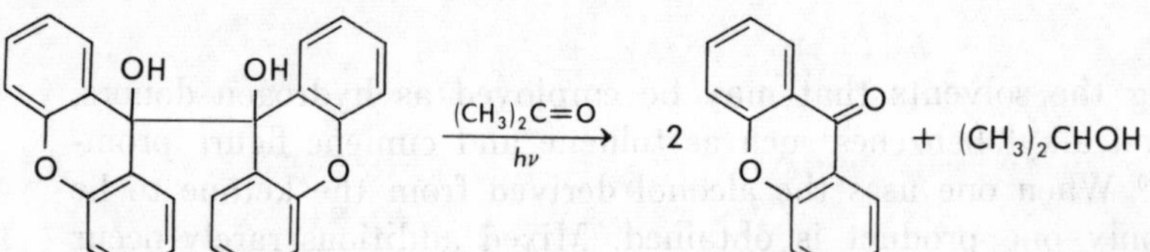

[44]

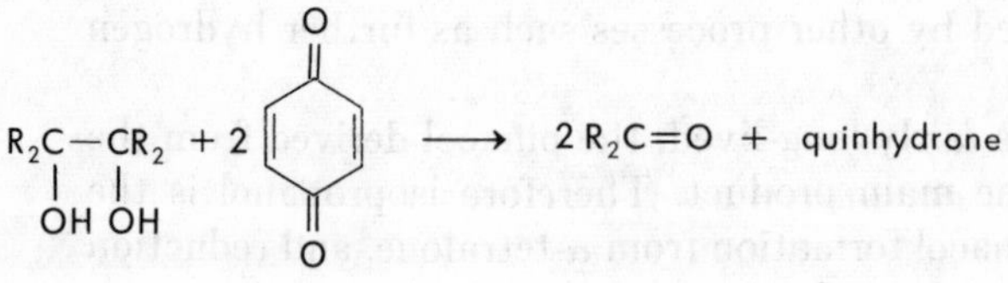

$$R_2C-CR_2 \;+\; 2\;\text{[quinone]} \;\longrightarrow\; 2\,R_2C=O \;+\; \text{quinhydrone}$$
$$\underset{OH\;\;OH}{|\quad\;|}$$

[45]

Two additional factors may be noted. First, reductive couplings of this type are not limited merely to carbonyl compounds and alcohols but can occur whenever the addition or abstraction of hydrogen produces a reasonably stable radical. One such case is the reductive coupling of acridine.

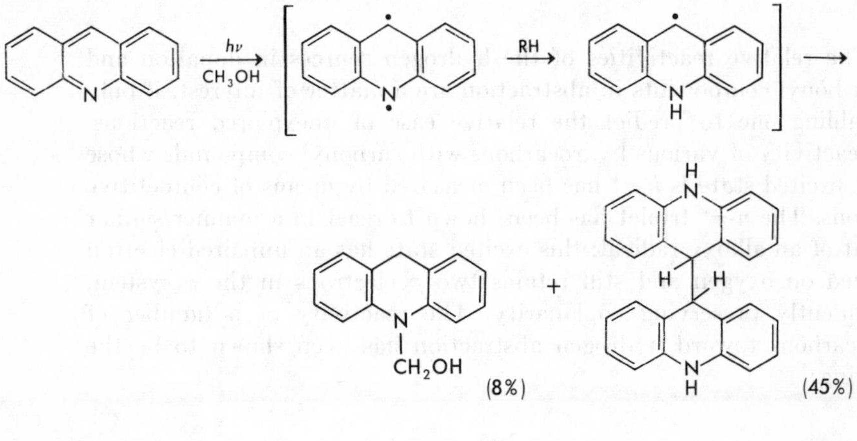

hν
CH₃OH
RH
N
H
CH₂OH
(8%)
(45%)

[45]

Another example is the coupling of nitrosobenzene to form azoxybenzene;[46] 1,3,5,-trinitrobenzene gives similar coupling products on photolysis in ethanol. The solvent is probably oxidized in the reaction, since acetaldehyde has been isolated from the reaction mixture:[47]

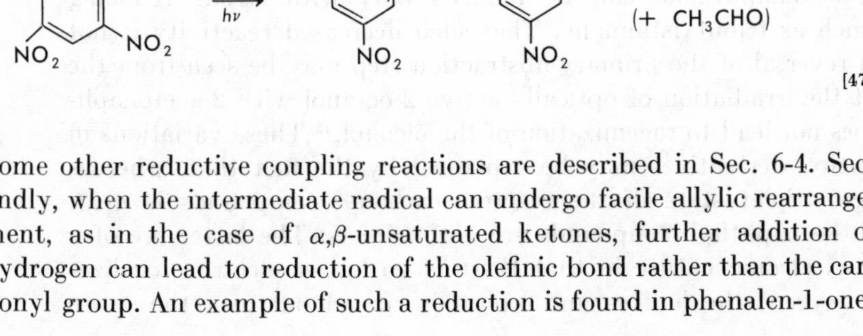

NO
hν
O
N=N
+ nitroderivatives
and diphenylamines
(<10%)
[46]
NO₂
EtOH
hν
(+ CH₃CHO)
[47]

Some other reductive coupling reactions are described in Sec. 6-4. Secondly, when the intermediate radical can undergo facile allylic rearrangement, as in the case of α,β-unsaturated ketones, further addition of hydrogen can lead to reduction of the olefinic bond rather than the carbonyl group. An example of such a reduction is found in phenalen-1-one:

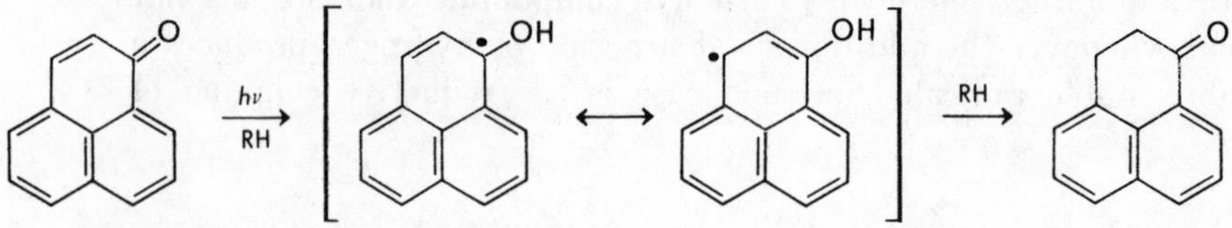

The relative reactivities of the hydrogen sources in donation and the carbonyl components in abstraction are a matter of interest, if only in enabling one to predict the relative ease of unexplored reactions. The reactivity of various hydrocarbons with carbonyl compounds whose lowest excited state is n-π^* has been measured by means of competitive reactions. The n-π^* triplet has been shown to react in a manner similar to that of an alkoxy radical; this excited state has an unpaired electron localized on oxygen and still retains two p electrons in the π system, consequently preserving coplanarity. The reactivity of a number of hydrocarbons toward hydrogen abstraction has been shown to be the following:

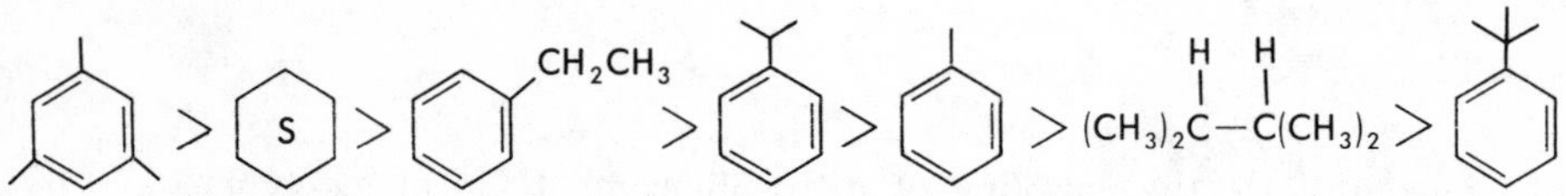

Although the place of cyclohexane in this series is in dispute,[50] it might be observed in general that the order follows the strength of the C—H bond to be broken. Thus, the tertiary protons in 2,3-dimethylbutane are removed in preference over the primary ones. Reactivity differences among carbonyl compounds in the abstraction of hydrogen have also been studied, and some significant differences have come to light. Most prominent is the greatly reduced activity of 2-acetonaphthone and 1-naphthaldehyde as well as of p-amino- and p-hydroxybenzophenones. Thus, 2-acetonaphthone can be reduced only with strong reducing agents such as tributylstannane. That such decreased reactivity is not due to a reversal of the primary abstraction step may be seen from the fact that the irradiation of optically active 2-octanol with 2-acetonaphthone does not lead to racemization of the alcohol.[33] These variations in the naphthyl derivatives may be explained by the fact that, whereas the lowest triplet state of the reactive carbonyl compounds is n-π^*, those of the naphthyl compounds are π-π^* triplets. The latter are of a different electronic nature in that there is no longer electron localization on oxygen; the half-vacant orbital is spread out over the entire ring system, requiring extensive electron reorganization for hydrogen abstraction.[33]

The reduction of *p*-amino- and *p*-hydroxybenzophenones is dependent on the solvent employed, being almost completely suppressed in isopropanol, while reduction does take place in paraffinic solvents such as cyclohexane.[51] Spectroscopic evidence for a change in excitation with the solvent exists. In isopropanol it is the excited charge-transfer state that is of lowest energy, while in cyclohexane (where the reduction of *p*-amino-and *p*-hydroxybenzophenones proceeds in quantum yields of 20 and 100%, respectively) the n-π* state is the lowest-energy state. The intramolecular charge transfer from the electron-donating group to the carbonyl group will be enhanced by polar solvents, which help to decrease the energy of these states to a level below that of the n-π* state:

In accord with this theory it has been found that aminobenzophenones can be reduced easily in isopropanol when converted to their onium salts,[52] either by protonation or methylation, because the charge-transfer states no longer form. Whether the nature of the lowest excited state is the only factor responsible in these cases remains to be seen. The quantum yield of 1- and 2-acetonaphthone and of 2-naphthylphenyl ketone in oxetane formations is also smaller than that of acetophenone and benzophenone.[53]

Mercaptans and disulfides generally retard the reduction of benzophenone not by triplet quenching, but rather by interrupting radical coupling through hydrogen abstraction from the thiol or through donation to the disulfide:[54]

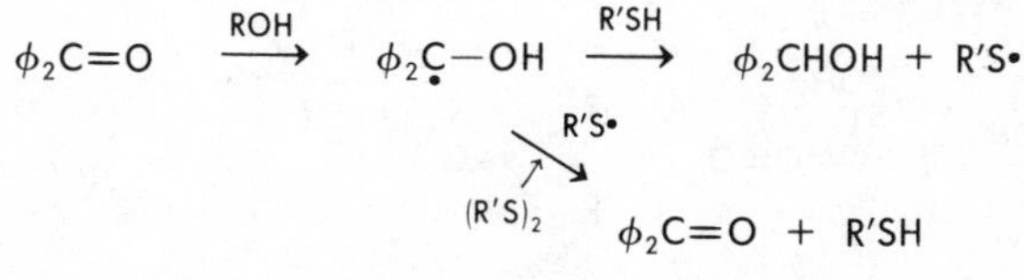

Acetophenone is even more sensitive to these reagents. Disulfides, and especially benzyl mercaptan, can accelerate the decarbonylation of 2-ethylhexanal by a factor of 5 to 10, probably through rapid hydrogen transfer to the alkyl radicals formed:

$$R-\overset{*}{\underset{H}{C}}=O + R'SH \longrightarrow R\overset{\cdot}{C}HOH + R'S\cdot$$

$$R'S\cdot + RCHO \longrightarrow R'SH + R\overset{\cdot}{C}=O \longrightarrow R\cdot + CO$$

$$R\cdot + R'SH \longrightarrow RH + R'S\cdot$$

[55]

$$(R = n\text{-}C_4H_9(C_2H_5)CH-)$$

The reductive coupling of alkyl phenyl glyoxalates is similar in nature to the formation of pinacols. At higher temperatures intramolecular hydrogen transfer by a Norrish type II process may take place if the ester is derived from a primary or secondary alcohol. Alcohol exchange follows the hydrogen-transfer step:[56,57]

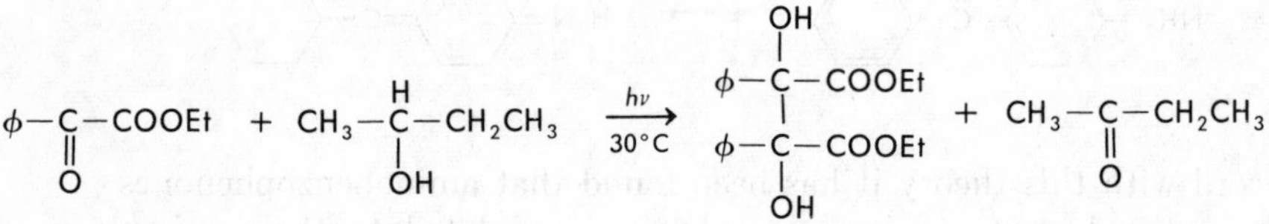

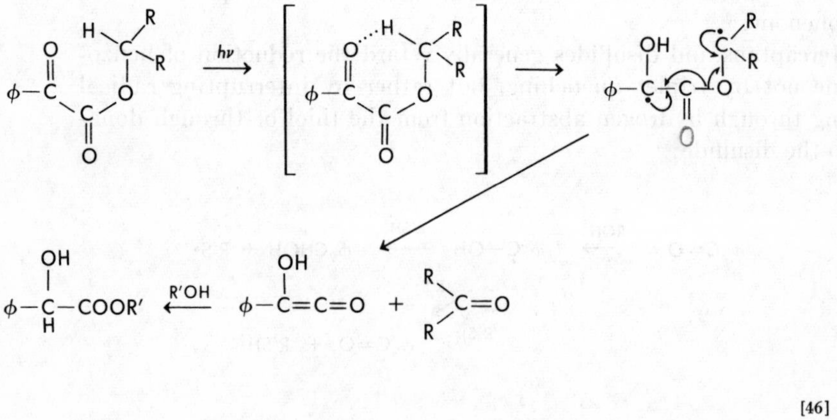

$$\phi-\overset{O}{\underset{\|}{C}}-COOEt + CH_3-\overset{H}{\underset{OH}{C}}-CH_2CH_3 \xrightarrow[30°C]{h\nu} \begin{array}{c} \phi-\overset{OH}{\underset{|}{C}}-COOEt \\ \phi-\overset{|}{\underset{OH}{C}}-COOEt \end{array} + CH_3-\overset{O}{\underset{\|}{C}}-CH_2CH_3$$

[46]

In this way the photolysis of cyclohexylphenylglyoxalate in ethanol at 40° leads to ethyl mandelate and cyclohexanone.[56]

The formation of 1,3-dibenzoylpropane from the benzophenone-sensitized photolysis of *trans*-1,2-dibenzoylcyclopropane in 2-propanol is related to the latter type of reaction. The following sequence is likely to occur:

[58]

Thioesters undergo coupling to form sulfur-free olefins on their photolysis in the absence of a solvent:

[59]

References

1. H. S. Johnson and J. Heicklen, *J. Am. Chem. Soc.*, **86**, 4249, 4255 (1964).
2. K. Gollnick and G. O. Schenck, *Pure Appl. Chem.*, **9**, 507 (1964), and references cited therein.
3. G. O. Schenck, H. D. Becker, K. H. Schulte-Elte, and C. H. Krauch, *Ber.*, **96**, 509 (1963).
3a. L. T. Allan and G. A. Swan, *J. Chem. Soc.*, 4822 (1965).
4. C. S. Foote, S. Wexler, and W. Ando, *Abstract of Papers*, Am. Chem. Soc., April, 1965, 52 P.
5. C. S. Foote and S. Wexler, *J. Am. Chem. Soc.*, **86**, 3880 (1964).
6. G. O. Schenck, *Angew. Chem.*, **69**, 579 (1957), and references cited therein; G. O. Schenck and E. Koch, *Z. Elektrochem.*, **64**, 170 (1960).

7. G. R. Evanega, W. Bergmann, and J. English, Jr., *J. Org. Chem.*, **27**, 13 (1962).
8. G. O. Schenck and C. H. Krauch, *Ber.*, **96**, 517 (1963).
9. G. O. Schenck, K. Gollnick, G. Buchwald, S. Schroeter, and G. Ohloff, *Ann.*, **674**, 93 (1964).
9a. E. Klein, W. Rojahn, *Tetrahedron*, **21**, 2173 (1965); *Ber.*, **98**, 3045 (1965); C. S. Foote, S. Wexler, W. Ando, *Tetrahedron Letters*, 4111, (1965); K. R. Kopecky, H. J. Reich, *Can. J. Chem.*, **43**, 2265 (1965).
10. A. Nickon and J. F. Bagli, *J. Am. Chem. Soc.*, **83**, 1498 (1961); A. Nickon and W. L. Mendelson, *J. Am. Chem. Soc.*, **85**, 1894 (1963).
11. C. S. Foote and S. Wexler, *J. Am. Chem. Soc.*, **86**, 3879 (1964).
12. E. J. Corey and W. C. Taylor, *J. Am. Chem. Soc.*, **86**, 3881 (1964).
13. S. J. Arnold, E. A. Ogryzlo, and H. Witzke, *J. Chem. Phys.*, **40**, 1769 (1964); A. U. Khan and A. Kasha, *J. Chem. Phys.*, **39**, 2105 (1963).
14. H. H. Wasserman and A. R. Doumaux, Jr., *J. Am. Chem. Soc.*, **84**, 4612 (1962).
15. A. W. Johnson and S. W. Tam, *Chem. Ind. (London)*, **1964**, 1425. See also T. Matsuura, K. Omura, R. Nakashima, *Bull. Chem. Soc. (Japan)*, **38**, 1358 (1965).
16. G. Büchi and D. E. Ayer, *J. Am. Chem. Soc.*, **78**, 689 (1956).
17. J. A. Berson and E. Brown, *J. Am. Chem. Soc.*, **77**, 447 (1955).
18. P. A. Leighton and F. A. Lucy, *J. Chem. Phys.*, **2**, 756 (1934).
19. F. B. Mallory, C. S. Wood, and J. T. Gordon, *J. Am. Chem. Soc.*, **86**, 3094 (1964).
20. C. S. Wood and F. B. Mallory, *J. Org. Chem.*, **29**, 3373 (1964).
21. R. Srinivasan and J. C. Powers, Jr., *J. Am. Chem. Soc.*, **85**, 1355 (1963).
22. F. B. Mallory, C. S. Wood, J. T. Gordon, L. C. Lindquist, and M. L. Sarita, *J. Am. Chem. Soc.*, **84**, 4361 (1962).
23. N. Kharasch and P. Friedman, *Abstract of papers, Am. Chem. Soc., Chicago,* September, 1964, 27S; E. N. Ugochukwu and R. L. Wain, *Chem. Ind. (London),* **1965**, 35; J. J. Hlavka and H. M. Krazinski, *J. Org. Chem.*, **28**, 1422 (1963).
24. W. Wolf and N. Kharasch, *J. Org. Chem.*, **30**, 2493 (1965); N. Kharasch, T. G. Alston, *Chem. Ind. (London)*, 1463 (1965).
24a. E. E. van Tamelen, J. I. Brauman, L. E. Ellis, *J. Am. Chem. Soc.*, **87**, 4964 (1965).
25. W. M. Moore, D. D. Morgan, and F. R. Stermitz, *J. Am. Chem. Soc.*, **85**, 829 (1963).
26. M. V. Sargent and C. J. Timmons, *J. Am. Chem. Soc.*, **85**, 2186 (1964).
27. F. B. Mallory, J. T. Gordon, and C. S. Wood, *J. Am. Chem. Soc.*, **85**, 828 (1963).
28. R. E. Buckles, *J. Am. Chem. Soc.*, **77**, 1040 (1955); H. Stobbe, *Ber.*, **40**, 3372 (1907).
29. G. E. Lewis, *Tetrahedron Letters*, **9**, 12 (1960); P. Hugelshofer, J. Kalvoda, and K. Schaffner, *Helv. Chim. Acta*, **43**, 1322 (1960). See also: W. Carruthers and H. N. M. Stewart, *Tetrahedron Letters*, **1965**, 301; G. M. Badger, C. P. Joshua, and G. E. Lewis, *Tetrahedron Letters*, **1964**, 3711; *Aust. J. Chem.* **18**, 1639 (1965); S. M. Kupchan and H. C. Wormser, *Tetrahedron Letters*, **1965**, 359.
30. A Schönberg, A. F. A. Ismail, and W. Asker, *J. Chem. Soc.*, **1946**, 442; A. F. A. Ismail and Z. M. Eli-Shafei, *J. Chem. Soc.*, **1957**, 3393. A. Schönberg and K. Junghans, *Ber.*, **98**, 2539 (1965).
31. J. S. Shannon, H. Silberman, and S. Sternhell, *Tetrahedron Letters*, **1964**, 659.
32. A. Schönberg and A. Mustafa, *Chem. Rev.*, **40**, 181 (1947).
33. G. S. Hammond and P. A. Leermakers, *J. Am. Chem. Soc.*, **84**, 207 (1962).
34. W. M. Moore, G. S. Hammond, and R. P. Foss, *J. Am. Chem. Soc.*, **83**, 2789 (1961).

35. J. N. Pitts, Jr., J. K. S. Wan, and E. A. Schuck, *J. Am. Chem. Soc.*, **86**, 3606 (1964).
36. G. S. Hammond and W. M. Moore, *J. Am. Chem. Soc.*, **81**, 6334 (1959).
37. A. Schönberg, "Präparative Organische Chemie," pp. 109–116, Springer, Berlin, 1958.
38. G. Ciamician and P. Silber, *Ber.*, **44**, 1280 (1911).
39. G. S. Hammond, W. P. Baker, and W. M. Moore, *J. Am. Chem. Soc.*, **83**, 2795 (1961).
40. A. Beckett and G. Porter, *Trans. Faraday Soc.*, **59**, 2038 (1963).
41. F. Bergmann and Y. Hirshberg, *J. Am. Chem. Soc.*, **65**, 1429 (1943).
42. R. Moubasher and A. M. Othman, *J. Am. Chem. Soc.*, **72**, 2667 (1950).
43. A. Mustafa, *J. Chem. Soc.*, **1949**, 83.
44. A. Schönberg and A. Mustafa, *J. Chem. Soc.*, **1944**, 67.
45. F. Mader and V. Zanker, *Ber.*, **97**, 2418 (1964); M. A. Kellmann, *Bull. Soc. Chim. Belges*, **71**, 811 (1962). H. Göth, P. Cerutti, H. Schmid, *Helv. Chim. Acta*, **48**, 1395 (1965).
46. E. Bamberger, *Ber.*, **35**, 1606 (1902). M. Shamma, J. K. Whitesell, and P. L. Warner, Jr., *Tetrahedron Letters*, **1965**, 3869.
47. V. I. Stenberg and D. J. Holter, *J. Org. Chem.*, **29**, 3420 (1964).
48. H. Köller, G. P. Rabold, K. Weiss, and T. K. Mukherjee, *Proc. Chem. Soc.*, **1964**, 332.
49. A. Padwa, *Tetrahedron Letters*, **1964**, 3465.
50. C. Walling and M. J. Gibian, *J. Am. Chem. Soc.*, **86**, 3902 (1964). **87**, 3361 (1965).
51. G. Porter and P. Suppan, *Proc. Chem. Soc.*, **1964**, 191; G. Porter and P. Suppan, *Pure Appl. Chem.*, **9**, 499 (1964).
52. S. G. Cohen and M. N. Siddiqui, *J. Am. Chem. Soc.*, **86**, 5048 (1964).
53. N. C. Yang, M. Nussim, M. J. Jorgenson, and S. Murov, *Tetrahedron Letters*, **1964**, 3657.
54. S. G. Cohen, D. A. Laufer, and W. V. Sherman, *J. Am. Chem. Soc.*, **86**, 3060 (1964); S. G. Cohen and S. Aktipis, *Tetrahedron Letters*, **1965**, 579.
55. S. G. Cohen, J. D. Berman, and S. Orman, *Tetrahedron Letters*, **1962**, 43.
56. E. S. Huyser and D. C. Neckers, *J. Org. Chem.*, **29**, 276 (1964).
57. N. C. Yang and A. Morduchowitz, *J. Org. Chem.*, **29**, 1654 (1964).
58. G. W. Griffin, E. J. O'Connell, and H. A. Hammond, *J. Am. Chem. Soc.*, **85**, 1001 (1963).
59. U. Schmidt and K. H. Kabitzke, *Angew. Chem.*, **64**, 687 (1964). U. Schmidt, K. H. Kabitzke, O. Boie, and C. Osterroht, *Ber.*, **98**, 3819 (1965).

Substitution Reactions

8-1 The Photolysis of Nitrite Esters and Related Compounds

The photolysis of nitrite esters and hypohalites[1,2] has acquired great synthetic utility in recent years. It leads to a wide variety of products, even though the primary process is the same in all cases: homolytic fission of a N—O or X—O bond. The products from the fission step are nitric oxide, or a halogen radical, and the reactive alkoxy radical:

$$RONO \longrightarrow RO\cdot + NO$$

$$ROX \longrightarrow RO\cdot + X\cdot$$

The subsequent events in the sequence really place the reaction among the substitution reactions, and it is therefore discussed separately. The alkoxy radical has, like most radicals, several paths[3] available to stabilize itself, such as:

1. Recombination:

$$RO\cdot + X\cdot \longrightarrow ROX$$

2. Addition to olefinic bonds:

$$RO\cdot + \;>C=C<\; \longrightarrow \; RO-\overset{|}{\underset{|}{C}}-\overset{|}{\underset{|}{C}}\cdot$$

3. Disproportionation:

$$2RR'CHO\cdot \longrightarrow RR'C=O + RR'CHOH$$

4. Radical fission:

$$RR'CHO\cdot \longrightarrow R\cdot + R'CHO \text{ or } R'\cdot + RCHO$$

5. Intramolecular or intermolecular hydrogen abstraction:

$$RCH-(CH_2)_n-\overset{|}{CH}- \;\xrightarrow{\;R'H\;}\; RCH-(CH_2)_n-\overset{|}{CH}- \;+\; R'\cdot$$
$$\underset{\overset{|}{\underset{\bullet}{O}}}{} \qquad\qquad\qquad \underset{OH}{}$$

$$\searrow$$

$$RCH-(CH_2)_n-\overset{|}{\underset{\bullet}{C}}-$$
$$\underset{OH}{|}$$

When the last process, that of intramolecular hydrogen abstraction, takes place, a free radical is generated elsewhere in the molecule, and it can combine with any $X\cdot$ or NO that might still be in the vicinity. When the combination with nitric oxide leads to nitroso dimers or oximes, the process has become known as the Barton reaction, after D. H. R. Barton, who discovered the sequence and developed it into the reaction of considerable synthetic utility that it is today.[4] The complete chain of events in the Barton reaction is as follows:

The reaction has found application predominantly in the chemistry of steroids, mainly because of its great selectivity in the hydrogen-abstraction step; the step takes place only from the position δ to the nitrite ester. One of the first examples reported by Barton was the partial synthesis of aldosterone acetate:

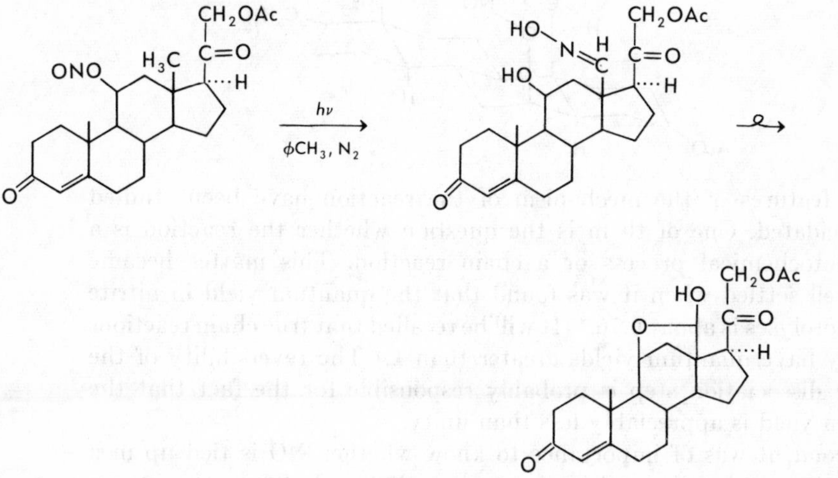

[5,6]

Two other typical examples are given below:

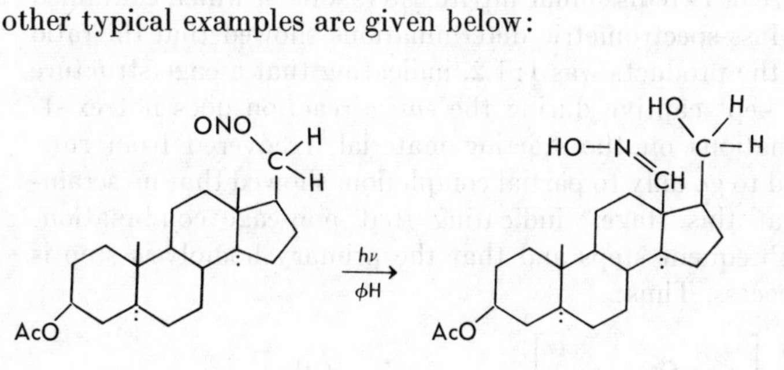

[7]

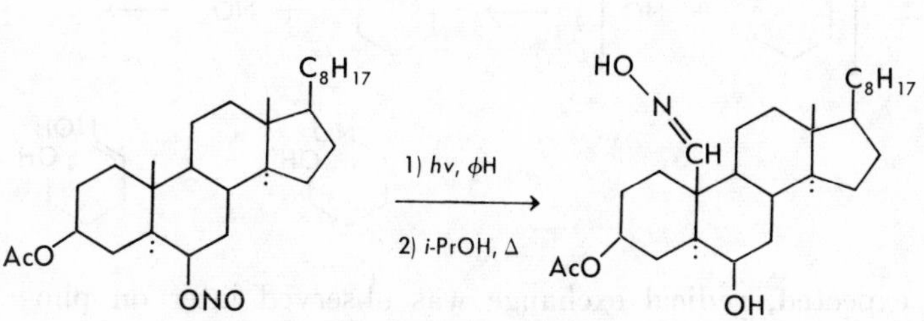

[4]

As presented above, the sequence suggests that a six-membered transition state is desired, if not required, for hydrogen abstraction.[7] From the examples presented above it may be noted that all groups involved are in axial positions, facilitating such a transition state:

Several features of the mechanism of the reaction have been studied and elucidated. One of them is the question whether the reaction is a true photochemical process or a chain reaction. This matter became fairly well settled when it was found that the quantum yield in nitrite ester photolyses is about 0.76.[8] (It will be recalled that true chain reactions typically have quantum yields greater than 1.) The reversibility of the primary dissociation step is probably responsible for the fact that the quantum yield is appreciably less than unity.

Second, it was of importance to know whether NO is tied up in a solvent cage during the entire sequence, so that each NO group returns to its molecule of origin, or whether there is a looser association in which intermolecular transfer can take place. This point was studied[9] by photolyzing a mixture of two dissimilar nitrite esters, one of which contained 98.3% of N^{15}. Mass-spectrometric determinations showed that the ratio of N^{14} to N^{15} in the products was 1:1.2, indicating that a cage structure in which NO is kept captive during the *entire* reaction does not exist. Similar determinations on the starting material, recovered from runs that were allowed to go only to partial completion, showed that no scrambling occurred at this stage,[9] indicating that non-cage combinations occur only in subsequent steps and that the primary homolysis step is indeed a cage process. Thus:

As would be expected, radical exchange was observed later on photolysis in the presence of iodine or bromotrichloromethane:

[10]

A third question is whether a six-membered transition state is indeed a requirement in the hydrogen-abstraction step. It was studied by Kabas-akalian, Townley, and Yudis.[11] These workers have found that, except for some side reactions, no nitroso dimers are obtained on photolysis of a series of ω-phenylalkylnitrites whenever an insufficient number of carbon atoms was present in the chain to enable a six-membered transition state to form; the presence of a larger number of atoms than needed resulted in abstraction from the γ position in spite of the greater reactivity of benzyl hydrogens in other positions:

These results show that seven- or five-membered transition states are not involved in nitrite ester photolyses. (In similar free-radical decompositions of hypohalites, however, small amounts of products have been observed, which point to a seven-membered transition state for hydrogen abstraction.[12])

The photochemical behavior of aliphatic nitrite esters is similar.[13] Among these, tertiary nitrite esters undergo alkoxy radical decomposition in preference to the Barton reaction. (An exception is the case of 2-methyl-2-hexylnitrite.[13]) The same occurs in primary or secondary nitrite esters unable to react through a six-membered transition state. The photolysis of isobutylnitrite is shown here as an example:

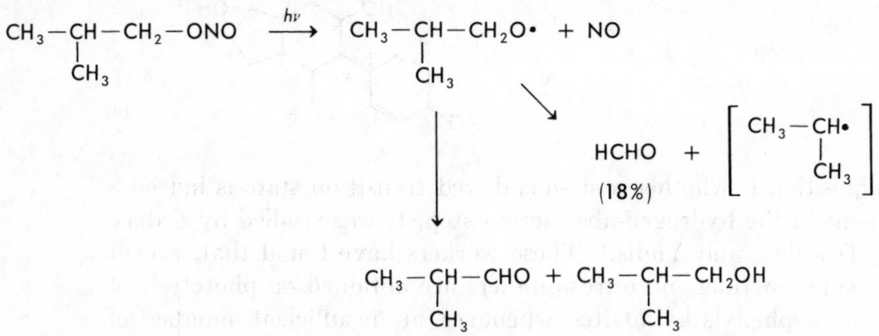

$$CH_3-CH-CH_2-ONO \xrightarrow{h\nu} CH_3-CH-CH_2O\cdot + NO$$

with CH_3 groups below, then:

$$HCHO + \left[\begin{array}{c} CH_3-CH\cdot \\ | \\ CH_3 \end{array} \right]$$

(18%)

$$CH_3-CH-CHO + CH_3-CH-CH_2OH$$

with CH_3 groups, (12%) and (27%)

[14]

The products obtained from alicyclic nitrite esters on their photolysis give further evidence for the requirement of a six-membered transition state. Thus, 2-methyl-1-cyclohexylnitrite will give only traces of a nitroso dimer, while the 2-ethyl homolog reacts readily to give about 30% of the dimer.[15,16] Hydrogen abstraction can occur readily in the latter case:

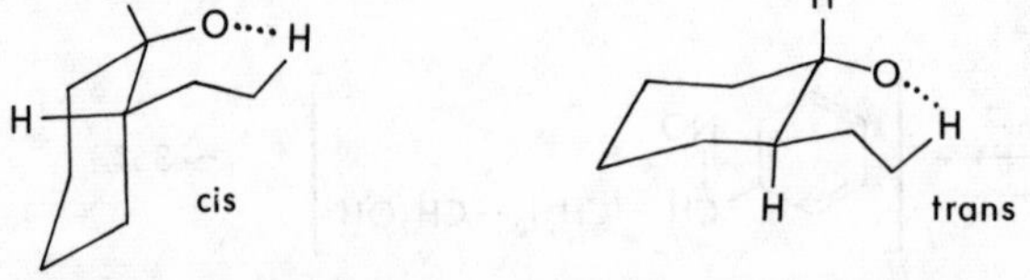

cis   trans

Cyclohexyl nitrite fails to react; this compound, as well as its four- and five-membered analogs (and to a lesser extent the seven-membered one), undergoes ring opening in a secondary radical fission process:

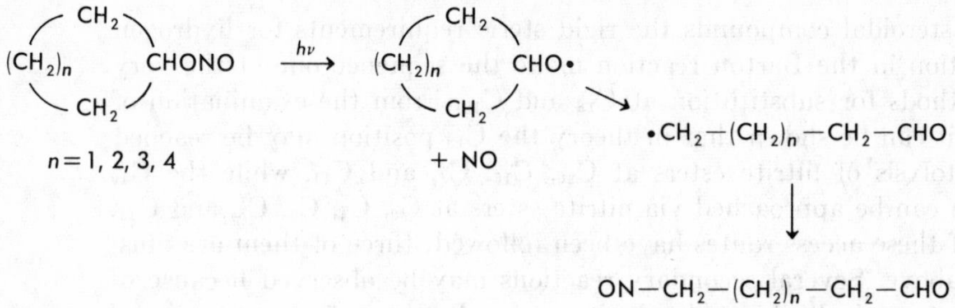
CH2
(CH2)n
CHONO
CH2
hν
CH2
(CH2)n
CHO•
CH2
•CH2—(CH2)n—CH2—CHO
n=1, 2, 3, 4
+ NO
ON—CH2—(CH2)n—CH2—CHO

The higher homologs, cycloheptyl- and, especially, cyclooctylnitrite, possess the prerequisites for intramolecular hydrogen abstraction from the γ positions, and rearrangement occurs quite readily. It has not been established, however, whether a cyclic transition state is indeed involved:

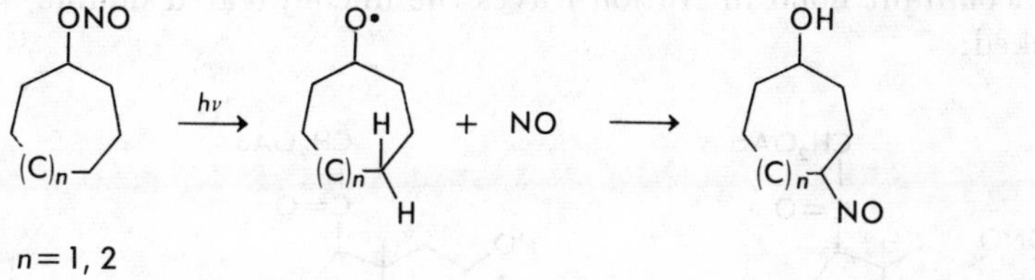
ONO
(C)n
hν
O•
H
(C)n
H
+ NO
OH
(C)n
NO
n=1, 2

As mentioned, other radical processes may compete with the Barton reaction. Thus, the photolysis of *dl*-bornyl and *dl*-isobornyl nitrites leads to the same mixture of products:

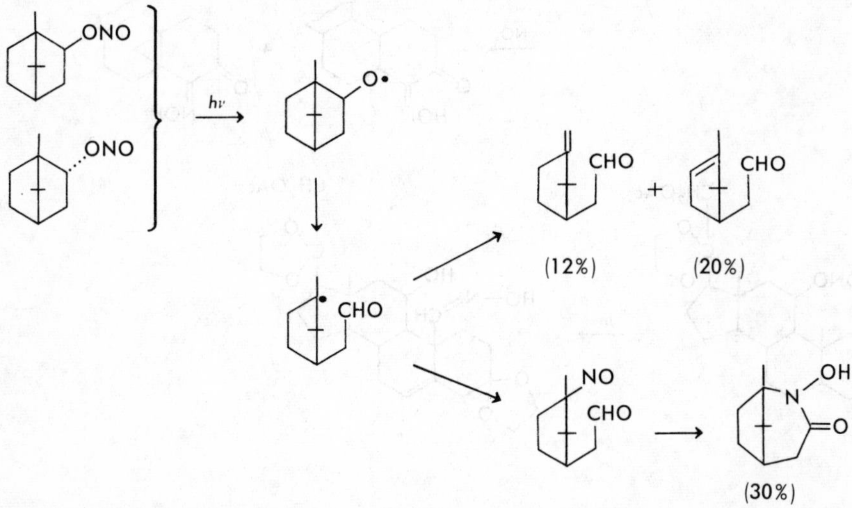
ONO
ONO
hν
O•
CHO
CHO
+
CHO
(12%)
(20%)
NO
CHO
OH
N
O
(30%)

[17,18]

In steroidal compounds the rigid steric requirements for hydrogen abstraction in the Barton reaction make the sequence one of the very few methods for substitution at C_{18} and C_{19}. From the examination of models it can be shown that in theory the C_{18} position may be reached by photolysis of nitrite esters at C_{20}, C_{15}, C_8, and C_{11}, while the C_{19} position can be approached via nitrite esters at C_2, C_4, C_6, C_8, and C_{11}. Most of these access routes have been followed; three of them are illustrated above. Several secondary reactions may be observed because of certain strategically located substituents or because of some structural features of the molecule. One of them is the attack of the C_{19}-methylene radical on the conjugated double bond in Δ^4-3-ketosteroids. The driving force for such attack is probably participation of the conjugated carbonyl group system in resonance stabilization of the new radical. This is supported by the fact that conversion of the carbonyl group to the ketal with concomitant bond migration leaves the unconjugated double bond unattacked:

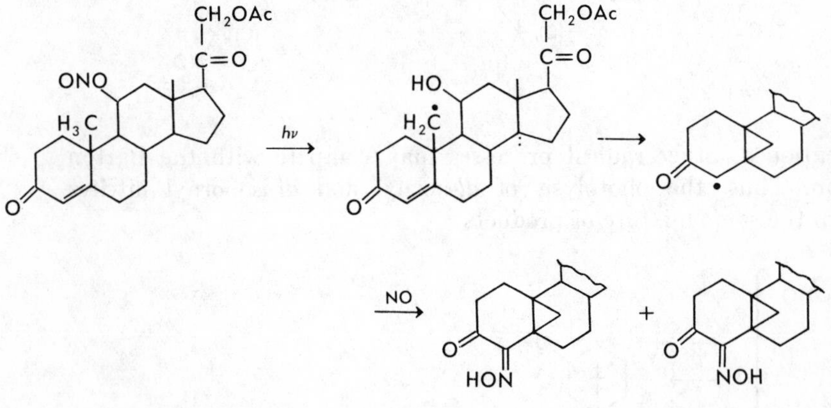

But

[6]

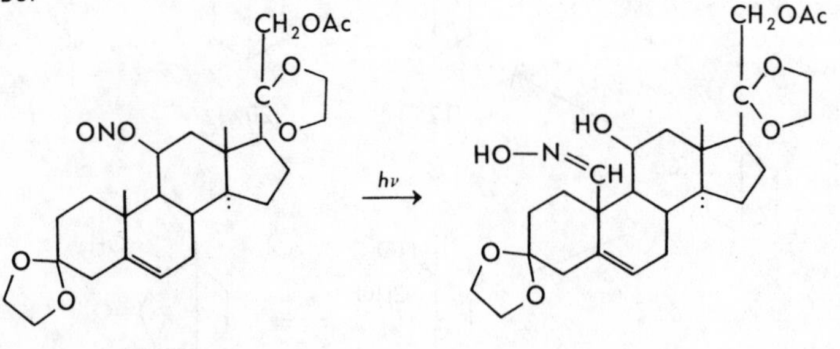

[19]

A second reaction is the attack of the oximino group on neighboring carbonyl groups:

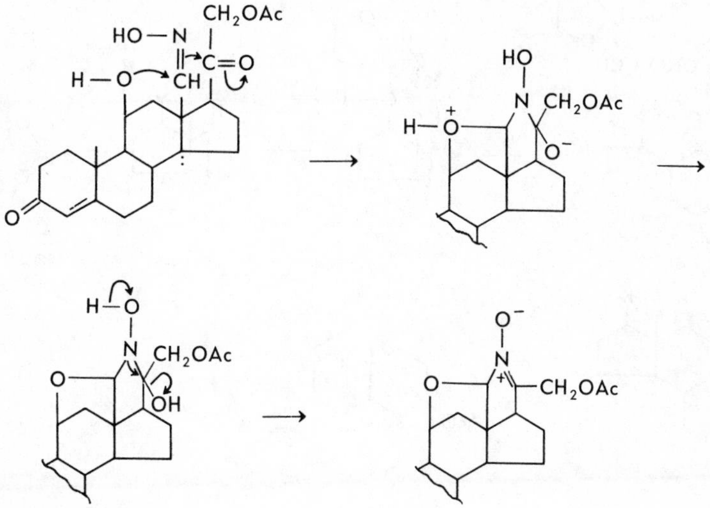

[6,20]

Other processes result in C—C fission due to free-radical rearrangements. One leads to the incorporation of the C_{18} methyl group in the ring expansion of ring D:

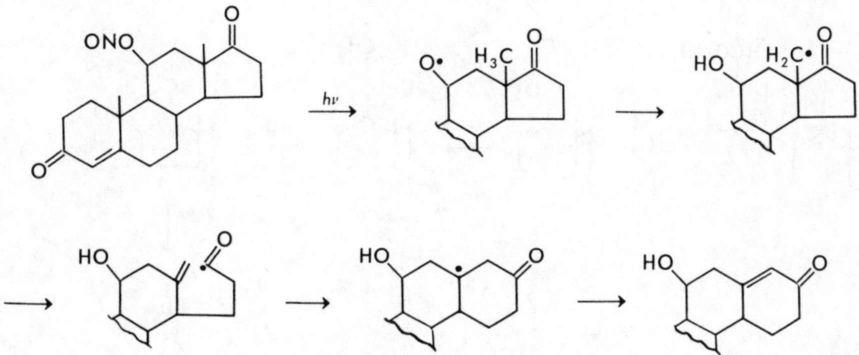

[21]

Alternatively, radical expulsion by C—C bond fission may take place prior to hydrogen abstraction:

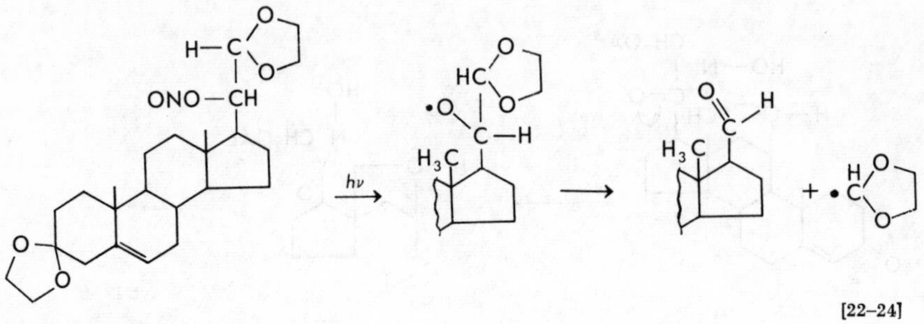

[22–24]

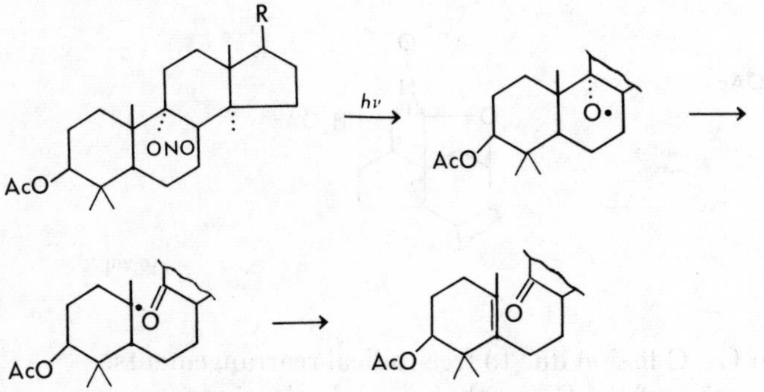

[67]

A fifth variation is epoxide formation by addition of the alkoxy radical
to a double bond:

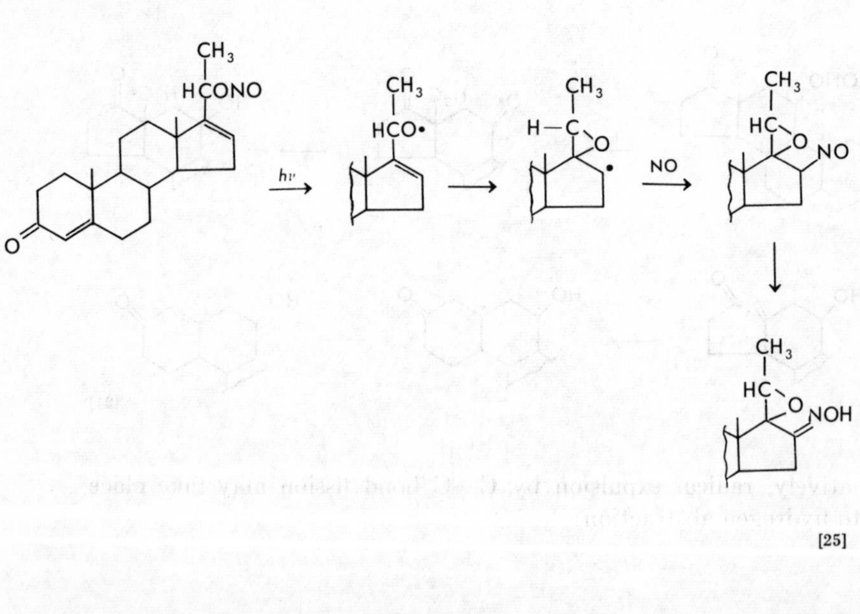

[25]

Finally, hydroxamic acids may form by the following route:

[26]

The rearrangements of 9-nitroanthracene and 2,3-dimethyl-1-nitronaphthalene bear resemblance to the rearrangement of nitrite esters. Chapman and coworkers[27] found that 2,3-dimethyl-1-nitronaphthalene rearranges to 2,3-dimethyl-1,4-naphthoquinone on photolysis in 95% ethanol and that 9-nitroanthracene undergoes a series of transformations, depending on the conditions used:[27]

The isolation of NO among the products of the reaction is probably due to the intermediate formation of 9-nitrosoanthracene. A subsequent rearrangement may then lead to 10,10'-bianthrone and the monoxime:

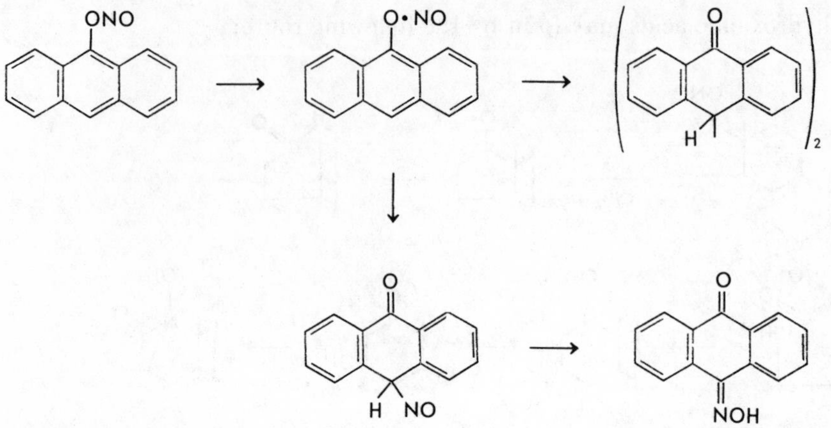

Two mechanisms for the formation of the nitrite ester can be considered.[27] The first would involve C—N bond fission with the formation of NO_2 followed by recombination and formation of a C—O bond. Although such a mechanism seems to be operative in the nitromethane–methyl nitrite conversion, the absence of any NO_2 among the products forces one to consider alternative routes such as that presented below:

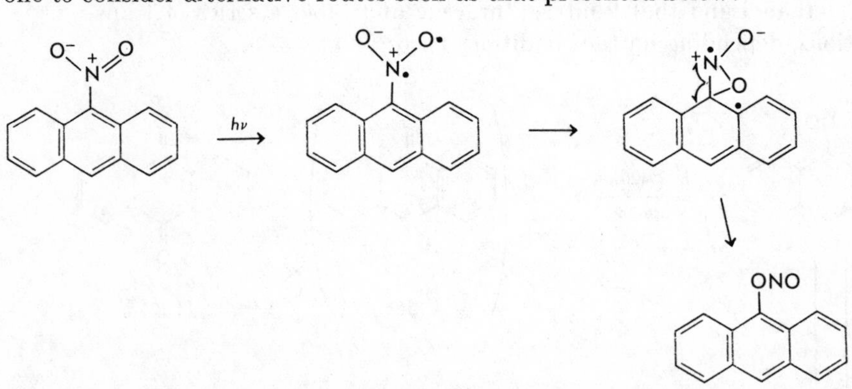

A similar course of events was observed earlier in the photolysis of nitrobenzene, where *p*-nitrophenol and nitrosobenzene are the main products obtained:

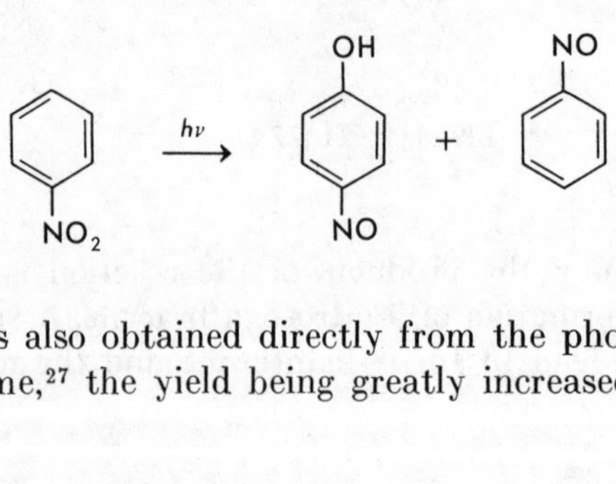

[68]

Anthraquinone is also obtained directly from the photolysis of anthraquinone monoxime,[27] the yield being greatly increased by the addition of NO:

This reaction is difficult to rationalize. The only conceivable possibility that incorporates the dependence on NO gas necessitates the presence of nitrous oxide (N_2O) among the products:

$$\longrightarrow \quad + \; N_2O \quad (NO + H\cdot \longrightarrow HNO \longrightarrow N_2O + H_2O)$$

There is no information on this point, and the mechanism presented here is therefore entirely speculative.

A reaction related to the nitroanthracene rearrangement is that of β-methyl-β-nitrostyrene.[27] A ketoxime is formed; it can best be seen to occur as involving rearrangement to a nitrite ester followed by migration of the nitroso group:[27]

(98%)

In the photolysis of *N*-nitrosoamines in the presence of a proton source, migration of the nitroso group from N to C occurs, leading to *N*-substituted amidoximes:

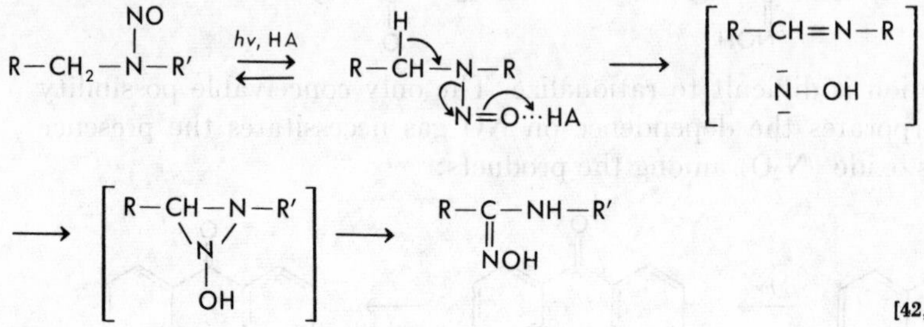

$$[42,43]$$

One further item of interest is the migration of a nitrile group from a cyanohydrin at C_{20} to a site at C_{18} in steroids:

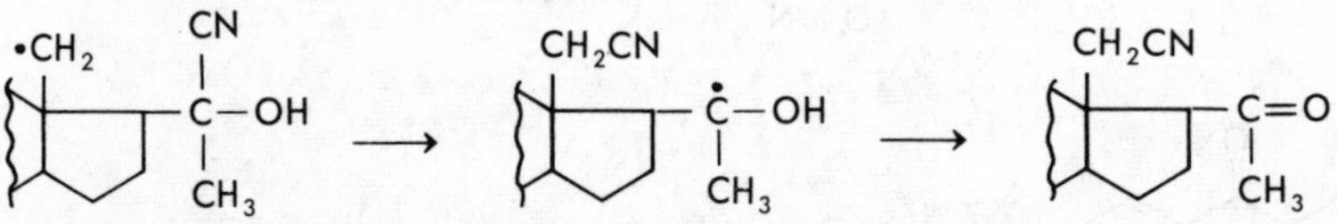

$[31]$

The photolysis of hypohalites needs little discussion, since it proceeds in a fashion similar to that of nitrite esters,[28] even though it may bear the characteristics of a free-radical chain reaction.

Treatment with base converts the chlorohydrins, which are formed initially, to ethers:

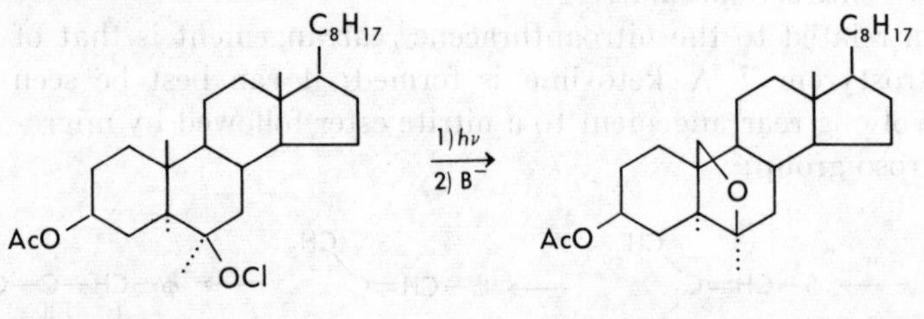

$$[29]$$

Although the hypochlorites must be prepared separately, hypoiodites may be generated *in situ* with lead tetraacetate and iodine. Iodine is frequently lost from the product with the spontaneous formation of ethers. For example:

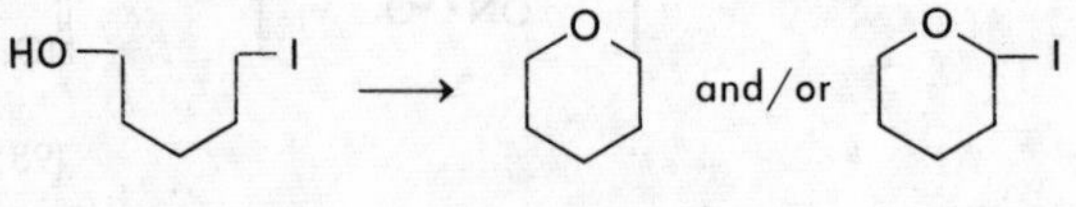

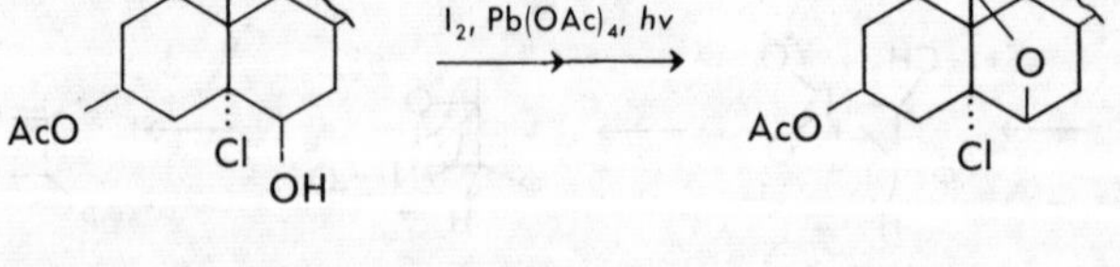

$[30]$

In the absence of circumstances permitting a Barton type of reaction to occur, alkoxy radical decomposition takes place along the various paths available in a manner paralleling that observed in the photolysis of nitrite esters.

Acyl hypoiodites, prepared *in situ* from lead tetraacetate, iodine, and a carboxylic acid, lead primarily to decarboxylation on photolysis, with the production of the corresponding alkyl iodides. In fact, this reaction provides a good method for decarboxylation:[69]

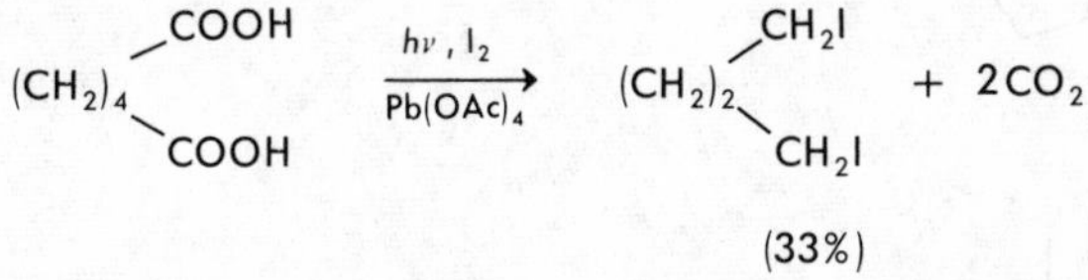

$$(CH_2)_4 \underset{COOH}{\overset{COOH}{\diagup}} \quad \xrightarrow[Pb(OAc)_4]{h\nu,\ I_2} \quad (CH_2)_2 \underset{CH_2I}{\overset{CH_2I}{\diagup}} \quad + \ 2CO_2$$

(33%)

The N-halogen bond undergoes facile rupture upon photolysis. Barton[70] has made use of this reaction to develop a useful method for the synthesis of γ-lactones. The reaction takes place through the intermediate formation of γ-iodoamides, followed by their cyclization to iminolactones, which undergo rapid hydrolysis:

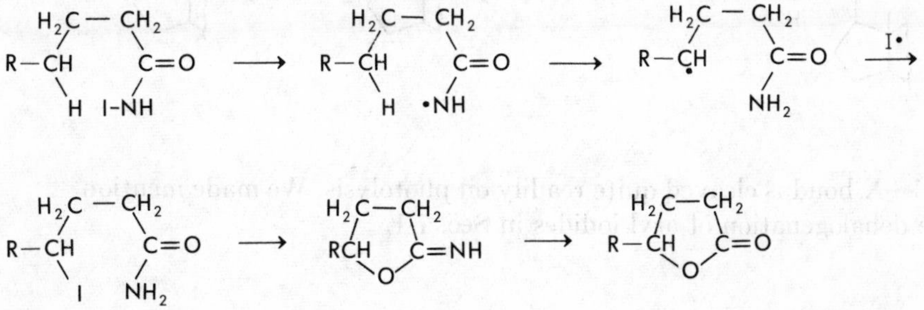

The *N*-iodoamides may be prepared either with lead tetraacetate-iodine or by a *t*-butylhypochlorite–iodine mixture. A similar hydrogen abstraction has been reported in the photolysis of derivatives of *N*-chloroamides. However, subsequent cyclization apparently did not occur:[71]

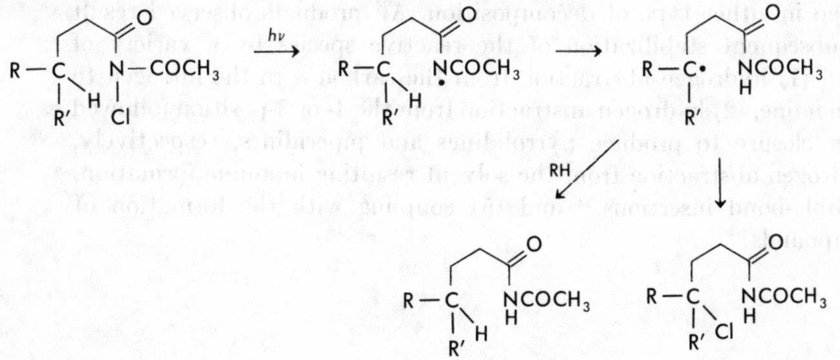

A related reaction is the photolysis of *N*-chloroamines. In one example reported, fragmentation took place along the route indicated below:[72]

The C—X bond is cleaved quite readily on photolysis. We made mention of the dehalogenation of aryl iodides in Sec. 7-1.

8-2   The Photolysis of Azides

The thermal and photochemical properties of azides are much the same; the loss of nitrogen with the formation of an electron-deficient species which goes by a variety of names (nitrene, azene, etc.)[32] is the first step in either type of decomposition. All products observed result from subsequent stabilization of the reactive species by a variety of routes:[33] (1) hydrogen abstraction from the carbon α to the nitrogen to form an imine, (2) hydrogen abstraction from the 4- or 5-position followed by ring closure to produce pyrrolidines and piperidines, respectively, (3) hydrogen abstraction from the solvent resulting in amine formation, (4) double-bond insertions,[34] and (5) coupling with the formation of azocompounds:

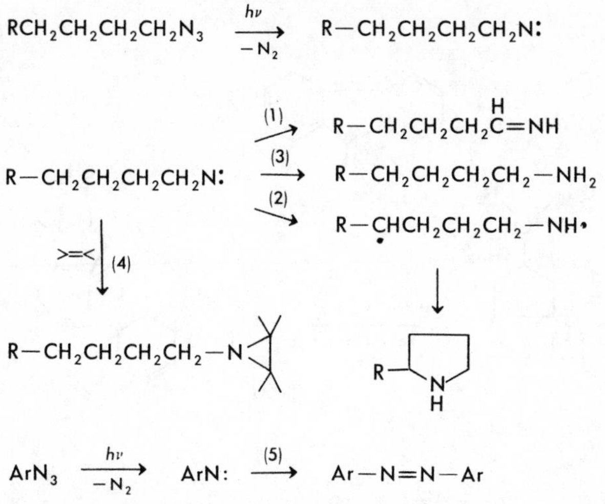

$$RCH_2CH_2CH_2CH_2N_3 \xrightarrow[-N_2]{h\nu} R-CH_2CH_2CH_2CH_2N:$$

$$R-CH_2CH_2CH_2CH_2N: \begin{array}{l} \xrightarrow{(1)} \quad R-CH_2CH_2CH_2\overset{\text{H}}{C}=NH \\ \xrightarrow{(3)} \quad R-CH_2CH_2CH_2CH_2-NH_2 \\ \xrightarrow{(2)} \quad R-\underset{\cdot}{C}HCH_2CH_2CH_2-NH\cdot \end{array}$$

$$\downarrow \begin{array}{c} \text{>=<} \\ (4) \end{array}$$

$$R-CH_2CH_2CH_2CH_2-N\overset{\displaystyle \bigvee}{\underset{\displaystyle \bigwedge}{}}$$

$$R-\underset{\underset{\text{H}}{\text{N}}}{\bigg\langle} \bigg\rangle$$

$$ArN_3 \xrightarrow[-N_2]{h\nu} ArN: \xrightarrow{(5)} Ar-N=N-Ar$$

Examples of each of these reaction paths have been reported. Thus, the photolysis of *n*-heptyl azide leads to an imine and a pyrrolidine,† while cyclohexylamine is observed on photolysis of cyclohexyl azide:

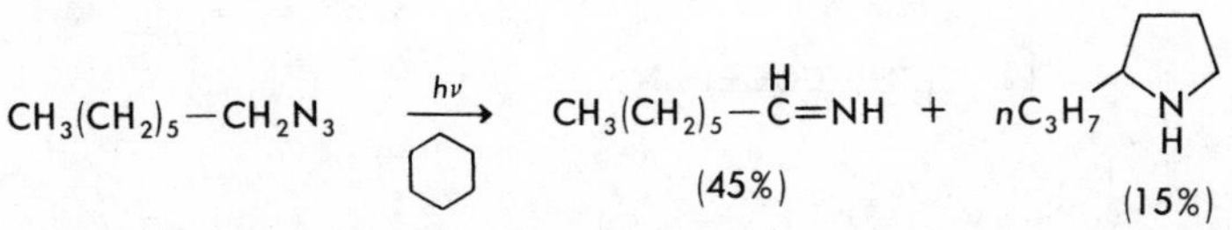

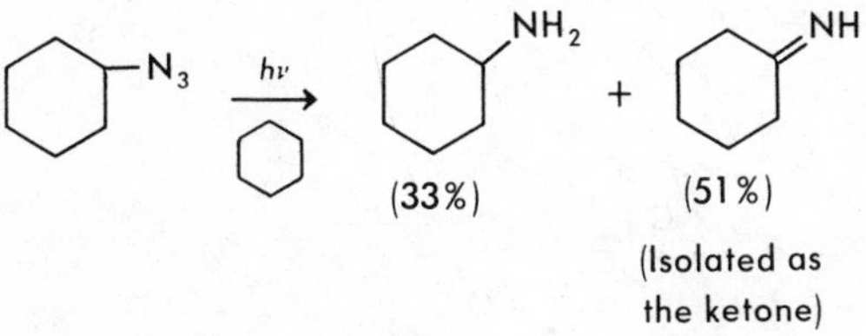

$$CH_3(CH_2)_5-CH_2N_3 \xrightarrow{h\nu} CH_3(CH_2)_5-\overset{\text{H}}{C}=NH + nC_3H_7\underset{\underset{\text{H}}{\text{N}}}{\bigg\langle} \bigg\rangle$$

$$(45\%) \qquad\qquad (15\%)$$

$$\bigcirc-N_3 \xrightarrow{h\nu} \bigcirc-NH_2 + \bigcirc=NH$$

$$(33\%) \qquad (51\%)$$

$$\text{(Isolated as the ketone)}$$

[33]

Abstraction of hydrogen from the 4 position may be further illustrated by the formation of carbazole from *o*-azidobiphenyl and by the elegant application of the reaction in the synthesis of conessine:

† The formation of pyrrolidine derivatives reported here has been shown to be a rather precarious process,[33a] for both the original and later investigators have commented on its difficult reproducibility.

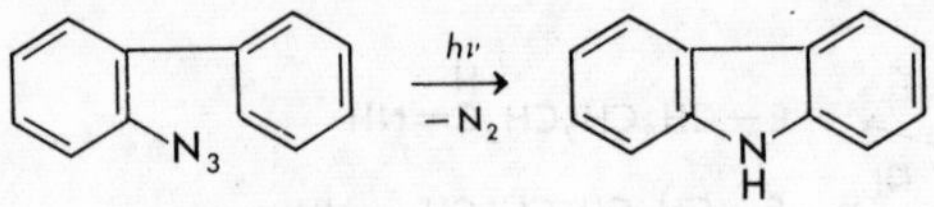

[35]

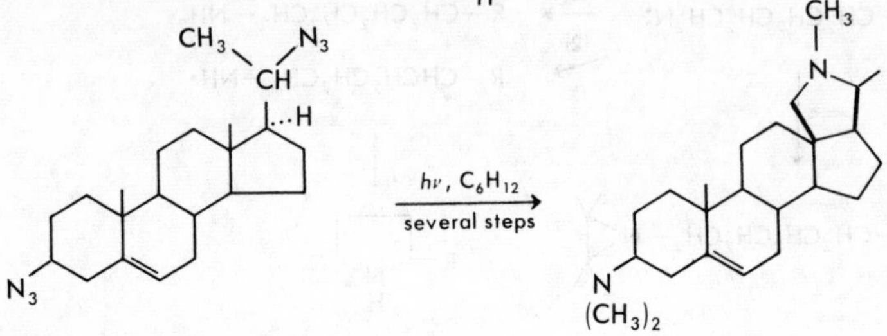

[33]

It is clear that the type of product one obtains will depend on the medium in which the photolysis is conducted, which may be further seen from the products formed on photolysis of azidoformates:

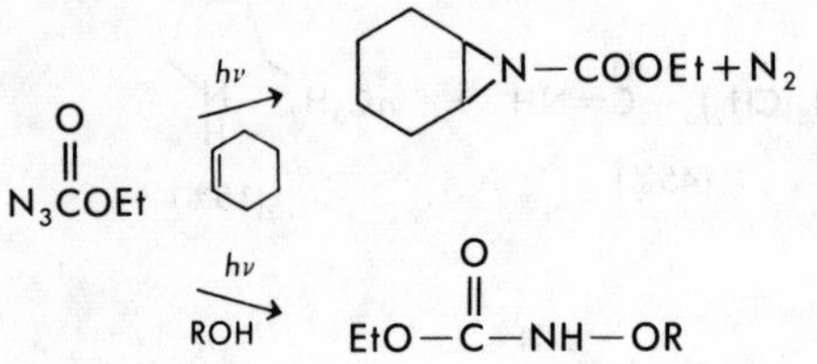

[34,36]

However

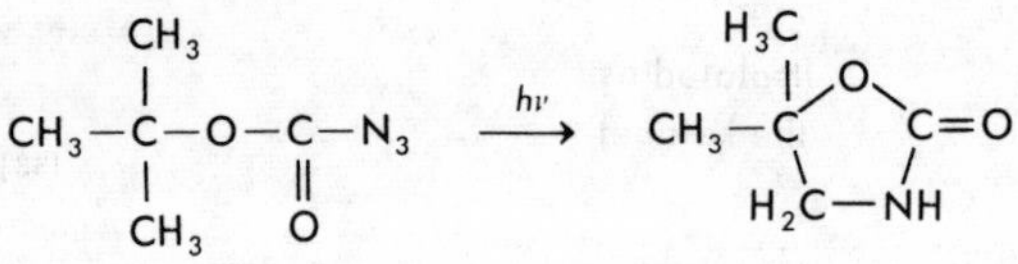

and

[36]

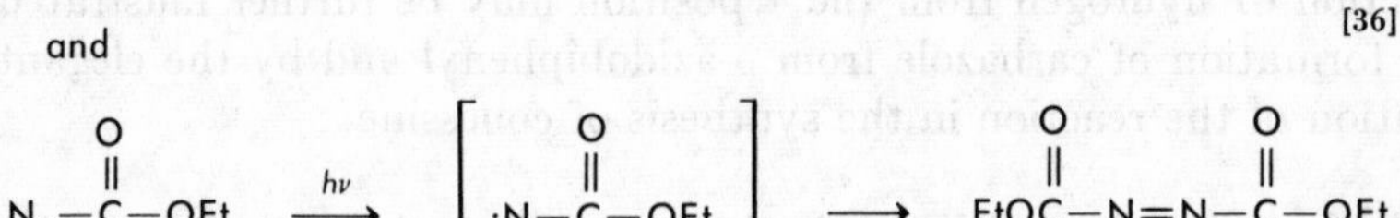

$$\xrightarrow{\quad} \;\; :N-\overset{\overset{\displaystyle O}{\|}}{C}-OEt$$

$$EtO-\overset{\overset{\displaystyle O}{\|}}{C}-\overset{\overset{\displaystyle}{N}}{\underset{\overset{\displaystyle}{N'}}{\|}}-\overset{\overset{\displaystyle O}{\|}}{C}-OEt \quad\longrightarrow\quad EtO\overset{\overset{\displaystyle O}{\|}}{C}-N=\overset{+}{N}-\overset{-}{N}-\overset{\overset{\displaystyle O}{\|}}{C}-OEt$$

$$O=C-OEt \qquad\qquad\qquad\qquad \overset{\displaystyle C=O \quad O}{\underset{\displaystyle OEt}{|}}$$

$$\longleftrightarrow \quad EtO-\overset{\overset{\displaystyle O}{\|}}{C}-\overset{-}{N}-\overset{+}{N}=N-\overset{\overset{\displaystyle O}{\|}}{C}-OEt \quad\longrightarrow\quad (EtOOC)_2N-N=N-COOEt$$

$$\overset{\displaystyle C=O \quad O}{\underset{\displaystyle OEt}{|}}$$

$$\longrightarrow \quad N_2 + (EtOOC)_3N \qquad\qquad\qquad\qquad\qquad\qquad [37,38]$$

The lifetime of the reactive $R-\overset{\overset{\displaystyle O}{\|}}{C}-N$: species is enhanced by certain substituents, such as in the case where $R = NH_2$.[74]

Similar reactive species are produced in the photolysis of 1,2,3-triazolines:[75]

The photolysis of acyl azides leads to hydrogen abstraction and ring closure as well as to Curtius rearrangement; the isocyanate produced often reacts further with the solvent or with neighboring groups:

[39]

[40]

There is some indication that the multiplicity of the electron-deficient nitrogen species produced photochemically is triplet.[41] Among the photolysis of other nitrogen derivatives that of azo compounds is of interest in that it proceeds in two ways: (1) In solution, double-bond isomerization favors the cis isomer. (2) Decomposition leads to the formation of free radicals and nitrogen gas.

In gas-phase photolyses where facility for the dissipation of excess vibrational energy is lacking, rupture of the C—N bonds to produce nitrogen gas and radicals occurs as the main process. The radicals subsequently may combine.[32] The N=N bond is apparently not broken, for none of the products that would result from such reactive species have been reported.†

$$R-N=N-R \longrightarrow \left[R-N=N-R \right]^* \longrightarrow 2R\cdot + N_2$$

The R—N=N · radical has been observed only as a reactive species, short-lived even at −196°C.[73]

8-3 Methylene

Although a broad review of the chemistry of divalent carbon is beyond the scope of this book, the photolysis of diazomethane deserves

† Ogilvie,[73a] however, has reported the formation of methylenimine in the photolysis of formaldazine in the solid state at 20°K. This must occur via the radical $CH_2=N\cdot$.

to be mentioned. Methylene produced in the gas-phase photolysis of diazomethane adds indiscriminately to olefins,[44] and it has been shown to be in the singlet state. Under high pressure in the presence of an inert gas, intersystem crossing to the triplet state occurs.[45] Hammond[46,47] has produced a selective (triplet) form of :CH₂ in solution from the benzophenone-sensitized photolysis of diazomethane. The different product ratios obtained from its addition to *cis-* and *trans-*2-butene indicate that spin inversion, which must occur prior to bond formation, takes place faster than rotation of the C—C bond.[46]

The photolysis of diazoacetophenone in alcohols yields two products: the ester resulting from Wolff rearrangement and ketene-solvent addition and acetophenone, formed by hydrogen abstraction from the solvent:

$$\phi-\underset{\substack{\|\\O}}{C}-CHN_2 \xrightarrow[ROH]{h\nu} \phi CH_2CO_2R + \phi COCH_3$$

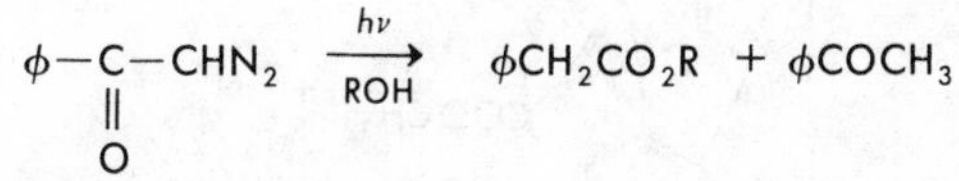

Padwa and Layton[77] have found that the direct photolysis of diazoacetophenone, which gives rise to the singlet, yields ratios of ester/acetophenone that depend on the solvent in the manner shown below; the ratio decreases as the size of the alcohol increases, a fact that may be explained by the enhanced intersystem crossing to the triplet as hydrogen bonding of solvent to excited singlet decreases. Photolysis in the presence of a 2 *M* excess of Michler's ketone with the use of filters that eliminate radiation below 330 mμ leads to the triplet; acetophenone is the only product formed in the photolysis conducted in isopropanol. It is significant, however, that ester formation again becomes an important process in ethanol and methanol. This feature has been interpreted to mean that, assuming no conversion of excited triplet to higher ground-state vibrational levels occurs, endothermic triplet → singlet conversion takes place, but only when hydrogen abstraction from the solvent becomes energetically less favorable. This would be the first chemical evidence for such interconversions.

Method	Solvent	Ester/acetophenone
Direct	CH_3OH	300:1
photolysis	C_2H_5OH	5.9:1
	$i\text{-}C_3H_7OH$	2.5:1
Sensitized	CH_3OH	7.3:1
photolysis	C_2H_5OH	1.1:1
	$i\text{-}C_3H_7OH$	0:1

The photolysis of other diazocompounds, or their precursors, results in the loss of nitrogen and the formation of divalent carbon species which undergo the usual addition and substitution reactions. A few of the more atypical examples known are shown below:

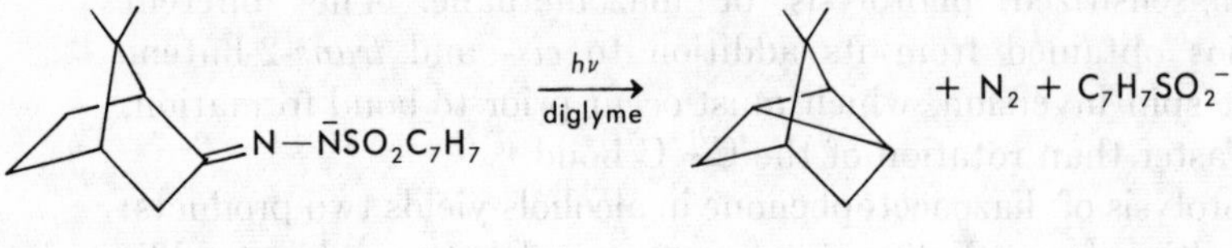

[48]

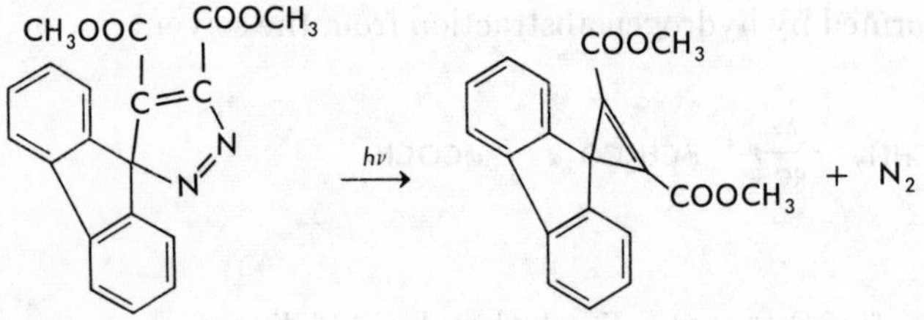

[49]

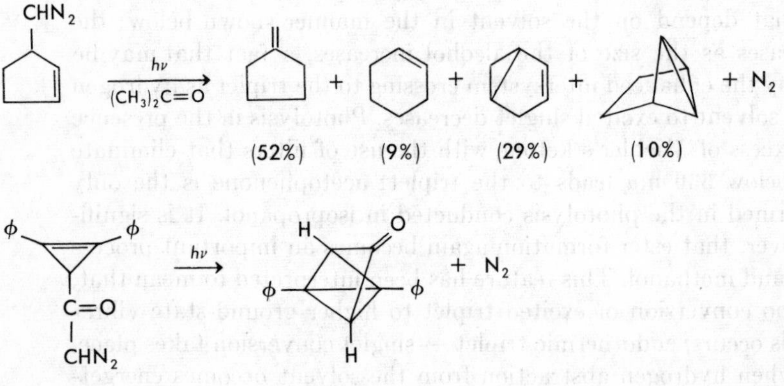

(52%)   (9%)   (29%)   (10%)

[50]

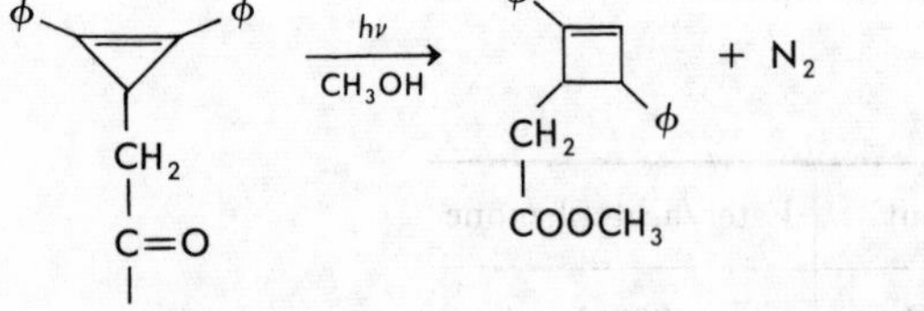

[51]

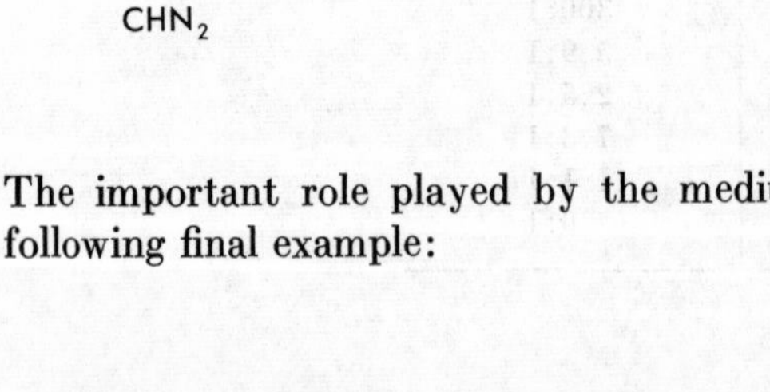

[52]

The important role played by the medium is well illustrated by the following final example:

The photolysis of diazirines (cyclic three-membered diazo compounds) also leads to carbenes.[76]

8-4 *Photochemical Substitution Reactions in Solution*

From LCAO-type molecular-orbital calculations of electron densities in aromatic π systems[54,55] it may be shown that a rather striking change in the relative electron densities of benzene rings occurs upon changing from the ground state to the lowest excited π-π^* state. Thus, calculations for the benzene ring substituted by electron-withdrawing groups show that the location of greatest electron density changes from the *meta* position in the ground state to the *para* position in the first excited state:

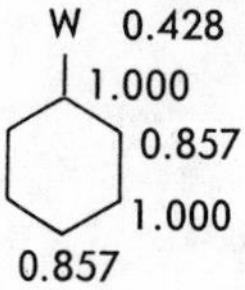

W   0.428
  1.000
      0.857
      1.000
0.857

Ground state

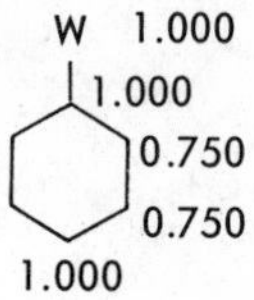

W   1.000
  1.000
      0.750
      0.750
1.000

First excited state

$$W = CH_2^+ \qquad [55]$$

In contrast, calculations show that the greatest electron density in rings substituted by electron-donating groups changes from the *para* to the *meta* position on excitation, as shown below for anisole:

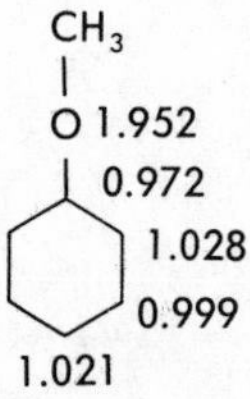

CH$_3$
|
O 1.952
  0.972
      1.028
      0.999
1.021

Ground state

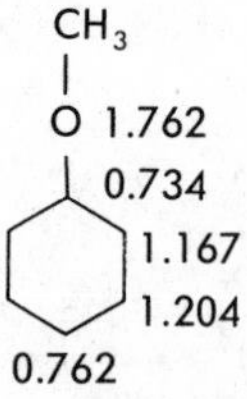

CH$_3$
|
O 1.762
  0.734
      1.167
      1.204
0.762

First excited state

[55]

Zimmerman[54] has had some measure of success in correlating the results of these calculations with experimental facts. Thus, the photolysis of benzyl acetates assumes an increasingly ionic character as one and two *meta* methoxy groups are introduced, which, according to calculations, should be able to stabilize a positive charge in the meta position of the excited state. 4-Methoxybenzyl acetate yields, on photolysis in aqueous dioxane, products derived only from radical intermediates that are created by homolytic fission:

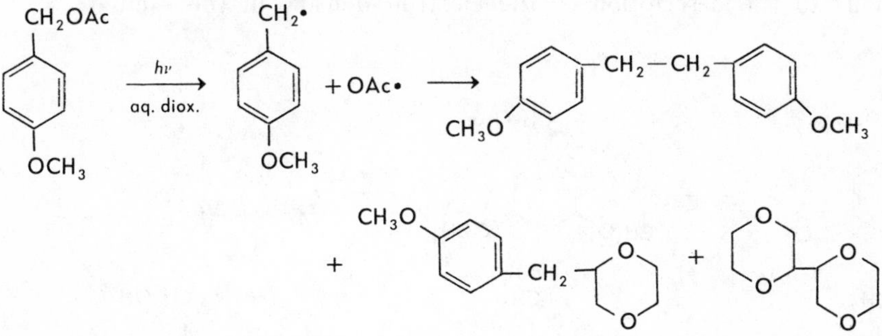
CH2OAc
hν
aq. diox.
CH2•
+OAc•
CH2—CH2
CH3O
OCH3
OCH3
OCH3
CH3O
+
CH2
O
O
+
O
O
O
O

[55]

The introduction of one *m*-methoxy group causes the formation of 4-methoxybenzyl alcohol, formed by an ionic process, in addition to the products derived from free-radical reactions:

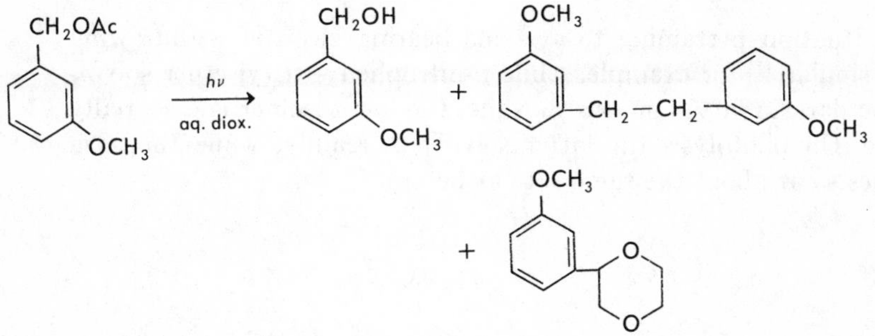
CH2OAc
hν
aq. diox.
OCH3
CH2OH
+
OCH3
OCH3
CH2—CH2
OCH3
OCH3
+
O
O

A second *m*-methoxy group leads to the formation of the alcohol as the *sole* product, indicating that all vestiges of a radical mechanism have disappeared:

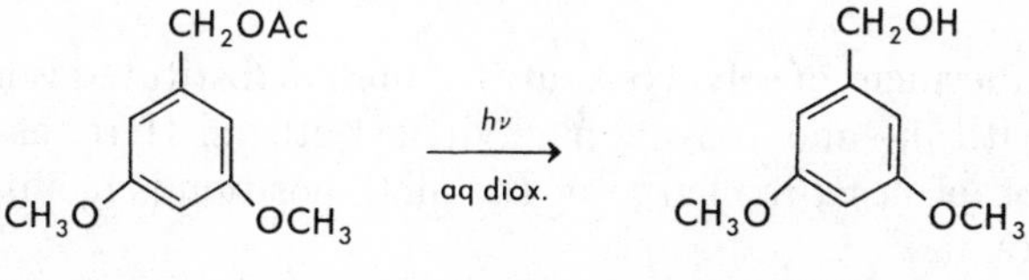
CH2OAc
CH3O
OCH3
hν
aq diox.
CH2OH
CH3O
OCH3

[55]

In ethanol the ethyl ether rather than the alcohol is obtained as the major product; similar results are obtained from the photolysis of benzyl chlorides. Thus meta-electron-donating groups appear to favor ionic-displacement reactions on photolysis through stabilization of the positive charge in the excited state. Although difficult to represent in normal valence-bond terminology, Zimmerman has applied valence-bond representations to the description of the electron density in the excited states:

[55]

The situation pertaining to systems bearing electron withdrawing groups is similar.[56] For example, while *p*-nitrophenyl trityl ether solvolyses in the dark in 90% aqueous dioxane, the meta isomer is essentially unreactive. On photolysis the latter solvolyses readily, while the para isomer does so at about the same rate as before.

A similar enhancement of solvolysis rates of meta-substituted isomers has been found with *m*- and *p*-cyanophenyltrityl ethers. Here, as predicted, stabilization of *negative* charge in the meta position is facilitated in the excited state.

Havinga and coworkers[57] had noted earlier similar rate enhancements in the hydrolysis of nitrophenylphosphate and sulfate esters. Here the rate of hydrolysis of the meta nitro esters is about 300 times that for the ortho or para isomer; nucleophilic substitutions are facilitated by para withdrawing groups in the ground state and by meta withdrawing groups in the excited state. The following example is an excellent illustration of the effect of the nitro group under two sets of conditions:

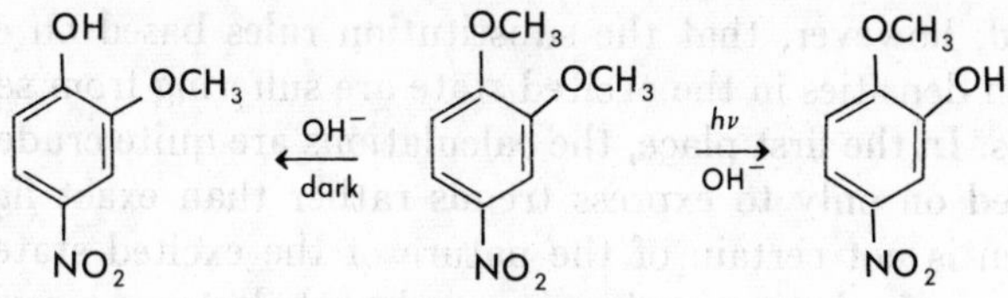

[58]

Other illustrations are presented below. Each case should be regarded as a nucleophilic displacement in the excited state:

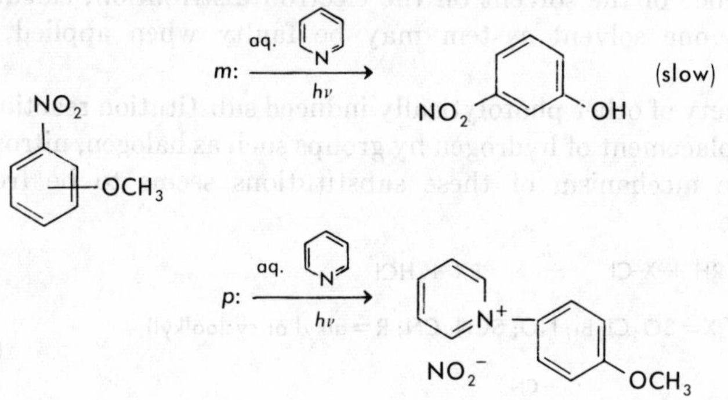

m: (slow)

[59]

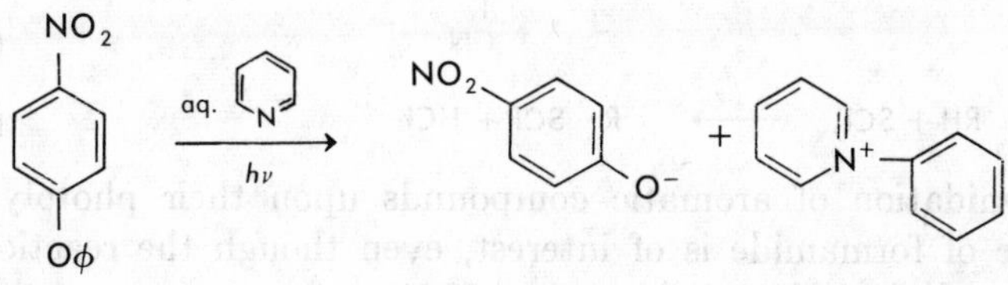

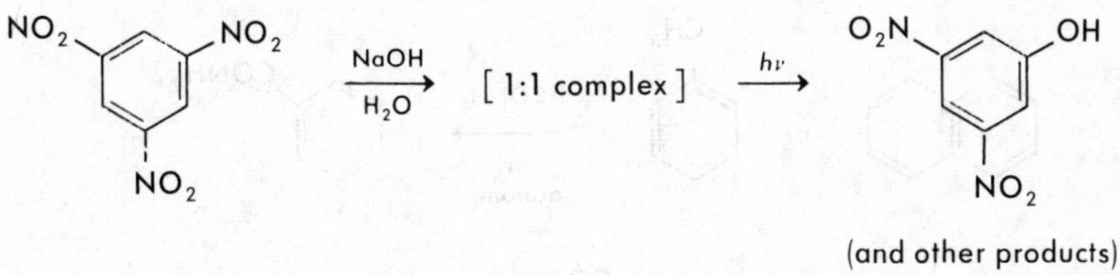

p:

[60]

(and other products)

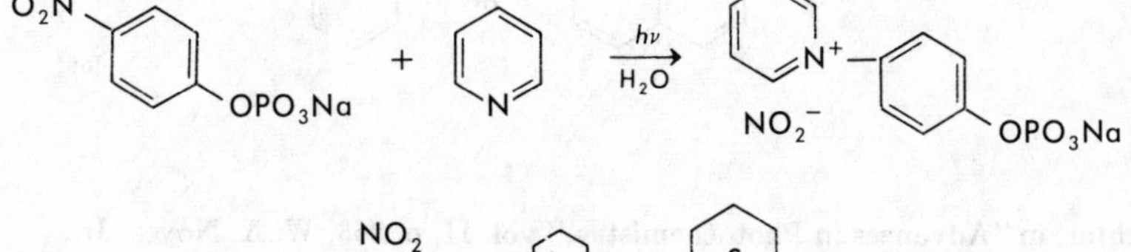

[61]

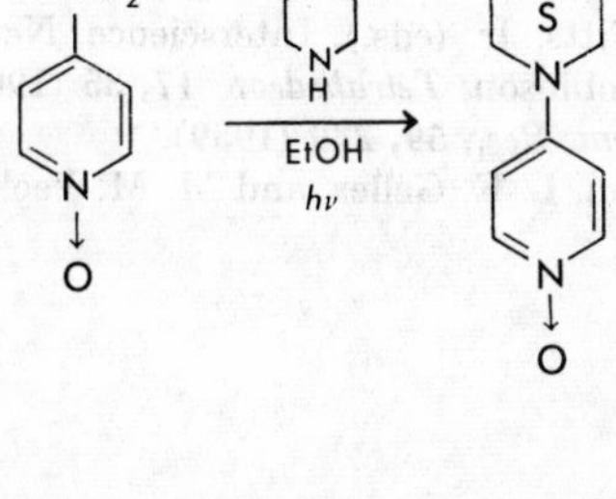

[62]

It must be noted, however, that the substitution rules based on calculations of electron densities in the excited state are suffering from several severe limitations. In the first place, the calculations are quite crude, and they can be relied on only to express trends rather than exact figures. Second, one often is not certain of the nature of the excited state; the presence or absence of substituents bearing unshared electrons may cause changes from π-π^* to n-π^*. Finally, very little information is available about the influence of the solvent on the electron distribution; calculations based on one solvent system may be faulty when applied to another.

A large variety of other photolytically induced substitution reactions results in the replacement of hydrogen by groups such as halogen, nitroso, and cyano. The mechanism of these substitutions seems to be free-radical in nature.

$$RH + X\text{-}Cl \xrightarrow{h\nu} RX + HCl$$

$$(X = SO_2Cl;\ Br;\ NO;\ SCN;\ CN;\ R = alkyl\ or\ cycloalkyl)$$

[63]

$$ROCH_2R' \xrightarrow[h\nu]{Cl-CN} R-O-CH-R' + HCl$$
$$\qquad\qquad\qquad\qquad |$$
$$\qquad\qquad\qquad\qquad CN$$

[64]

$$RH + SCl_2 \xrightarrow{h\nu} R-SCl + HCl$$

[65]

Finally, the amidation of aromatic compounds upon their photolysis in the presence of formamide is of interest, even though the reactions proceed only in relatively low yields (15 to 32%):

[66]

References

1. M. Akhtar, in "Advances in Photochemistry," vol. II, p. 263, W. A. Noyes, Jr., G. S. Hammond, and J. N. Pitts, Jr. (eds.), Interscience, New York, 1964.
2. A. L. Nussbaum and C. H. Robinson, *Tetrahedron*, **17**, 35 (1962).
3. P. Gray and A. Williams, *Chem. Rev.*, **59**, 239 (1959).
4. D. H. R. Barton, J. M. Beaton, L. E. Geller, and M. M. Pecket, *J. Am. Chem. Soc.*, **82**, 2640 (1960).

5. D. H. R. Barton and J. M. Beaton, *J. Am. Chem. Soc.*, **82**, 2641 (1962).

6. D. H. R. Barton and J. M. Beaton, *J. Am. Chem. Soc.*, **83**, 4083 (1961).

7. D. H. R. Barton, J. M. Beaton, L. E. Geller, and M. M. Pecket, *J. Am. Chem. Soc.*, **83**, 4076 (1961).

8. P. Kabasakalian and E. R. Townley, *J. Am. Chem. Soc.*, **84**, 2711 (1962).

9. M. Akhtar and M. M. Pecket, *J. Am. Chem. Soc.*, **86**, 265 (1964).

10. M. Akhtar, D. H. R. Barton, and P. G. Sammes, *J. Am. Chem. Soc.*, **86**, 3394 (1964).

11. P. Kabasakalian, E. R. Townley, and M. D. Yudis, *J. Am. Chem. Soc.*, **84**, 2716 (1962).

12. C. Walling and A. Padwa, *J. Am. Chem. Soc.*, **85**, 1597 (1963).

13. P. Kabasakalian, E. R. Townley, and M. D. Yudis, *J. Am. Chem. Soc.*, **84**, 2718 (1962).

14. P. Kabasakalian and E. R. Townley, *J. Am. Chem. Soc.*, **84**, 2723 (1962).

15. P. Kabasakalian and E. R. Townley, *J. Am. Chem. Soc.*, **84**, 2724 (1962).

16. P. Kabasakalian and E. R. Townley, *J. Org. Chem.*, **27**, 2918 (1962).

17. P. Kabasakalian and E. R. Townley, *J. Org. Chem.*, **27**, 3562 (1962).

18. M. Nakazaki and K. Naemura, *Bull. Chem. Soc. (Japan)*, **37**, 532 (1964).

19. D. H. R. Barton and J. M. Beaton, *J. Am. Chem. Soc.*, **84**, 199 (1962).

20. Ref. 1, p. 270.

21. H. Reimann, A. S. Capomaggi, T. Strauss, E. P. Oliveto, and D. H. R. Barton, *J. Am. Chem. Soc.*, **83**, 4481 (1961).

22. K. Tauda, V. Ikewawa, and S. Nozor, *Chem. Pharm. Bull. (Tokyo)*, **1**, 519 (1959).

23. A. L. Nussbaum, E. P. Yuan, C. H. Robinson, A. Mitchell, E. P. Oliveto, J. M. Beaton, and D. H. R. Barton, *J. Org. Chem.*, **27**, 20 (1962).

24. A. L. Nussbaum, C. H. Robinson, E. P. Oliveto, and D. H. R. Barton, *J. Am. Chem. Soc.*, **83**, 2400 (1961).

25. A. L. Nussbaum, R. Wayne, E. Yuan, O. Zagneetko, and E. P. Oliveto, *J. Am. Chem. Soc.*, **84**, 1070 (1962).

26. C. H. Robinson, O. Gnoj, A. Mitchell, R. Wayne, E. Townley, P. Kabasakalian, E. P. Oliveto, and D. H. R. Barton, *J. Am. Chem. Soc.*, **83**, 1771 (1961); C. H. Robinson, O. Gnoj, A. Mitchell, E. P. Oliveto, and D. H. R. Barton, *Tetrahedron*, **21**, 743 (1965).

27. O. L. Chapman, A. A. Griswold, E. Hoganson, G. Lenz, and J. Reasoner, *Pure Appl. Chem.*, **9**, 585 (1964); O. L. Chapman, P. G. Cleveland, and E. D. Hoganson, *Chem. Commun.*, **1966**, 101.

28. E. L. Jenner, *J. Org. Chem.*, **27**, 1031 (1962).

29. A. Akhtar and D. H. R. Barton, *J. Am. Chem. Soc.*, **83**, 2213 (1961).

30. H. Ueterwasser, K. Heusler, J. Kalvoda, C. Meystre, P. Wieland, G. Anner and A. Wettstein, *Helv. Chim. Acta*, **46**, 344 (1963).

31. C. Meystre, K. Heusler, J. Kalvoda, G. Anner, and A. Wettstein, *Angew. Chem.*, **73**, 738 (1961).

32. P. A. S. Smith, "The Chemistry of Open-chain Organic Nitrogen Compounds," Benjamin, New York, 1965.

33. D. H. R. Barton and L. R. Morgan, *J. Chem. Soc.*, **1962**, 622; however, see also D. H. R. Barton and A. N. Starratt, *J. Chem. Soc.*, **1965**, 2444.

33a. R. M. Moriarty and M. Rahman, *Tetrahedron*, **21**, 2877 (1965).

34. W. Lwowsky and T. W. Mattingly, *Tetrahedron Letters*, **1962**, 277.

35. P. A. S. Smith and B. B. Brown, *J. Am. Chem. Soc.*, **74**, 2435 (1952).

36. R. Kreher and G. H. Bockhorn, *Angew. Chem.*, **76**, 681 (1964); see also W. Lwowsky and T. W. Mattingly, Jr., *J. Am. Chem. Soc.*, **87**, 1947 (1965).

37. W. Lwowsky, T. W. Mattingly, and T. J. Maricich, *Tetrahedron Letters*, **1964**, 1591.

38. J. Hancock, *Tetrahedron Letters*, **1964**, 1585.

39. W. L. Meyer and A. S. Levinson, *J. Org. Chem.*, **28**, 2859 (1963).

40. L. Horner and E. Spietschka, *Ber.*, **85**, 225 (1952).

41. W. H. Saunders, Jr. and E. A. Caress, *J. Am. Chem. Soc.*, **86**, 861 (1964).

42. E. M. Burgess and J. M. Lavanish, *Tetrahedron Letters*, **1964**, 1221.

43. Y. L. Chow, *Tetrahedron Letters*, **1964**, 2333.

44. W. Von E. Doering, R. G. Buttery, R. G. Laughlin, and N. Chaudhuri, *J. Am. Chem. Soc.*, **78**, 3224 (1956).

45. G. Herzberg and J. Shoosmith, *Nature*, **183**, 1801 (1959); see also R. F. W. Bader, and J. I. Generosa, *Can. J. Chem.*, **43**, 1631 (1965).

46. K. R. Kopecky, G. S. Hammond, and P. A. Leermakers, *J. Am. Chem. Soc.*, **83**, 2397 (1961).

47. K. R. Kopecky, G. S. Hammond, and P. A. Leermakers, *J. Am. Chem. Soc.*, **84**, 1015 (1962).

48. W. G. Dauben and F. G. Willey, *J. Am. Chem. Soc.*, **84**, 1497 (1962).

49. G. Ege, *Tetrahedron Letters*, **1963**, 1667.

50. D. M. Lemal and K. S. Shim, *Tetrahedron Letters*, **1964**, 3231.

51. S. Masamune, *J. Am. Chem. Soc.*, **86**, 735 (1964).

52. S. Masamune and N. T. Castelluci, *Proc. Chem. Soc.*, **1964**, 298.

53. E. J. Moriconi and J. J. Murray, *J. Org. Chem.*, **29**, 3577 (1964).

54. H. E. Zimmerman, in "Advances in Photochemistry," vol. I, p. 200, W. A. Noyes, Jr., G. S. Hammond, J. N. Pitts, Jr. (eds.), Interscience, New York, 1963.

55. H. E. Zimmerman and V. R. Sandel, *J. Am. Chem. Soc.*, **85**, 915 (1963).

56. H. E. Zimmerman and S. Somasekhara, *J. Am. Chem. Soc.*, **85**, 922 (1963).

57. E. Havinga, R. O. de Jongh, and W. Dorst, *Rec. Trav. Chim.*, **75**, 378 (1956). For a recent discussion see D. A. de Bie and E. Havinga, *Tetrahedron*, **21**, 2363 (1965).

58. E. Havinga and R. O. de Jongh, *Bull. Soc. Chim. Belges*, **71**, 803 (1962). See also E. Havinga and D. F. Nijhoff, *Tetrahedron Letters*, **1965**, 4199.

59. R. L. Letsinger, O. B. Ramsay, and J. H. McCain, *J. Am. Chem. Soc.*, **87**, 2945 (1965).

60. V. Gold and C. H. Rochester, *Proc. Chem. Soc.*, **1960**, 403.

61. R. L. Letsinger and O. B. Ramsay, *J. Am. Chem. Soc.*, **86**, 1447 (1964).

62. R. M. Johnson and C. W. Rees, *Proc. Chem. Soc.*, **1964**, 213.

63. E. Müller and H. Huber, *Ber.*, **96**, 670 (1963); E. Müller, G. Fiedler, *Ber.*, **98**, 3493 (1965); E. Müller, M. Salamon, *Ber.*, **98**, 3501 (1965).

64. E. Müller, and H. Huber, *Ber.*, **96**, 2319 (1963).

65. E. Müller and E. W. Schmidt, *Ber.*, **96**, 3050 (1963).

66. D. Elad, *Tetrahedron Letters*, **1963**, 77. See also D. Elad and J. Rokach, *J. Org. Chem.*, **30**, 3361 (1965).

67. J. Fried, J. W. Brown, and M. Applebaum, *Tetrahedron Letters*, **1965**, 849.

68. S. H. Hastings and F. A. Matsen, *J. Am. Chem. Soc.*, **70**, 3514 (1948).

69. D. H. R. Barton, H. P. Faro, E. P. Serebryakov, and N. F. Woolsey, *J. Chem. Soc.*, **1965**, 2438.

70. D. H. R. Barton, A. L. J. Beckwith, and A. Goosen, *J. Chem. Soc.*, **1965**, 181.

71. R. C. Petterson and A. Wambsgans, *J. Am. Chem. Soc.*, **86**, 1648 (1964).

72. G. Adam and K. Schreiber, *Tetrahedron Letters*, **1965**, 923.

73. P. B. Ayscough, B. R. Brooks, and H. E. Evans, *J. Phys. Chem.*, **68**, 3889 (1964).

73a. J. F. Ogilvie, *Chem. Commun.*, **1965**, 359.

74. R. Kreher and G. H. Berger, *Tetrahedron Letters*, **1965**, 369.

75. P. Scheiner, *J. Org. Chem.*, **30**, 7 (1965).

76. H. M. Frey, *Pure Appl. Chem.*, **9**, 461 (1964); H. M. Frey and I. D. R. Stevens, *J. Chem. Soc.*, **1964**, 4700.

77. A. Padwa and R. Layton, *Tetrahedron Letters*, **1965**, 2167.

Author Index

The numbers following the author's name refer to the chapter and reference numbers respectively.

Adam, G., 8–72
Adamson, A. W., 1–4a
Akhtar, A., 8–1, 9, 10, 29
Aksentijevich, R. I., 2–125
Aktipis, S., 7–54
Allan, L. T., 7–3a
Alston, T. S., 7–24
Altenburger, E., 4–27
Altwicker, E. R., 4–13
Alumbaugh, R. L., 3–10
Amada, T., 2–123
Amin, J. H., 4–80
Anastrasiov, A., 5–21
Anderson, J. C., 4–40, 63
Ando, W., 7–4, 9a
Angus, H. J. F., 6–22, 25
Anner, G., 8–30, 31
Anselme, J. P., 3–35
Applebaum, M., 8–67
Applequist, D. E., 5–13, 17
Arigoni, D., 3–25; 4–15, 21, 25, 32, 41
Arnett, E. M., 2–51
Arnold, D. R., 6–41, 45
Arnold, S. J., 7–13
Asker, W., 7–30
Atkinson, J. G., 6–38
Auerbach, J., 3–40
Ausloos, P., 1–14a; 3–15, 16
Autrey, R. L., 2–46; 3–70
Axelrod, M., 3–40
Ayer, D. E., 6–38, 39; 7–16
Ayer, W. A., 5–87
Ayscough, P. B., 8–73

Back, M. H., 2–120
Backer, H. J., 2–30

Bader, R. F. W., 8–45
Badger, G. M., 4–79; 7–29
Bagli, J. F., 7–10
Bailey, P. S., 2–23
Baker, W. P., 7–39
Bakunim, M., 5–55
Baldwin, J. E., 2–85
Ball, Jr. J. S., 5–93, 94
Bamberger, E., 7–46
Bamford, C. H., 3–1
Barakat, M. Z., 5–59
Barltrop, J. A., 6–16, 17, 50
Barnasconi, R., 3–25
Barrett, J. H., 2–54
Bartlett, P. D., 6–48
Barton, D. H. R., 2–46, 48, 32; 3–25, 56–58, 60, 70; 4–23, 24, 28–30, 33, 37; 8–4, 7, 10, 19, 21, 23–25, 29, 33, 69, 70
Basinski, J. E., 5–66, 69
Bass, J. D., 5–2; 6–10
Baum, E. J., 3–1a
Baum, J. W., 3–38
Bauslaugh, G., 6–68
Beaton, J. M., 8–4–7, 19, 23
Becher, J., 4–76a
Becker, H. D., 7–3
Beckett, A., 7–40
Beckwith, A. L. J., 8–70
Beereboom, J. J., 6–47
Bellamy, A. J., 3–24
Bennett, R. G., 1–17
Benson, S. W., 3–5
Bereza, S., 4–9
Berger, G. H., 8–74
Bergmann, F., 7–41
Bergmann, W., 4–57; 7–7
Berman, J. D., 7–55

263

Subject Index